ExplOring maths

maths

Teacher's Book

4

PEARSON
Longman

**Anita Straker, Tony Fisher, Rosalyn Hyde,
Sue Jennings and Jonathan Longstaffe**

Published and distributed by Pearson Education Limited, Edinburgh Gate, Harlow, Essex, CM20 2JE, England
www.longman.co.uk

First published 2008

ISBN-13 978-1-405-89610-8

Cover illustration by M.C. Escher

Typeset by Tech-Set, Gateshead

Printed by Ashford Colour Press Ltd., Gosport

The publisher's policy is to use paper manufactured from sustainable forests.

Every effort has been made to trace the copyright holders and we apologise in advance for any unintentional omissions. We would be pleased to insert the appropriate acknowledgement in any subsequent edition of this publication.

Picture Credits

The publisher would like to thank the following for their kind permission to reproduce their photographs:

(Key: b-bottom; c-centre; l-left; r-right; t-top)

Alamy Images: Nick Hanna 159t; Jeff Greenberg 334 (russian market); Maurice Joseph 344; Photofusion Picture Library 135; Robert Fried 276c; Frances Roberts 334 (roman numerals); Sebastien Baussais 276r; **Ancient Art & Architecture:** 334tr; Ronald Sheridan 276l; **The Art Archive:** Bibliothèque des Arts Décoratifs Paris/Gianni Dagli Orti 210t; **Bridgeman Art Library Ltd:** British Museum, London, UK 333tl; **Corbis:** Bettmann 334tl; Blue Lantern Studio 67; Moodboard 216tr; Rolf Bruderer 334 (bank); **Danita Delimont.com:** Nik Wheeler 210b, 212tr; **DK Images:** Alan Hills & Barbara Winter(c)The British Museum 216bl; Coral Mula 332tl; Ian O'Leary 186, 187; Stephen Oliver 216br; Steve Gorton 189b; The British Museum 334bl; **Getty Images:** Keren Su/Taxi 334 (chinese school); Paul Chesley/Stone 332bl; **iStockphoto:** 63, 69t, 133br, 133tl, 158br, 189t, 193c, 212bc, 212bl, 212tc, 212tl, 214, 334bc, 334br, 360r; **Jupiter Unlimited:** 62l, 133bl; Brand X 62r; Comstock Images 216tl; PhotoObjects.net 360l; **Ordnance Survey:** Reproduced by permission of Ordnance Survey on behalf of HMSO©Crown Copyright, All Rights Reserved 191c, 191b; **Pearson Education Ltd:** Pearson Learning Photo Studio 361; PH College 253; PH Merrill Publishing 258; Prentice Hall 158bl, 158tr, 159b; Prentice Hall School Division 193l; Silver Burdett Ginn 133tr, 158tl; **Robert Harding World Imagery:** Pearl Bucknall 191t; Bruno Morandi 210c; **The M.C Escher Company-Holland:** M.C Escher's Symmetry Drawing E67(c)2007 The M.C Escher Company-Holland. All rights reserved. www.mcescher.com 212br

Front Cover: The M.C Escher Company-Holland: M.C Escher's Symmetry Drawing E55(c)27 The M.C Escher Company-Holland. All rights reserved. www.mcescher.com

All other images © Pearson Education

Picture Research by: Louise Edgeworth

Autograph and The Geometer's Sketchpad are distributed in the UK and Ireland by Chartwell-Yorke Ltd. www.chartwellyorke.com

MSW Logo can be downloaded for free from www.softronix.com

Every effort has been made to trace the copyright holders and we apologise in advance for any unintentional omissions. We would be pleased to insert the appropriate acknowledgement in any subsequent edition of this publication.

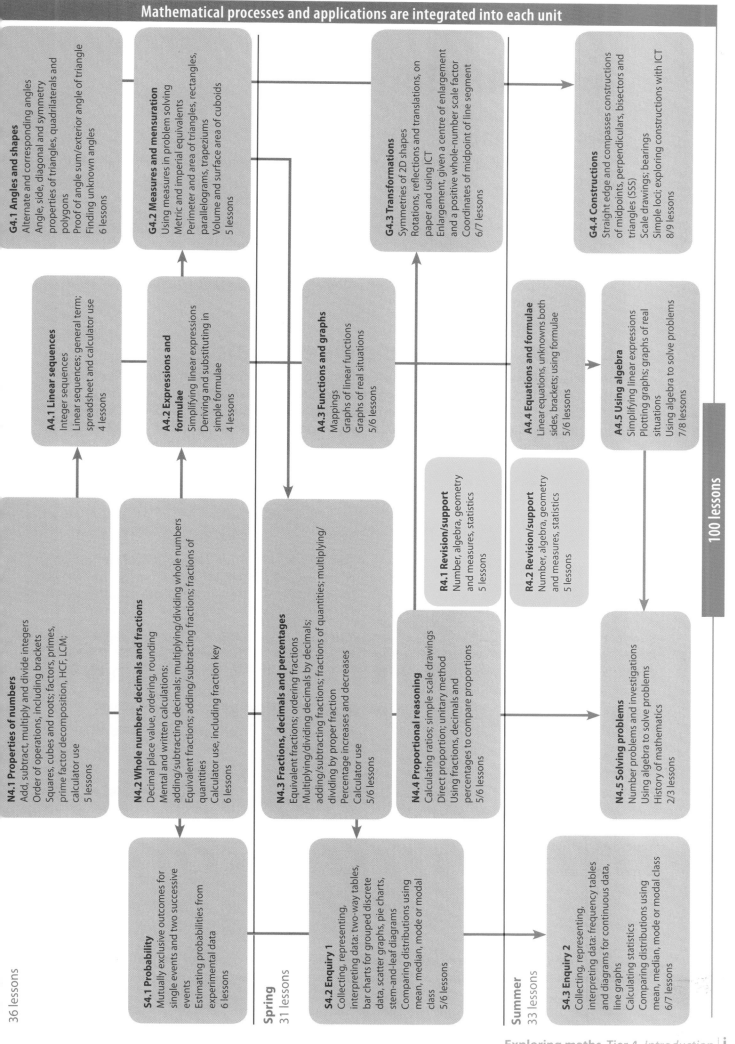

G4.1 Angles and shapes
Alternate and corresponding angles
Angle, side, diagonal and symmetry properties of triangles, quadrilaterals and polygons
Proof of angle sum/exterior angle of triangle
Finding unknown angles
6 lessons

G4.2 Measures and mensuration
Using measures in problem solving
Metric and imperial equivalents
Perimeter and area of triangles, rectangles, parallelograms, trapeziums
Volume and surface area of cuboids
5 lessons

G4.3 Transformations
Symmetries of 2D shapes
Rotations, reflections and translations, on paper and using ICT
Enlargement, given a centre of enlargement and a positive whole-number scale factor
Coordinates of midpoint of line segment
6/7 lessons

G4.4 Constructions
Straight edge and compasses constructions of midpoints, perpendiculars, bisectors and triangles (SSS)
Scale drawings; bearings
Simple loci; exploring constructions with ICT
8/9 lessons

A4.1 Linear sequences
Integer sequences
Linear sequences; general term; spreadsheet and calculator use
4 lessons

A4.2 Expressions and formulae
Simplifying linear expressions
Deriving and substituting in simple formulae
4 lessons

A4.3 Functions and graphs
Mappings
Graphs of linear functions
Graphs of real situations
5/6 lessons

A4.4 Equations and formulae
Linear equations, unknowns both sides, brackets; using formulae
5/6 lessons

A4.5 Using algebra
Simplifying linear expressions
Plotting graphs; graphs of real situations
Using algebra to solve problems
7/8 lessons

N4.1 Properties of numbers
Add, subtract, multiply and divide integers
Order of operations, including brackets
Squares, cubes and roots; factors, primes, prime factor decomposition, HCF, LCM; calculator use
5 lessons

N4.2 Whole numbers, decimals and fractions
Decimal place value, ordering, rounding
Mental and written calculations: adding/subtracting decimals; multiplying/dividing whole numbers
Equivalent fractions; adding/subtracting fractions; fractions of quantities
Calculator use, including fraction key
6 lessons

N4.3 Fractions, decimals and percentages
Equivalent fractions; ordering fractions
Multiplying/dividing decimals by decimals; adding/subtracting fractions; fractions of quantities; multiplying/dividing by proper fraction
Percentage increases and decreases
Calculator use
5/6 lessons

N4.4 Proportional reasoning
Calculating ratios; simple scale drawings
Direct proportion; unitary method
Using fractions, decimals and percentages to compare proportions
5/6 lessons

N4.5 Solving problems
Number problems and investigations
Using algebra to solve problems
History of mathematics
2/3 lessons

R4.1 Revision/support
Number, algebra, geometry and measures, statistics
5 lessons

R4.2 Revision/support
Number, algebra, geometry and measures, statistics
5 lessons

S4.1 Probability
Mutually exclusive outcomes for single events and two successive events
Estimating probabilities from experimental data
6 lessons

S4.2 Enquiry 1
Collecting, representing, interpreting data: two-way tables, bar charts for grouped discrete data, scatter graphs, pie charts, stem-and-leaf diagrams
Comparing distributions using mean, median, mode or modal class
5/6 lessons

S4.3 Enquiry 2
Collecting, representing, interpreting data: frequency tables and diagrams for continuous data, line graphs
Calculating statistics
Comparing distributions using mean, median, mode or modal class
6/7 lessons

36 lessons

Spring
31 lessons

Summer
33 lessons

100 lessons

Introduction

The materials

The *Exploring maths* scheme has seven tiers, indicated by the seven colours in the table below. Each tier has:

- a class book for pupils;
- a home book for pupils;
- a teacher's book, organised in units, with lesson notes, mental tests (for number units), facsimiles of resource sheets, and answers to the exercises in the class book and home book;
- a CD with interactive books for display, either when lessons are being prepared or in class, and ICT resources for use in lessons.

Content, structure and differentiation

The tiers are linked to National Curriculum levels so that they have the maximum flexibility. They take full account of the 2007 Programme of Study for Key Stage 3, the Secondary Strategy's renewed *Framework for teaching mathematics in Years 7 to 11*, published in 2008, and the possibility of taking the statutory Key Stage 3 test before the end of Year 9. Level 1 standards for functional skills for mathematics are embedded and, in the higher tiers, the groundwork laid for level 2.

Labels such as 'Year 7' do not appear on the covers of books but are used in the table below to explain how the materials might be used.

	Year 7	Year 8	Year 9
Extra support For pupils who achieved level 2 or a weak level 3 at KS2, who will enter the level 3–5 test at KS3 and who are likely to achieve Grade F–G at GCSE.	**Tier 1** NC levels 2–3 (mainly level 3)	**Tier 2** NC levels 3–4 (mainly level 4)	**Tier 3** NC levels 4–5 (both levels 4 and 5)
Support For pupils who achieved a good level 3 or weak level 4 at KS2, who will enter the level 4–6 test at KS3 and who are likely to achieve Grade D–E at GCSE.	**Tier 2** NC levels 3–4 (mainly level 4)	**Tier 3** NC levels 4–5 (both levels 4 and 5)	**Tier 4** NC level 5–6 (mainly level 5)
Core For pupils who achieved a secure level 4 at KS2, who will enter the level 5–7 test at KS3 and who are likely to achieve B–C at GCSE.	**Tier 3** NC levels 4–5 (both levels 4 and 5)	**Tier 4** NC level 5–6 (mainly level 5)	**Tier 5** NC levels 5–6 (mainly level 6)
Extension For pupils who achieved level 5 at KS2, who will enter the level 6–8 test at KS3 and who are likely to achieve A or A* at GCSE.	**Tier 4** NC level 5–6 (mainly level 5)	**Tier 5** NC levels 5–6 (mainly level 6)	**Tier 6** NC levels 6–7 (mainly level 7)
Gifted and talented For gifted pupils who achieved a strong level 5 at KS2, who will be entered early for the level 6–8 test for KS3 and who are likely to achieve A* at GCSE.	**Tier 5** NC levels 5–6 (mainly level 6)	**Tier 6** NC levels 6–7 (mainly level 7)	**Tier 7** NC levels 7–8 (mainly level 8)

The *Exploring maths* scheme as a whole offers an exceptional degree of differentiation, so that the mathematics curriculum can be tailored to the needs of individual schools, classes and pupils.

There are at least five tiers available for each of the year groups 7, 8 and 9. The range of tiers to be used in Year 7 can be chosen by the school to match the attainment of their incoming pupils and their class organisation. Teachers of mixed-ability classes can align units from different tiers covering related topics (see Related units, p. x).

The *Results Plus Progress* entry test, published separately, guides teachers on placing pupils in an appropriate tier at the start of Year 7. The test analysis indicates which topics in that tier may need special emphasis. Similar computer assessments are available for other years (see Computer-mediated assessments, p. vii).

Pupils can progress to the next tier as soon as they are ready, since the books are not labelled Year 7, Year 8 or Year 9. Similarly, work on any tier could take more than a year where pupils need longer to consolidate their learning.

Pupils in any year group who have completed Tier 4 or above successfully could be entered early for the Key Stage 3 test if the school wishes. Single-level tests for pupils working at particular national curriculum levels, which pupils can take in the winter or summer of any calendar year, are currently being piloted in ten local authorities as part of the *Making good progress* project. The tiered structure of *Exploring maths* is ideally suited to any extension of this pilot.

Each exercise in the class book offers differentiated questions, so that teachers can direct individual pupils to particular sections of the exercises. Each exercise starts with easier questions and moves on to harder questions, identified by underscored question numbers. More able pupils can tackle the extension problems.

If teachers feel that pupils need extra support, one or more lessons in a unit can be replaced with or supplemented by lessons from revision units.

Organisation of the units

Each tier is based on 100 lessons of 50 to 60 minutes, plus 10 extra lessons to use for revision or further support, either instead of or in addition to the main lessons.

Lessons are grouped into units, varying in length from three to ten lessons. The number of lessons in a unit increases slightly through the tiers so that there are fewer but slightly longer units for the higher tiers.

Each unit is identified by a code: N for number, A for algebra, G for geometry and measures, S for statistics and R for revision. For example, Unit N4.2 is the second number unit for Tier 4, while Unit G6.3 is the third geometry and measures unit for Tier 6. Mathematical processes and applications are integrated throughout.

The units are shown in a flowchart giving an overview for the year (see p. i). Some units need to be taught before others but schools can determine the precise order.

Schools with mixed-ability classes can align units from different tiers covering related topics. For example, Unit G4.2 *Measures and mensuration* in Tier 4 can be aligned with the Tier 3 Unit G3.1 *Mensuration* and the Tier 5 Unit G5.2 *Measures and mensuration*. For more information on where to find related units, see p. x.

Revision units

Each optional revision unit consists of five stand-alone lessons on different topics. These lessons include national test questions to help pupils prepare for tests.

Revision lessons can be taught in any order whenever they would be useful. They could be used with a whole class or part of a class. Schools that are entering pupils for national tests may wish to use, say, five of the revision lessons at different points of the spring term and five in the early summer term.

The revision lessons can either replace or be taught in addition to lessons in the main units. Units where the indicative number of lessons is given as, say, 5/6 lessons, are units where a lesson could be replaced by a revision lesson if teachers wish.

Balance between aspects of mathematics

In the early tiers there is a strong emphasis on number and measures. The time dedicated to number then decreases steadily, with a corresponding increase in the time for algebra, geometry and statistics. Mathematical processes and applications, or using and applying mathematics, are integrated into the content strands in each tier.

The lessons for each tier are distributed as follows.

	Number	Algebra	Geometry and measures	Statistics
Tier 1	54	1	30	15
Tier 2	39	19	23	19
Tier 3	34	23	24	19
Tier 4	26	28	27	19
Tier 5	20	29	29	22
Tier 6	19	28	30	23
Tier 7	17	29	29	25
TOTAL	209	157	192	142
	30%	23%	27%	20%

The teacher's book, class book and home book

Teacher's book

Each unit starts with a two-page overview of the unit. This includes:

- the necessary previous learning and the objectives for the unit, with the process skills and applications listed first for greater emphasis;
- the titles of the lessons in the unit;
- a brief statement on the key ideas in the unit and why they are important;
- brief details of the assessments integrated into the unit;
- common errors and misconceptions for teachers to look out for;
- the key mathematical terms and notation used in the unit;
- the practical resources required (equipment, materials, paper, and so on);
- the linked resources: relevant pages in the class book and home book, resource sheets, assessment resources, ICT resources, and so on;
- references to useful websites (these were checked at the time of writing but the changing nature of the Internet means that some may alter at a later date).

The overview is followed by lesson notes. Each lesson is described on a two-page spread. There is enough detail so that non-specialist teachers could follow the notes as they stand whereas specialist mathematics teachers will probably adapt them or use them as a source of ideas for teaching.

Each lesson identifies the main learning points for the lesson. A warm-up starter is followed by the main teaching activity and a plenary review.

The lesson notes refer to work with the whole class, unless stated otherwise. For example, where pupils are to work in pairs, the notes make this clear.

All the number units include an optional mental test for teachers to read out to the class, with answers on the same sheet.

All units in the teacher's book include answers to questions in the class book, home book, check ups and resource sheets. The answers are repeated in the answer section at the back of the teacher's book.

Class book

The class book parallels the teacher's book and is organised in units. The overall objectives for the unit, in pupil-friendly language, are shown at the start of the unit, and the main objective for each individual lesson is identified.

Interesting information to stimulate discussion on the cultural and historical roots of mathematics is shown throughout the units in panels headed 'Did you know that…?'

The exercises include activities, games or investigations for groups or individuals, practice questions and problems to solve. Questions are differentiated, with easier questions at the beginning of each exercise. Harder questions are shown by underlining of the question number. Challenging problems are identified as extension problems. The exercises for each lesson conclude with a summary of the learning points for pupils to remember.

Answers to exercises in the class book are given in the teacher's book.

Each unit ends with a self-assessment section for pupils called 'How well are you doing?' to help them to judge for themselves their grasp of the work. Answers to these self-assessment questions are at the back of the class book for pupils to refer to.

Home book

Each lesson has an optional corresponding homework task. Homework tasks are designed to take most pupils about 15 to 20 minutes for Tiers 1 and 2, 25 minutes for Tiers 3, 4 and 5, and 30 minutes for Tiers 6 and 7.

Homework is normally consolidation of class work. It is assumed that teachers will select from the homework tasks and will set, mark and follow up homework in accordance with the school's timetable. Because each school's arrangements for homework are different, feedback and follow-up to homework is not included in the lesson notes. It is assumed that teachers will add this as appropriate.

If the homework is other than consolidation (e.g. Internet research, collecting data for use in class), the lesson notes state that it is essential for pupils to do the homework. The next lesson refers to the homework and explains how it is to be used.

Answers to the homework tasks are given in the teacher's book.

The ActiveTeach CD-ROM

The *ActiveTeach* contains interactive versions of the **Teacher's Book, Class Book, Home Book** and a variety of ICT resources. Full notes on how to use the *ActiveTeach* are included on the CD-ROM in the Help tab.

Teachers can use the interactive version of the Teacher's Book when they are planning or teaching lessons.

From the contents page of the Teacher's Book, teachers can navigate to the lesson notes for the relevant unit, which are then displayed in a series of double page spreads.

Clicking on the thumbnail of the PowerPoint slide or the triangular icon shown on the edges of the pages allows teachers to view ICT resources, resource sheets, and other Microsoft Office program files. All these resources, as well as exercises in the Class Book and tasks in the Home Book, can be accessed by clicking on the reference to the resource in the main text.

There is also an option for teachers to use a resource palette to put together their own set of resources ready for a particular lesson, choosing from any of the *Exploring maths* resources in any tier, and adding their own if they wish. This option will be especially useful for teachers of mixed ability classes.

Interactive versions of the Class Book and Home Book can be displayed in class. From the contents page, teachers can go to the relevant unit, which is then shown in a series of double page spreads. It is possible to zoom in and enlarge particular worked examples, diagrams or photographs, points to remember, homework tasks, and so on. Just as in the Teacher's Book, clicking on the triangular icon launches the relevant resource.

ICT resources

Each tier has a full range of ICT resources, including: a custom-built toolkit with over 60 tools, Flash animations, games and quizzes, spreadsheets and slides.

The different resources are coded as follows.

⊙ **Check ups (CU)**

Each unit is supplemented by an optional check-up for pupils in the form of a PDF file to print and copy (see also the section on Assessment for learning).

⊙ **Resource sheets (RS)**

Some units have PDF files of resource sheets to print and copy for pupils to write on in class.

⊙ **Tools (TO)**

These general purpose teaching tools can be used in many different lessons. Examples are:
  – an interactive calculator, similar to an OHP calculator (in most cases, the scientific calculator will be needed);
  – a number line;
  – a graph plotter;
  – simulated dice and spinners;
  – squared paper and dotty paper;
  – drawing tools such as a protractor, ruler and compasses.

⊙ **Simulations (SIM)**

Some of these are animations to play and pause like a video film. Others are interactive and are designed to generate discussion; for example, the teacher may ask pupils to predict an outcome on the screen.

⊙ **Quizzes (QZ)**

These are quizzes of short questions for pupils to answer, e.g. on their individual whiteboards, usually at the start or end of a lesson.

⊙ **Interactive teaching programs (ITP)**

These were produced by the Primary Strategy and are included on the CD-ROM with permission from the DCSF.

⊙ **PowerPoint presentations (thumbnails)**

These are slides to show in lessons. Projected slides can be annotated, either with a whiteboard pen or with the pen tool on an interactive whiteboard. Teachers without access to computer and data projector in their classrooms can print the slides as overhead projector transparencies and annotate them with an OHP pen.

- **Excel files (XL)**

  These are spreadsheets for optional use in particular lessons.

- **Geometer's Sketchpad files (GSP)**

  These are dynamic geometry files for optional use in particular lessons.

  Other ICT resources, such as calculators, are referred to throughout the units.

  The table on p. ix identifies those lessons where pupils have an opportunity to use ICT for themselves.

Assessment for learning

There is a strong emphasis on assessment for learning throughout *Exploring maths*.

- Learning objectives for units as a whole and for individual lessons are shown on slides and in the class book for discussion with pupils.

- Potential misconceptions are listed for teachers in the overview pages of each unit.

- Key questions for teachers to ask informally are identified in the lesson notes.

- The review that concludes every lesson allows the teacher to judge the effectiveness of the learning and to stress the learning points that pupils should remember.

- The points to remember are repeated in the class book and home book.

- A self-assessment section for pupils, 'How well are you doing?', is included in each unit in the class book to help pupils to judge for themselves their grasp of the work.

- Optional revision lessons provide extra support in those areas where pupils commonly have difficulty.

- Each unit on the CD-ROM includes an optional check-up of written questions.

- Each number unit of the teacher's book includes an optional mental test of 12 questions for teachers to read to the class.

The mental test could be used as an alternative to part of the last lesson of the unit. About 20 minutes of lesson time is needed to give the test and for pupils to mark it. Answers are on the same sheet.

The written check-ups include occasional questions from national tests. Teachers could use some or all of the questions, not necessarily on the same occasion, and pupils could complete them in class, at home, or as part of an informal test. For example, some written questions could be substituted for the final homework of a unit and the mental test could be used as an alternative to part of the last lesson. Answers to the written check-ups are given in the teacher's book.

Computer-mediated assessments

Exploring maths is complemented by *Results Plus Progress*, a series of stimulating on-line computer-mediated assessments supporting Key Stage 3 mathematics, available separately.

There is an entry test for Year 7 to guide teachers on placing pupils in an appropriate tier at the start of the course. For each of Years 7, 8 and 9, there are two end-of-term assessments for the autumn and spring terms, and an end-of-year assessment.

Each product offers sets of interactive test questions that pupils answer on computers, either in school or on home computers with internet access. Because the tests are taken electronically, the products offer instant marking and analysis tools to identify strengths and weaknesses of individuals or groups of pupils. Future units from *Exploring maths* that are dependent on the same skills are identified so that teachers are aware of the units that they may need to adapt, perhaps by adding in extra revision or support lessons.

Results Plus Progress has been developed by the Test Development Team at Edexcel, who have considerable experience in producing the statutory national end-of-key-stage tests and the optional tests for Years 7 and 8.

Where can I find...?

Historical and cultural references

N4.1	Brahmagupta and the use of negative numbers and zero	Class book p. 3
	Euclid, who proved the existence of an infinite number of prime numbers	Class book p. 11
G4.1	Euclid	Class book p. 21
	Euclid and the Elements of Geometry	Home book p. 10
N4.2	The discovery of Kaprekar's constant for four digit numbers	Class book p. 48
S4.1	Pascal and Fermat, and their contribution to the mathematics of probability	Class book p. 58
G4.2	The first computer spreadsheet	Class book p. 84
A4.2	The origin and common uses of imperial measures	Class book p. 88
N4.3	George Salmon and his work on recurring decimals	Class book p. 109
	The evolution of the percent sign	Class book p. 119
S4.2	William Playfair and the use of the first pie chart	Class book p. 128
	Florence Nightingale and the use of statistical diagrams for persuasion	Class book p. 139
A4.3	Descartes and his naming of Cartesian Coordinates	Class book p. 146
N4.4	The first use of the ratio symbol in 1633	Class book p. 162
	Old tables of weights and measures	Class book p. 174
	The 200 BCE Chinese text, the *Jiuzhang suanshu*, on how to use mathematics to solve problems	Class book p. 177
G4-3	M.C. Escher and tessellating shapes	Class book p. 189
A4.4	Fibonacci and the earliest known use of the word 'equation'	Class book p. 203
	Al-Khwarizmi and the origins of algebra	Class book p. 212
S4.3	The units of length used by the ancient Egyptians in 3000 BCE	Class book p. 219
	Murphy's law	Class book p. 230
G4.4	Leonardo da Vinci and his love of geometry, particularly constructions	Class book p. 288
	The origin of the Olympic logo of interlocking circles	Class book p. 241
N4.5	The early Chinese decimal number system and the abacus	Class book p. 286
	The Rhind papyrus and the Egyptian method of multiplication, based on doubling	Class book p. 288
	The evolution of Hindu-Arabic numerals	Class book p. 290
	The puzzles of the American puzzlist Sam Lloyd (1841–1911)	Class book p. 291
	The SEND + MORE = MONEY magazine puzzle	Class book p. 292
	The history of counting	Slide presentation

ICT lessons: hands-on for pupils

Pupils have many opportunities for hands on use of ICT.

N4.1	Lesson 2: Using the $(-)$ or $+/-$ key on a calculator	Teacher's book p. 6
	Lesson 3: Using the $(-)$ or $+/-$ key on a calculator	Teacher's book p. 8
	Lesson 4: Using the $\sqrt[x]{}$ and x^y keys on a calculator	Teacher's book p. 10
A4.1	Lesson 3: Using a spreadsheet to generate sequences	Teacher's book p. 46
N4.2	Lesson 4: Using the memory keys on a calculator	Teacher's book p. 62
	Lesson 5: Using the fraction key on a calculator	Teacher's book p. 64
S4.1	Lesson 4 (optional): Using the probability tools	Teacher's book p. 82
	Lesson 6 (optional): Using ICT number spinners	Teacher's book p. 86
N4.3	Lesson 1: Using a calculator to convert fractions to decimals	Teacher's book p. 126
	Lesson 2: Using a calculator to multiply fractions	Teacher's book p. 128
	Lesson 5: Using a calculator to find percentages	Teacher's book p. 134
	Lesson 6: Using a spreadsheet to calculate discounts	Teacher's book p. 136
A4.3	Lesson 4: Using graph-plotting software to investigate graphs of the form $y = ax$	Teacher's book p. 176
G4.3	Lesson 2: Exploring transformations using Transformation Golf	Teacher's book p. 212
S4.3	Lessons 3 and 4: Using ICT to create statistical diagrams and present reports	Teacher's book p. 258
G4.4	Lesson 4: Constructing triangles using dynamic geometry software	Teacher's book p. 284
	Lesson 9: Using ICT to explore loci	Teacher's book p. 294

Related units

Units from different tiers can be aligned if necessary.

For example, Unit N4.1 *Properties of numbers* in Tier 4 can be used alongside the Tier 3 Unit N3.1 *Properties of numbers* and the Tier 5 Unit N5.1 *Powers and roots*.

Tier 3	Tier 4	Tier 5
N3.1 Properties of numbers	N4.1 Properties of numbers	N5.1 Powers and roots
N3.2 Whole numbers and decimals	N4.2 Whole numbers, decimals and fractions	
N3.3 Fractions and percentages N3.4 Decimals and measures	N4.3 Fractions, decimals and percentages	N5.3 Calculations and calculators
N3.5 Percentages, ratio and proportion	N4.4 Proportional reasoning	N5.2 Proportional reasoning
N3.6 Solving number problems	N4.5 Solving problems	N5.4 Solving problems
A3.1 Patterns and sequences A3.3 Sequences, functions and graphs	A4.1 Linear sequences A4.3 Functions and graphs	A5.1 Sequences and graphs A5.3 Functions and graphs
A3.2 Equations and formulae A3.4 Functions, equations and graphs	A4.2 Expressions and formulae A4.4 Equations and formulae	A5.2 Equations and formulae A5.5 Equations, formulae and graphs
	A4.5 Using algebra	A5.4 Using algebra
G3.4 Properties of shapes		
G3.2 Angles	G4.1 Angles and shapes	G5.4 2D and 3D shapes
G3.5 Constructions	G4.4 Constructions	G5.1 Angles and constructions
G3.3 Transformations	G4.3 Transformations	G5.3 Transformations
G3.1 Mensuration N3.4 Decimals and measures	G4.2 Measures and mensuration	G5.2 Measures and mensuration
S3.1 Grouped data and simple statistics		
S3.3 Enquiry 1	S4.2 Enquiry 1	S5.1 Enquiry 1
S3.4 Enquiry 2	S4.3 Enquiry 2	S5.3 Enquiry 2
S3.2 Probability 1	S4.1 Probability	S5.2 Probability 1
S3.5 Probability 2		S5.4 Probability 2
R3.1 Revision unit 1	R4.1 Revision unit 1	R5.1 Revision unit 1
R3.2 Revision unit 2	R4.2 Revision unit 2	R5.2 Revision unit 2

Contents

Properties of numbers

Before they start, pupils should be able to:

- ◉ order, add and subtract positive and negative integers in context
- ◉ use simple tests of divisibility
- ◉ recognise square numbers to 12 × 12 and the corresponding roots
- ◉ use the bracket keys and memory of a calculator.

Objectives based on NC levels 5 and 6 (mainly level 5)

In this unit, pupils learn to:

- ◉ identify the mathematical features of a context or problem
- ◉ try out and compare mathematical representations
- ◉ conjecture and generalise, identifying exceptional cases
- ◉ calculate accurately, selecting mental methods or a calculator as appropriate
- ◉ use accurate notation
- ◉ refine own findings and approaches on the basis of discussion with others
- ◉ record methods, solutions and conclusions

and to:

- ◉ add, subtract, multiply and divide integers
- ◉ use the order of operations, including brackets, with more complex calculations
- ◉ use multiples, factors, common factors, highest common factor, lowest common multiple and primes
- ◉ find the prime factorisation of a number (e.g. $8000 = 2^6 \times 5^3$)
- ◉ use squares, positive and negative square roots, cubes and cube roots, and index notation for small positive integer powers
- ◉ strengthen and extend mental methods of calculation
- ◉ use the function keys of a calculator for sign change, brackets, powers and roots, and interpret the display in context.

Lessons

1. **Order of operations**
2. **Adding and subtracting directed numbers**
3. **Multiplying and dividing directed numbers**
4. **Powers and roots**
5. **Multiples, factors and primes**

About this unit

A good 'feel for number' means that pupils are aware of relationships between numbers and know at a glance which properties they possess and which they do not. A sound understanding of the order of operations and powers and roots of numbers helps them to generalise the principles in their later work in algebra.

Assessment

This unit includes:

- ◉ an optional mental test that could replace part of a lesson (p. 14);
- ◉ a self-assessment section (*N4.1 How well are you doing?* class book p. 14);
- ◉ a set of questions to replace or supplement questions in the exercises or homework tasks, or to use as an informal test (*N4.1 Check up*, CD-ROM).

Common errors and misconceptions	Look out for pupils who:

Common errors and misconceptions

Look out for pupils who:

- disregard brackets, e.g. $7 - (4 + 1) = 7 - 4 + 1$;
- wrongly apply the order of operations, including when using a calculator;
- confuse positive and negative integers with addition and subtraction operations, e.g. $(-3) + (-2) = 5$, $(-8) + (+6) = 2$;
- confuse the highest common factor (HCF) and lowest common multiple (LCM);
- assume that the lowest common multiple of a and b is always $a \times b$;
- think that n^2 means $n \times 2$, or that $\sqrt{n}$ means $\frac{n}{2}$.

Key terms and notation

problem, solution, method, pattern, relationship, expression, order, solve, explain, systematic

calculate, calculation, calculator, operation, add, subtract, multiply, divide, divisible, sum, total, difference, product, quotient

greater than ($>$), less than ($<$), value

positive, negative, integer, odd, even, multiple, factor, prime, power, square, cube, root, square root, cube root, digit sum, notation n^2 and $\sqrt{n}$, n^3 and $\sqrt[3]{n}$

Practical resources

scientific calculators for pupils   individual whiteboards

Exploring maths

Tier 4 teacher's book
N4.1 Mental test, p. 14
Answers for N4.1, pp. 16 – 19

Tier 4 CD-ROM
PowerPoint files
    N4.1 Slides for lessons 1 to 5
Tools and prepared toolsheets
    N4.1 Toolsheets for lesson 2
    Calculator tool
    Number jumps tool
Tier 4 programs
    Target
    Directed numbers ($+$ and $-$) quiz
    Directed numbers ($\times$ and $\div$) quiz
    Ladder method

Tier 4 class book
N4.1, pp. 1 – 14
N4.1 How well are you doing?, p. 14

Tier 4 home book
N4.1, pp. 1 – 3

Tier 4 CD-ROM
N4.1 Check up
N4.1 Pupil resource sheets
    2.1 One per pupil
    3.1 One per pupil

Useful websites

Circle 0, Diffy, Factor tree
nlvm.usu.edu/en/nav/category_g_3_t_1.html

Grid game
www.bbc.co.uk/education/mathsfile/gameswheel.html

Multiplication square jigsaw
nrich.maths.org/public/viewer.php?obj_id=5573

Factor squares
nrich.maths.org/public/viewer.php?obj_id=5468

1 Order of operations

Learning points

- Deal with brackets first.
- When there are no brackets, multiply and divide before you add and subtract.

Starter

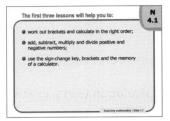

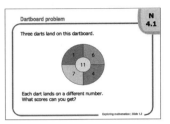

Show **slide 1.1**. Discuss the objectives for the first three lessons. Say that this lesson is about working out calculations in the correct order.

Show **slide 1.2**. Say that three darts have landed on different numbers.

> **What is the least possible score?** [11]
> **What is the greatest possible score?** [24]

Ask pupils to write the numbers 11 to 24 in a list in their books. Record $1 + 4 + 6$ next to 11, and $6 + 7 + 11$ next to 24.

> **What other scores are possible?**

Give pupils a minute or two to find the scores that they can make with three darts on different numbers. They should discover that 13, 15, 20 and 23 are not possible.

> **Can you make the missing scores if two darts land on the same number?**
> [e.g. $1 + 1 + 11 = 13$; $4 + 4 + 7 = 15$; $6 + 7 + 7 = 20$; $6 + 6 + 11 = 23$]

Main activity

Revise the order of operations: brackets first, then squares, then multiplication and division, then addition and subtraction. Demonstrate some examples.

Example 1	$6 \times 3^2 - 15 \div 3$
Work out the square:	$6 \times 9 - 15 \div 3$
Then the division:	$6 \times 9 - 5$
Then the multiplication:	$54 - 5$
Finally, the subtraction:	49

Example 2	$(2 + 4)^2 \times 5 \div 6$
Work out the bracket:	$6^2 \times 5 \div 6$
Then the square:	$36 \times 5 \div 6$
Then the multiplication:	$180 \div 6$
Finally, the division:	30

Introduce nested brackets (usually round brackets inside square ones).

Example 3	$45 \div [11 - (5 - 3)]$
Work out the inside bracket:	$45 \div [11 - 2]$
Then the remaining bracket:	$45 \div 9$
Finally, the division:	5

Example 4	$50 \div [50 \div (20 \div 2)]$
Work out the inside bracket:	$50 \div [50 \div 10]$
Then the remaining bracket:	$50 \div 5$
Finally, the division:	10

Remind pupils of the meaning of the square-root sign (√). As a class, work through **N4.1 Exercise 1** questions 1 and 2 in the class book (p. 2). Ask pupils to write answers on their whiteboards.

Use the **Calculator tool** to show or remind pupils how to use their calculator bracket keys. Repeat examples 2, 3 and 4 above using a calculator.

TO

Ask pupils to do the rest of **N4.1 Exercise 1** in the class book (p. 2).

Review   Give pupils a target number, say 16. Ask them to make a calculation using all the numbers 2, 4, 7 and 10 once, with 16 as the answer, e.g. $(2 \times 7 - 10) \times 4$.

Launch **Target** to give further problems. Use the operation signs, brackets and the given single-digit numbers to make the target number.
Remind pupils of the learning points for the lesson.

SIM

Homework   Ask pupils to do **N4.1 Task 1** in the home book (p. 1).

2 Adding and subtracting directed numbers

Learning points

☺ When you are adding or subtracting positive and negative numbers, two signs together can be regarded as one sign:

$+ \ +$ is $+$ $+ \ -$ is $-$ $- \ +$ is $-$ $- \ -$ is $+$

Two signs that are the same can be regarded as $+$.
Two signs that are different can be regarded as $-$.

Starter

Say that this lesson is about adding and subtracting positive and negative numbers.

Use **Toolsheet 2.1**, a number line from -5 to 5. Remind pupils that positive numbers have a $+$ sign in front of them, although we don't always write it. Negative numbers have a $-$ sign in front of them. We always write the $-$ sign.

Point to zero. Give an instruction, such as 'add 3'. Ask pupils as a whole class to say where this would take them on the line. Repeat with another instruction, such as 'subtract 5'. Ask again where this would take them. Give more instructions, including some that land on numbers beyond the line on the board.

If you wish, use the **Number jumps tool** to show the effect of 'add 3' by clicking on the line on the start and end values of the jump.

Main activity

Discuss examples of adding positive and negative numbers. You could interpret the first number as a starting temperature and the second as a rise or fall, for example:

$6 + (+2) = 8$ Start with 6°C, and add a rise of 2 degrees.
$2 + (-7) = -5$ Start with 2°C, and add a fall of 7 degrees.
$(-3) + (+4) = 1$ Start with -3°C, and add a rise of 4 degrees.
$(-5) + (-3) = -8$ Start with -5°C, and add a fall of 3 degrees.

Not all calculators have a sign-change key. If there is a sign-change key on your pupils' calculators (e.g. $\boxed{+/-}$ or $\boxed{(-)}$), point it out and explain that it can be used for calculations with negative numbers. Modify the instructions below to suit your calculators.

Use the **Calculator tool** to demonstrate how to input the negative number -2 by typing $\boxed{(-)}\boxed{2}$, which should give a display -2.
Repeat the calculations already on the board using the calculator:

Key in $\boxed{6}\boxed{+}\boxed{2}\boxed{=}$ The display should show 8.
Key in $\boxed{2}\boxed{+}\boxed{(-)}\boxed{7}\boxed{=}$ The display should show -5.
Key in $\boxed{(-)}\boxed{3}\boxed{+}\boxed{4}\boxed{=}$ The display should show 1.
Key in $\boxed{(-)}\boxed{5}\boxed{+}\boxed{(-)}\boxed{3}\boxed{=}$ The display should show -8.

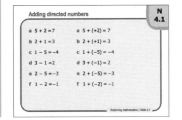

Refer pupils to the first set of calculations on **slide 2.1**. Get them to call out the answers as you run through them.

Display the second set of questions. This time ask pupils to use their own calculators to key in the calculation.

What do you notice about the two sets of answers?

Draw out the rules that two signs together can be thought of as one sign. Establish that $+ +$ is equivalent to $+$, and $+ -$ is equivalent to $-$.

Give out **N4.1 Resource sheet 2.1**. Complete the first addition table as a whole class, asking pupils to fill in the blank boxes as you go. Ask pupils to complete the second addition table in pairs. For answers, see p. 16.

> RS

Say that it is best to think of subtraction as a difference. Use the context of temperature differences to illustrate, recording each calculation on the board:

$5 - (-3) = 8$	From $-3°C$ to $5°C$ is a rise of 8 degrees.
$(-3) - (-8) = 5$	From $-8°C$ to $-3°C$ is a rise of 5 degrees.
$6 - 9 = -3$	From $9°C$ to $6°C$ is a fall of 3 degrees.
$(-3) - 4 = -7$	From $4°C$ to $-3°C$ is a fall of 7 degrees.

Alternatively, use **Toolsheet 2.2** showing a vertical number line from -8 to 8.

> TO

As before, repeat the calculations on the board using calculators.

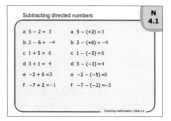

Refer pupils to the first set of calculations on **slide 2.2**. Get them to call out the answers as you run through them.

Display the second set of questions. This time ask pupils to key in the calculation and use the sign-change key to obtain the answers.

What do you notice about the two sets of answers?

Draw out that $- -$ is equivalent to $+$, and $- +$ is equivalent to $-$.

Refer pupils again to **Resource sheet 2.1**. Complete the first subtraction table as a class. Ask pupils to complete the second table on their own. For answers, see p. 19.

> RS

Select further individual work from **N4.1 Exercise 2** in the class book (p. 3).

Review   Launch **Directed numbers (+ and −)**. Use 'Next' and 'Back' to move through the questions. Ask pupils to answer on their whiteboards, or refer a question to an individual pupil to respond. Pause now and then to ask pupils how they worked out the answer. Discuss and rectify errors and misunderstandings. Summarise the rules for adding and subtracting directed numbers.

> QZ

Homework   Ask pupils to do **N4.1 Task 2** in the home book (p. 1).

3 Multiplying and dividing directed numbers

Learning points

◉ For addition or subtraction of directed numbers, two signs together can be regarded as one sign:
  $+\,+$ is $+$ $+\,-$ is $-$ $-\,+$ is $-$ $-\,-$ is $+$

◉ For multiplication or division of directed numbers, two signs that are the same results in $+$ and two signs that are different results in $-$.
  $+\times+$ is $+$ $+\times-$ is $-$ $-\times+$ is $-$ $-\times-$ is $+$

Starter

Say that the lesson is about multiplying and dividing positive and negative numbers.

Discuss the signs $<$ and $>$. Give some pairs of directed numbers (e.g. 4 and -2, -3 and -5) and ask pupils to insert $<$ or $>$ between them on their whiteboards.

Introduce the $\leqslant$ and $\geqslant$ signs. Explain that if n is an integer and $-2 \leqslant n \leqslant 1$, then the possible values for n are -2, -1, 0 or $+1$, and that if $-5 \geqslant n \geqslant -7$, then n could be -5, -6 or -7.

Tell pupils that N is an integer lying between -4 and $+6$, and that $N \neq 1$. Ask pupils to decide in pairs on some statements that describe the possible values of N (e.g. $-4 < N \leqslant 0$ and $2 \leqslant N < 6$).

Main activity

Remind pupils that $2 + 2 + 2 = 2 \times 3 = 6$.

Similarly, $(-2) + (-2) + (-2) = (-2) \times 3 = -6$. Explain that we can also write this as $3 \times (-2) = 6$.

Develop the multiplication table on the right. Point out the patterns. The left-hand column is decreasing by 1 and the right-hand column is increasing by 2.

$$(+3) \times (-2) = -6$$
$$(+2) \times (-2) = -4$$
$$(+1) \times (-2) = -2$$
$$(\,0\,) \times (-2) = 0$$
$$(-1) \times (-2) = +2$$
$$(-2) \times (-2) = +4$$
$$(-3) \times (-2) = +6$$

Use the patterns to continue the table.

RS

Give out **N4.1 Resource sheet 3.1**. Complete the first multiplication table as a whole class, asking pupils to fill in the blank boxes as you go along.

Ask pupils if they can see a quick way of working out products such as:

$(-2) \times (+3)$ or $(-3) \times (-2)$ or $(+1) \times (+3)$

They should notice that multiplication where the two signs are the same results in $+$ and multiplication where the two signs are different results in $-$. Demonstrate the use of the sign-change key on the calculator, adapting the instructions below for your calculators:

Key in $\boxed{3}\,\boxed{\times}\,\boxed{(-)}\,\boxed{4}\,\boxed{=}$ The display should show -12.
Key in $\boxed{(-)}\,\boxed{5}\,\boxed{\times}\,\boxed{(-)}\,\boxed{8}\,\boxed{=}$ The display should show 40.

Refer again to **N4.1 Resource sheet 3.1**. Complete the first multiplication table as a whole class, asking pupils to fill in the blank boxes as you go. Ask pupils to complete the second and third tables in pairs. For answers, see p. 16.

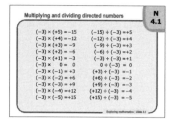

Remind pupils that if we know that $4 \times 8 = 32$, we also know that $32 \div 4 = 8$ and $32 \div 8 = 4$. Show **slide 3.1** and complete the patterns with the class.

Link to division, for example:

if $(-3) \times (+5) = -15$, then $(-15) \div (-3) = +5$ and $(-15) \div (+5) = -3$

Repeat with:

$(+3) \times (-6) = -18$, so $(-18) \div (-6) = +3$ and $(-18) \div (+3) = -6$

$(-4) \times (-7) = +28$, so $(+28) \div (-7) = -4$ and $(+28) \div (-4) = -7$

Pupils should notice that division where the two signs are the same results in $+$ and division where the two signs are different results in $-$.

Write on the board one or two questions for pupils to answer on whiteboards, for example:

$\square \times (-7) = 56$ \qquad $24 \div \square = -8$

Now ask them to evaluate some expressions, such as:

$(-7)^2 - 5$ \quad $[(-6) + 2]^2 + 3$ \quad $20 - (4 - 1)^2$ \quad $[(-4) + 2] \times (3 - 7)$

> Ask pupils to do **N4.1 Exercise 3** in the class book (p. 7).

Review Go through solutions to Exercise 3. Invite individual pupils to explain their methods.

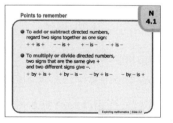

Launch **Directed numbers ($\times$ and $\div$)**. Use 'Next' and 'Back' to move through the questions. Ask pupils to answer on their whiteboards, or refer a question to an individual pupil. Discuss and rectify errors and misunderstandings.

Summarise the learning points from this and the previous lesson using **slide 3.2**.

Homework Ask pupils to do **N4.1 Task 3** in the home book (p. 2).

4 Powers and roots

Learning points

- The square of a number n is n^2 or $n \times n$.
  Examples: $9^2 = 9 \times 9 = 81$, $(-9)^2 = -9 \times -9 = 81$

- The square root of n is $\sqrt{n}$.
  Example: $\sqrt{81} = \pm 9$

- The cube of a number n is n^3 or $n \times n \times n$.
  Examples: $5^3 = 5 \times 5 \times 5 = 125$, $(-5)^3 = -5 \times -5 \times -5 = -125$

- The cube root of n is $\sqrt[3]{n}$.
  Example: $\sqrt[3]{125} = 5$

- When a negative number is raised to an even power, the result is positive.
  When a negative number is raised to an odd power, the result is negative.

Starter

Say that this lesson is about powers and roots of numbers.

Remind pupils that $(-2) \times (-2) = 4$ and $2 \times 2 = 4$. So every square number such as 4 has two square roots, one positive and one negative. Ask the class: 'What is the square root of …?' using some of the square numbers up to 12×12.

Discuss how to estimate the positive square root of a number that is not a perfect square. For example, $\sqrt{60}$ must lie between $\sqrt{49}$ and $\sqrt{64}$, i.e. $7 < \sqrt{60} < 8$, but as 60 is closer to 64 than to 49, $\sqrt{60}$ must be closer to 8 than to 7, perhaps about 7.8.

$$\underset{7}{\sqrt{49}} \qquad\qquad \underset{\uparrow}{\sqrt{60}} \quad \underset{8}{\sqrt{64}}$$

Use the **Calculator tool** to show how to use the square and square-root keys. You may need to explain that on some calculators the square-root key is pressed before the number and on others afterwards, and that most calculators give only the positive square root.

Explain that the cube root of 125 is 5, and that we write $\sqrt[3]{125} = 5$. The fourth root of 1296 is $+6$ or -6, and we write $\sqrt[4]{1296} = \pm 6$.

Some calculators have a cube root key $\boxed{\sqrt[3]{}}$. For other roots, keys vary from calculator to calculator, for example $\boxed{\sqrt[x]{}}$. Demonstrate how these keys work on your calculators.

Main activity

Explain the notation $13 \times 13 \times 13 = 13^3$, or 13 cubed. In general, a^3 means $a \times a \times a$, a^4 means $a \times a \times a \times a$, a^5 means $a \times a \times a \times a \times a$, and so on. Explain that a^n is usually read as 'a to the power n' and means a multiplied by itself n times.

If $a = 5$, what is a^3? If $a = -2$, what is a^3?

If $a = 3$, what is a^4? If $a = -1$, what is a^4?

Draw out that when a negative number is raised to an even power the result is positive, and when a negative number is raised to an odd power the result is negative.

Use the **Calculator tool** to show pupils how to use the x^y keys of their calculators.

Discuss the powers of 10 ($10^0 = 1$, $10^1 = 10$, $10^2 = 100$, $10^3 = 1000$, and so on) and their importance in the decimal number system.

Repeat with 3^5 and 4^6, then use the calculator to explore what happens when a number is raised to the power 0. Explain that this is always has the answer 1.

Write on the board: $\square \times \square \times \square = 2197$. Say that each box represents the same number. Let pupils try to find a solution with their calculators. After a couple of minutes stop them and explain that using reasoning will lead more quickly to the answer.

> Could the number in each box be a negative number?

> Is the number greater than 10? Is it greater than 20?
> How do you know?

> What would be a good number to try next?

Agree that trying $15 \times 15 \times 15$ to see whether it is too big or too small cuts the possibilities by half. The remaining possibilities are 11, 12, 13 and 14.

> If the box represents an even number, is the answer odd or even?

Say that there are now two possibilities: 11 and 13. Ask which is more likely?

Get pupils to consider the last digit in each case. Confirm that 13 is correct by getting pupils to find $13 \times 13 \times 13$ using their calculators.

> Select individual work from **N4.1 Exercise 4** in the class book (p. 9).

Review

Pose the problems on **slide 4.1**.

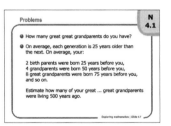

Establish that each person has $2 = 2^1$ birth parents, $4 = 2^2$ grandparents, $8 = 2^3$ great grandparents, …, $2^5 = 32$ great great great grandparents.

500 years is about 20 generations, so each person had about $2^{20} = 1\,048\,576$ ancestors living 500 years ago. (The population of England in 1500 was roughly 1 million, so they could all be your ancestors, provided that all your ancestors were living in England at that time and families didn't intermarry too much.)

Ask pupils to remember the points on **slide 4.2**.

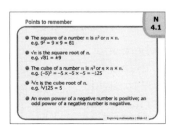

Homework

Ask pupils to do **N4.1 Task 4** in the home book (p. 2).

5 Multiples, factors and primes

Learning points

◉ Writing a number as the product of its prime factors is called the prime factor decomposition of the number.

◉ To find the highest common factor (HCF) of a pair of numbers, find the product of all the prime factors common to both numbers.

◉ To find the lowest common multiple (LCM) of a pair of numbers, find the smallest number that is a multiple of each of the numbers.

Starter

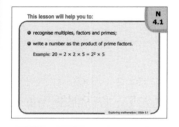

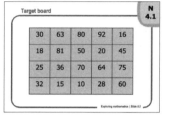

Use **slide 5.1** to discuss the objectives for this lesson. Remind pupils that:

◉ the factors of a number are all the numbers that divide into it exactly, so that the factors of 6 are 1, 2, 3 and 6, and the factors of 9 are 1, 3 and 9;

◉ factors can be paired (for 6, the factor pairs are 1 and 6, 2 and 3), except for square numbers, which have an odd number of factors (for 4, the factors are 1, 2 and 4);

◉ the number itself and 1 are always one of the factor pairs and, for prime numbers, they are the only factors.

Show the target board on **slide 5.2**. Point at a number and ask pupils to write all its factor pairs on their whiteboards.

Main activity

Write on the board a list of the first few primes: 2, 3, 5, 7, 11, 13, …

What are all these numbers?

Establish that they are all prime. Explain that when a number is expressed as the product of its prime factors we call it the *prime factor decomposition* of a number.

How can we find the prime factor decomposition of 48?

Explain the tree method, i.e. split 48 into a product such as 12×4, then continue factorising any number in the product that is not a prime. Repeat with 200.

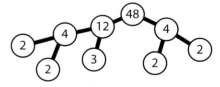

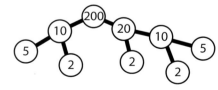

SIM

Launch **Ladder method**. Drag numbers from the grid to where you need them. For example, drag 75 from the grid to the box, then drag a prime factor of 75 (e.g. 3) to the circle, and so on. Continue to divide by prime numbers until the answer is 1. Express the answer as $75 = 5 \times 5 \times 3$. Repeat with another example, such as 98.

$$\begin{array}{r|r} 3 & 75 \\ 5 & 25 \\ 5 & 5 \\ \hline & 1 \end{array}$$

Show how to find the highest common factor (HCF) and lowest common multiple (LCM) of a pair of numbers.

Find the prime factors of 18 = 2 × 3 × 3 and 30 = 2 × 3 × 5. Represent the prime factors in a Venn diagram. Explain that:

- the overlapping prime factors give the HCF (2 × 3 = 6);

- all the prime factors give the LCM (2 × 3 × 3 × 5 = 90).
  Repeat with another example, e.g. 10 and 24 (HCF = 2; LCM = 120).

Ask pupils to do **N4.1 Exercise 5** in the class book (p. 12).

Review

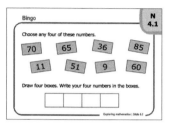

Finish with a game of Bingo. Show **slide 5.3**. Ask pupils to draw four boxes, choose four different numbers from the slide and write them in their boxes in any order.

Read out the clues below in any order. If pupil have the answer in one of their boxes they can cross it out. The first player to cross out all four numbers calls out 'Bingo!'.

- A multiple of 3 and of 4 less than 50 [36]
- An even multiple of 7 [84]
- The highest common factor of 81 and 18 [9]
- A multiple of 17 [51]
- The lowest common multiple of 12 and 20 [60]
- A multiple of 5 and of 7 [70]
- The highest common factor of 33 and 55 [11]
- A multiple of 13 [65]

Sum up the lesson using points on **slide 5.4**.

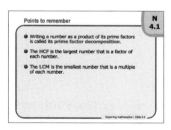

Round off the unit by referring again to the objectives. Suggest that pupils find time to try the self-assessment problems in **N4.1 How well are you doing?** in the class book (p. 14).

Homework Ask pupils to do **N4.1 Task 5** in the home book (p. 3).

N4.1 Mental test

Read each question aloud twice.

Allow a suitable pause for pupils to write answers.

1 What is the smallest whole number that is divisible by five and by three? *2003 KS3*

2 What is the next square number after thirty-six? *2005 PT*

3 The number one is a factor of both fifteen and twenty-four.
What other number is a factor of both fifteen and twenty-four? *2007 KS3*

4 Write down a factor of thirty-six that is greater than ten and less than twenty. *2005 KS3*

5 Write a multiple of nine that is bigger than seventy and smaller than eighty. *2006 KS3*

6 What is the next prime number after nineteen? *2002 KS3*

7 What number should you add to minus three to get the answer five? *2003 KS3*

8 I am thinking of a two-digit number that is a multiple of eight.
The digits add up to six. What number am I thinking of? *2003 KS3*

9 Subtract three from minus five. *2003 KS3*

10 Multiply minus four by minus five. *2007 KS3*

11 What number is five cubed? *2003 KS3*

12 Divide twenty-four by minus six. *2006 KS3*

Key:

KS3 Key Stage 3 test   PT Progress test
Questions 1 to 5 are at level 4; 6 to 9 are at level 5; 10 to 12 are at level 6.

Answers

1	15	**2**	49
3	3	**4**	12 or 18
5	72	**6**	23
7	8	**8**	24
9	-8	**10**	20
11	125	**12**	-4

Check up — N4.1

Write your answers in your book.

Properties of numbers (no calculator)

1. Here is a list of numbers:

   $-7 \quad -4 \quad -3 \quad -1 \quad 2 \quad 4 \quad 6$

   In each question, you must not use a number more than once.
   a Choose two numbers from the list that have a total of 2.
   b Choose two numbers from the list that have a total of -3.
   c Choose three numbers from the list that have the lowest possible total.
      Write the three numbers and their total.
   d Choose two numbers from the list that have a product of -12.
   e Choose two numbers from the list that have a product of 4.

2. Write two square numbers that total 45.
   $\square + \square = 45$

3. Look at these numbers.

   $6^1 \quad 5^2 \quad 4^3 \quad 3^4 \quad 2^5 \quad 1^6$

   a Which is the largest?
   b Which has the same value as 2^6?

Properties of numbers (calculator allowed)

4. Write the three prime numbers which multiply to make 231.
   $\square \times \square \times \square = 231$

5. This three-digit number has 2 and 9 as factors.
   378
   Write another three-digit number which has 2 and 9 as factors.

6. Write a multiple of 67 lying between 500 and 600.

Resource sheet 2.1 — N4.1

Write your answers on the sheet.

1. Complete these addition tables.

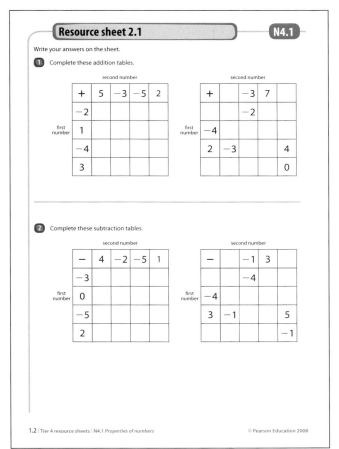

second number

+	5	-3	-5	2
-2				
1				
-4				
3				

first number (rows)

second number

+		-3	7	
		-2		
-4				
2	-3			4
				0

first number (rows)

2. Complete these subtraction tables.

second number

$-$	4	-2	-5	1
-3				
0				
-5				
2				

first number (rows)

second number

$-$		-1	3	
		-4		
-4				
3	-1			5
				-1

first number (rows)

Resource sheet 3.1 — N4.1

Write your answers on the sheet.

1. Complete this multiplication table. Use the patterns in the table to help you.

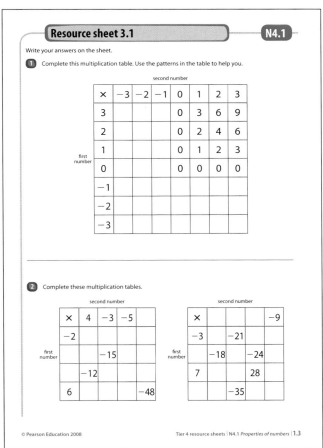

second number

×	-3	-2	-1	0	1	2	3
3				0	3	6	9
2				0	2	4	6
1				0	1	2	3
0				0	0	0	0
-1							
-2							
-3							

first number (rows)

2. Complete these multiplication tables.

second number

×	4	-3	-5	
-2				
		-15		
	-12			
6				-48

first number (rows)

second number

×				-9
-3		-21		
	-18		-24	
7			28	
		-35		

first number (rows)

Class book

Exercise 1

1 a 24 b 0.5 c 10
  d 50 e 12 f 10
  g 12.5 h 4 i 1.25

2 a $2 \times (9 - 1) = 16$
  b $(5 + 3) \times 2 = 16$
  c $(2 + 3) \times (1 + 4) = 25$
  d $3 + [7 \times (4 - 1)] = 24$
  e $10 - [6 \times (3 \div 2)] = 1$
  f $90 \div [20 - (13 - 2)] = 10$
  g $5 \times (6 - 3) - 2 = 13$
  h $[9 - (8 - 1)] \times 8 = 16$

3 a 4.41 b 12 c 41.811
  d 8.17 e 24.7 f 42.2
  g 76.25

4 a $(37 \times 21) + 223 = 1000$
  b $(756 \div 18) \times 29 = 1218$
  c $27 + (36 \times 18) = 675$
  d $31 \times (87 - 19) = 2108$
  e $(486 \div 18) - 15 = 12$
  f $(56 \times 63) \div 49 = 72$
  g $837 - (46 \times 12) = 285$
  h $52 \times (96 + 16) = 5824$

Exercise 2

1 a

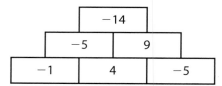

  b

  c

d

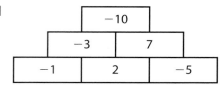

2 a

−5	−1	0
3	−2	−7
−4	−3	1

  b

−4	−3	−8
−9	−5	−1
−2	−7	−6

  c

3	−2	−4	−9
−7	−6	−4	5
−8	1	−3	−2
0	−5	−1	−6

3 a $2 + (-5) + \mathbf{7} = 4$
  b $(-3) - \mathbf{(-8)} - 8 = -3$
  c $7 - \mathbf{(-2)} + (-8) = 1$
  d $\mathbf{(-5)} + 6 - (-3) = 4$
  e $\mathbf{(-5)} + 7 + \mathbf{(-2)} = 0$
  f $12 - \mathbf{9} - \mathbf{3} = 0$
  g $3 + \mathbf{(-8)} + \mathbf{7} = 2$
  h $\mathbf{2} - \mathbf{(-2)} + \mathbf{(-5)} = -1$
  i $(-2) + \mathbf{(-8)} = -10$
  j $(-2) - \mathbf{9} = -11$
  k $(-1) - \mathbf{(-8)} = 7$
  l $\mathbf{9} - 4 = 5$

Extension problem

4 A = −4
  B = −2
  C = 0
  D = 2
  E = −5
  F = 1
  G = 5
  H = −1
  I = 7

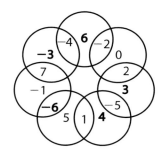

Exercise 3

1

A	B
3	−6
−15	−3
−8	−2
−3	2

A + B	A − B	A × B	A ÷ B
−3	9	−18	−0.5
−18	−12	45	5
−10	−6	16	4
−1	−5	−6	−1.5

2 a −24   b 5   c −2
    d 12   e −12   f −2.5
    g −72   h 200   i −6

3 a 20 points   b −3 points
    c −16 points   d 8 correct
    e 8 wrong   f 28 questions

4 a $2 \times [(-5) + 4] = -2$
    b $[(-2) + (-6)] \times 3 = -24$
    c $9 - (7 - 4) = 6$
    d $[(-3) \times (-4)] - 6 = 6$
    e $[8 - (-2)] \div (-5) = -2$
    f $14 - (6 - 7) = 15$

5 a 14°F   b 28.4°F   c 68°F
    d 23°F   e −40°F

Extension problem

6 a 12   b −3   c 9
    d 175   e −3   f −8
    g −10   h 4   i −2

Exercise 4

1 a 169   b 256
    c 128   d 1331

2 a 1296   b 117 649
    c 6561   d 177 147
    e 4096   f 24.1
    g 14 172.5   h 9133.7

3 a 56   b 9   c 9
    d 19   e 24   f 2
    g 8.7   h 4.2

4 a $80 = 8^2 + 4^2$ b $61 = 5^2 + 6^2$
    c $104 = 10^2 + 2^2$ d $145 = 8^2 + 9^2$

5 a $16 = 5^2 - 3^2$
    b $40 = 7^2 - 3^2$
    c $144 = 13^2 - 5^2$
    d $77 = 9^2 - 2^2$

6 a 81   b 88   c 27
    d 512   e 729

Extension problem

7

¹2	²1	³4	4
⁴9	1	⁵5	⁶5
⁷4	⁸2	⁹2	8
¹⁰1	4	7	8

Exercise 5

1 a $36 = 2^2 \times 3^2$ b $140 = 2^2 \times 5 \times 7$
    c $128 = 2^7$ d $250 = 2 \times 5^3$
    e $480 = 2^5 \times 3 \times 5$ f $408 = 2^3 \times 3 \times 17$

2 a $28 = 2^2 \times 7$ b $72 = 2^3 \times 3^2$
    c $180 = 2^2 \times 3^2 \times 5$ d $264 = 2^3 \times 3 \times 11$
    e $735 = 3 \times 5 \times 7^2$ f $1656 = 2^3 \times 3^2 \times 23$

3 a 40 and 90
      HCF = 10
      LCM = 360
    b 48 and 42
      HCF = 6
      LCM = 336

4 a 60 and 150
      HCF = 30
      LCM = 300
    b 126 and 210
      HCF = 42
      LCM = 630

5 a 175 and 200
      HCF = 25
      LCM = 1400
    b 112 and 140
      HCF = 28
      LCM = 560
    c 42 and 105
      HCF = 21
      LCM = 210

6 Consider units digits whose products fit the conditions. For example, in the first problem, the two units digits could be 0 and 1, or 4 and 5, or 5 and 6. The two numbers will also be close to $\sqrt{7500}$.

  a $75 \times 76 = 5700$

  b $7 \times 29 \times 37 = 7511$

  c $29 \times 31 \times 33 = 29\,667$

Extension problem

7 To give a zero on the end of a product, we need to consider a multiple of 10, or a multiple of 5 paired with a multiple of 2.

  10! has 2 zeros at the end of it.

  20! has 4 zeros at the end of it.

8 e.g. $1\,000\,000 = 10^6 = 5^6 \times 2^6 = 15\,625 \times 64$

How well are you doing?

1 a $3 + (-2) = 1$, or $6 + (-5) = 1$

  b $(-8) - (-2) = -6$, or $(-5) - 1 = -6$

  c $(-5) \times (-1) = 5$

  d $6 \div (-2) = -3$

2 36 and 64

3 $24^3 = 24 \times 24 \times 24$

  The last digit is the last digit of $4 \times 4 \times 4$, i.e. 4.

4 $5 \times 7 \times 13 = 455$

5 450 or 405

Home book

TASK 1

1 a $(56 - 38) \times 62 = 1116$

  b $(2030 \div 35) + 97 = 155$

  c $650 \div (48 - 35) = 50$

  d $27 \times (13 \times 15) = 5265$

TASK 2

1 a $2 + (-6) = \mathbf{-4}$ **b** $4 - (-1) = \mathbf{5}$

  c $(-4) + (-5) = \mathbf{-9}$ **d** $2 - (\mathbf{-5}) = 7$

  e $9 - \mathbf{6} = 3$ **f** $(\mathbf{-4}) + (-2) = -6$

  g $\mathbf{7} + (-7) = 0$ **h** $2 + (\mathbf{-8}) = -6$

  i $3 - (\mathbf{-5}) = 8$

TASK 3

1 a $2 \times (-6) = \mathbf{-12}$ **b** $4 \div (-1) = \mathbf{-4}$

  c $(-4) \times (-5) = \mathbf{20}$ **d** $14 \div (\mathbf{-7}) = -2$

  e $(-9) \times (\mathbf{-4}) = 36$ **f** $\mathbf{3} \times (-1) = -3$

  g $(-4) \times \mathbf{6} = -24$ **h** $\mathbf{0} \div (-7) = 0$

  i $2 \times (\mathbf{-3}) = -6$ **j** $\mathbf{10} \div (-5) = -2$

  k $3 \times \mathbf{7} = 21$ **l** $(\mathbf{-27}) \div (-3) = 9$

TASK 4

There are 8 different ways of writing 150 as the sum of four squares:

  $1 + 1 + 4 + 144$

  $1 + 4 + 64 + 81$

  $1 + 36 + 49 + 64$

  $4 + 9 + 16 + 121$

  $4 + 16 + 49 + 81$

  $9 + 16 + 25 + 100$

  $16 + 36 + 49 + 49$

  $25 + 25 + 36 + 64$

There are 3 different ways of writing 150 as the sum of three squares:

  $1 + 49 + 100$

  $4 + 25 + 121$

  $25 + 25 + 100$

TASK 5

1 a $84 = 2^2 \times 3 \times 7$ **b** $175 = 5^2 \times 7$

2 a $400 = 2^4 \times 5^2$ **b** $396 = 2^2 \times 3^2 \times 11$

3 a 100 and 150   **b** 78 and 91
     HCF = 50   HCF = 13
     LCM = 300   LCM = 546

4 $7 \times 11 \times 13 = 1001$

CD-ROM

Check up

1 a $6 + (-4) = 2$

  b $(-7) + 4 = -3$

  c $(-7) + (-4) + (-3) = -14$

  d $(-4) \times (-3) = 12$

  e $(-4) \times (-1) = 4$

2 $36 + 9 = 45$

3 a $3^4 = 81$ is the largest.

  b 4^3 has the same value as 2^6.

4 $3 \times 7 \times 11 = 231$

5 Any three-digit multiple of 18 other than 378

6 536

Resource sheet 2.1

1

+	5	−3	−5	2
−2	3	−5	−7	0
1	6	−2	−4	3
−4	1	−7	−9	−2
3	8	0	−2	5

+	−5	−3	7	2
1	−4	−2	8	3
−4	−9	−7	3	−2
2	−3	−1	9	4
−2	−7	−5	5	0

2

−	4	−2	−5	1
−3	−7	−1	2	−4
0	−4	2	5	−1
−5	−9	−3	0	−6
2	−2	4	7	1

−	4	−1	3	−2
−5	−9	−4	−8	−3
−4	−8	−3	−7	−2
3	−1	4	0	5
−3	−7	−2	−6	−1

Resource sheet 3.1

1

×	−3	−2	−1	0	1	2	3
3	−9	−6	−3	0	3	6	9
2	−6	−4	−2	0	2	4	6
1	−3	−2	−1	0	1	2	3
0	0	0	0	0	0	0	0
−1	3	2	1	0	−1	−2	−3
−2	6	4	2	0	−2	−4	−6
−3	9	6	3	0	−3	−6	−9

first number

2

×	4	−3	−5	−8
−2	−8	6	10	16
5	20	−15	−25	−40
−3	−12	9	15	24
6	24	−18	−30	−48

×	3	7	4	−9
−3	−9	−21	−12	27
−6	−18	−42	−24	54
7	21	49	28	−63
−5	−15	−35	−20	45

Angles and shapes

Previous learning

Before they start, pupils should be able to:

- use correct notation and labelling conventions for lines, angles and shapes
- identify parallel and perpendicular lines
- know the sum of angles at a point, on a straight line and in a triangle
- recognise vertically opposite angles
- estimate, measure and draw acute, obtuse and reflex angles.

Objectives based on NC levels 5 and 6 (mainly level 5)

In this unit, pupils learn to:

- make accurate mathematical diagrams and constructions on paper and on screen
- use accurate notation
- select appropriate procedures and tools, including ICT
- visualise and manipulate dynamic images and explore the effect of varying values
- use logical argument to establish the truth of a statement
- refine own findings and approaches on the basis of discussion with others
- evaluate the efficiency of alternative strategies and approaches

and to:

- identify alternate angles and corresponding angles
- solve geometrical problems using side and angle properties of triangles and special quadrilaterals, explaining reasoning with diagrams and text
- classify quadrilaterals by their geometrical properties
- know that if two shapes are congruent, corresponding sides and angles are equal
- understand a proof that:
  - the angle sum of a triangle is 180° and of a quadrilateral is 360°
  - the exterior angle of a triangle is equal to the sum of the two interior opposite angles.

Lessons

1 **Corresponding angles**

2 **Alternate angles**

3 **Angles in a triangle and a quadrilateral**

4 **Understanding congruence**

5 **Properties of quadrilaterals**

6 **Solving geometrical problems**

About this unit

Pupils need to identify parallel lines and transversals so that they can recognise corresponding and alternate angles, and use these to prove other geometric properties.

The ability to build on known information develops pupils' powers of reasoning and logical thinking, which are important in problem solving.

The starter in the first lesson is adapted from an activity in the *Interacting with mathematics: Year 9 geometrical reasoning pack* (DfES 0592-2002).

Assessment

This unit includes:

- a self-assessment section (*G4.1 How well are you doing?* class book p. 28);
- a set of questions to replace or supplement questions in the exercises or homework tasks, or to use as an informal test (*G4.1 Check up*, CD-ROM).

Common errors and misconceptions	Look out for pupils who:

Common errors and misconceptions

Look out for pupils who:
- think that congruent shapes must be of the same orientation;
- confuse exterior and interior angles;
- cannot identify corresponding and alternate angles, or state which is which.

Key terms and notation

parallel lines, corresponding angles, alternate angles, exterior angles, interior angles

angle, side, diagonal, properties of shapes, congruent, scalene, isosceles, right-angled, equilateral, acute, obtuse

extended, produced, transversal, proof, construction

Practical resources

large paper triangle

squared dotty paper

Exploring maths

Tier 4 teacher's book
Answers for G4.1, pp. 35–39

Tier 4 CD-ROM
PowerPoint files
  G4.1 Slides for lessons 1 to 6
Tier 4 programs
  Triangle break-up
  Angles in a triangle
  Congruence

Tier 4 class book
G4.1, pp. 15–29
G4.1 How well are you doing? p. 28

Tier 4 home book
G4.1, pp. 4–11

Tier 4 CD-ROM
G4.1 Check up
G4.1 Pupil resource sheets
  2.1 One per pupil
  3.1 One per pupil

Useful websites

Investigating the concept of triangle and properties of polygons
standards.nctm.org/document/eexamples/

Congruent triangles
matti.usu.edu/nlvm/nav/vlibrary.html

Problems about angles 1, Problems about angles 2
www.ies.co.jp/math/java/geo/angle.html

Two tapes
www.ies.co.jp/math/java/geo/twotapes/twotapes.html

1 Corresponding angles

Learning points

◉ Corresponding angles are formed when a transversal cuts a pair of straight parallel lines.

◉ Corresponding angles are equal.

◉ When you calculate angles, always include your reasons.

Starter

Say that this unit is about solving problems involving angles and shapes. The first two lessons are about finding equal angles when a pair of parallel lines is cut by a transversal.

Ask pupils to close their eyes and follow the instructions. Say:

> Imagine a horizontal straight line extending infinitely from left to right.
> Now imagine a vertical line, crossing the horizontal line, extending infinitely up and down.
>
> **How many right angles can you see?**
>
> Now fix your mind on the point where the two lines cross.
> This is the point of intersection.
> Keeping the horizontal line fixed, **very slowly** rotate the vertical line clockwise about this point.
>
> **What happens to the angles between the two lines?**
> **Are they still right angles?**
>
> Continue rotating the line very slowly until the angle is 45°.
>
> **How many 45° angles can you see?**
>
> **How big are the other angles? How did you work that out?**

Remind pupils that angles on a straight line add up to 180°, and that when two straight lines intersect two pairs of vertically opposite angles are formed.

Main activity

Extend the visualisation.

> Imagine a horizontal straight line, as before, cut by a straight line at 45° to it.
> Very slowly, translate the horizontal line upwards but keep it horizontal.
>
> **What happens to the point of intersection?**
>
> **What happens to the angles at this point? Do they change in size?**
>
> Now slowly translate the horizontal line downwards, past its original position.
>
> **What happens to the point of intersection?**
>
> **What happens to the angles at this point? Do they change in size?**

On the board, draw a pair of parallel straight lines and a transversal at 45° to the lines. Ask the class to copy the diagram on their whiteboards.

In turn, indicate each point of intersection. Ask pupils to write on their diagrams the sizes of all the angles. Write these on the diagram on the board [vertically opposite angles of 45° and supplementary angles of 135°].

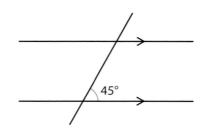

Select either point of intersection on the diagram. Demonstrate that each pair of adjacent angles sums to 180°, and that the four angles around the point sum to 360°, asking pupils for reasons.

Ask pupils to do questions 1 and 2 **G4.1 Exercise 1** in the class book (p. 16).

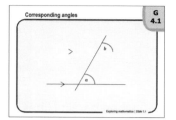

Show **slide 1.1**. Ask pupils to identify equal angles. Explain that they are *corresponding angles*. Make sure that pupils can identify corresponding angles in any position relative to the parallel lines and transversal.

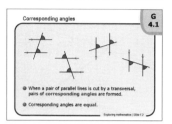

Show **slide 1.2**. Explain that each diagram shows a pair of parallel straight lines cut by a transversal.

> **What can you say about the two marked angles?**
> [the angles are equal; they are corresponding angles]

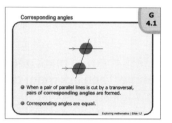

Confirm with **slide 1.3**.

Stress that to work out unknown angles in a geometric diagram, it can help to look for corresponding angles.

Ask pupils to do the rest of **G4.1 Exercise 1** in the class book (p. 17).

Review   Show **slide 1.4**. This shows parallel straight lines AB and CD cut by transversal EF at G and H.

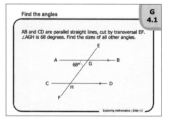

Ask pupils to copy the diagram and, working in pairs, to find the missing angles. Write on the board the possible reasons to choose from: *vertically opposite angles, angles on a straight line, corresponding angles, angles at a point.*

> **What do you notice about angles AGH and GHD? Explain why.**
>
> **What about angles DHG and AGH? Explain why.**

Sum up by reminding pupils of the learning points for this lesson.

Homework   Ask pupils to do **G4.1 Task 1** in the home book (p. 4).

2 Alternate angles

Learning points

- Alternate angles are formed when a transversal cuts a pair of parallel straight lines.
- Alternate angles are equal.
- When you calculate angles, always include reasons.
- You may need to work out other angles along the way.
- Draw diagrams neatly.

Starter

Say that this lesson continues to focus on the angles formed when parallel lines are cut by a transversal.

Draw on the board two pairs of intersecting parallel lines.

> What shape is enclosed by the two pairs of parallel lines?

Discuss the answers: a parallelogram or a rhombus. Establish the similarities and differences between these two shapes, including their symmetries.

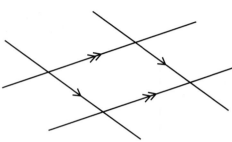

Ask pupils to draw a similar diagram on their whiteboards. Ask them to mark one of the interior angles of their shape and a corresponding angle. Then ask them to mark all the other angles that are equal to the two marked angles.

Invite a pupil to show their answer using the diagram on the board, and giving reasons [corresponding angles, vertically opposite angles].

Main activity

Show **slide 2.1**. Explain that each diagram shows parallel straight lines cut by a transversal. As each diagram appears, ask pupils:

> What can you say about the two marked angles?

Agree that they look as though they could be equal. Explain that these are *alternate angles*.

Draw this diagram on the board. Say that this is a pair of parallel straight lines cut by a transversal.

> What can you say about x, y and z?
> [$z = y$]
>
> How do you know for certain?

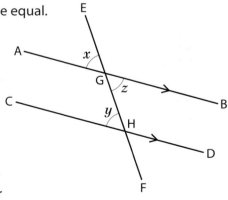

Explain that a *proof* is a sequence of steps or statements that follow on logically, one after another, to show that something is true. Write on the board:

To prove: Angle BGH = angle CHG
Angle AGE = x (given)
Angle BGH = angle AGE = x (vertically opposite angles)
Angle CHG = angle AGE = x (corresponding angles)
So angle BGH = angle CHG

Stress that the proof is built on information that they already know. Each step uses what is already known to derive or deduce new information. This proof would work for any angle x.

Mark angles a, b and c on the diagram.

Ask pupils, working in pairs, to prove that $a = c$.

Take feedback, writing the proof with reasons on the board.

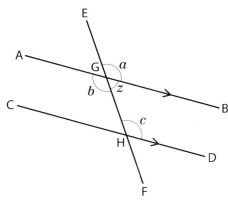

Establish that when a pair of parallel straight lines is cut by a transversal, alternate angles are formed. Alternate angles are equal. Explain that, just like corresponding angles, alternate angles can be given as a reason when they are finding missing or unknown angles.

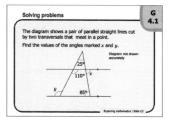

Show **slide 2.2**. Stress that the missing angles have to be calculated, not measured. Ask pairs to discuss the question. Discuss answers and possible reasons, e.g.

$x = 85°$ (alternate angles), $y = 110°$ (alternate angles)

Does it matter which angle you calculate first?

Ask pupils to do **G4.1 Exercise 2** in the class book (p. 19).

Review Work through the problem on **slide 2.3**, stressing again the importance of giving reasons to justify each step.

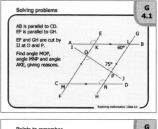

Ask pupils to remember the points on **slide 2.4**.

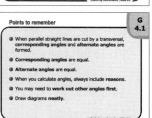

Homework Ask pupils to do **G4.1 Task 2** in the home book (p. 6).

3 Angles in a triangle and a quadrilateral

Learning points

- A proof is a sequence of steps or statements that follow on logically, one after another, to show that something is true.

- Each step in a proof uses information already known to derive new information.

- In a proof, you may need to join points in a diagram or to construct a line.

SIM

Starter

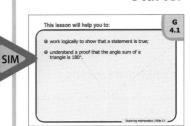

Show **slide 3.1** to discuss the objectives for this lesson. Say that this lesson focuses on the angle sum of triangles and quadrilaterals.

> **What is the sum of the angles in the triangle? How do you know?**

Launch **Triangle break-up** to demonstrate cutting off the corners of a triangle and placing the three angles together to form a straight line.

Explain that this demonstrates only that the three angles of this particular triangle form a straight line. A proof is needed to convince us that the three angles of any triangle will do the same.

Main activity

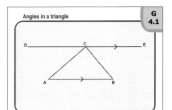

Show a proof that the sum of the angles of a triangle is 180°. Show **slide 3.2**.

Given: triangle ABC.

Through C, draw DE, parallel to AB

Angle $BCE = x$ (alternate angles)
Angle $ACD = z$ (alternate angles)

So $x + y + z = 180°$
(angles on a straight line)

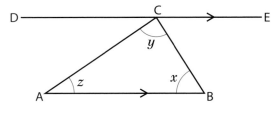

Draw a quadrilateral on the board, with one diagonal.

> **How could you use what you already know to find the angle sum of the quadrilateral?**

Write the proof on the board, using the fact that the diagonal divides the quadrilateral into two triangles with a total angle sum of 360°.

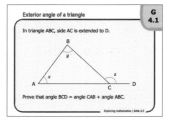

Show **slide 3.3**. Explain that angle BCD is the angle between side BC and side AC extended to D. This is called an *exterior angle* of the triangle.

Ask pupils, working in pairs, to prove the statement:

angle BCD = angle CAB + angle ABC

i.e. the exterior angle of a triangle equals the sum of the two interior opposite angles.

Write these possible reasons on the board as a reminder of what can be used.

- Angles on a straight line sum to 180°.

- Angles in a triangle sum to 180°.

- Alternate angles are equal.

- Corresponding angles are equal.

Choose one of the two proofs below and talk it through. You may prefer to write the word angle in full, rather than use the ∠ abbreviation.

Proof 1: To prove ∠BCD = ∠CAB + ∠ABC

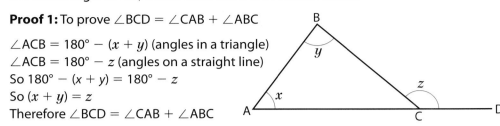

∠ACB = 180° − (x + y) (angles in a triangle)
∠ACB = 180° − z (angles on a straight line)
So 180° − (x + y) = 180° − z
So (x + y) = z
Therefore ∠BCD = ∠CAB + ∠ABC

Proof 2: To prove ∠BCD = ∠CAB + ∠ABC

Through C, draw CE parallel to AB.

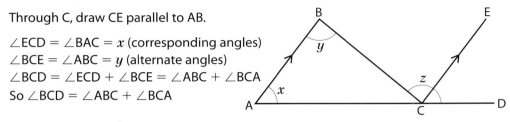

∠ECD = ∠BAC = x (corresponding angles)
∠BCE = ∠ABC = y (alternate angles)
∠BCD = ∠ECD + ∠BCE = ∠ABC + ∠BCA
So ∠BCD = ∠ABC + ∠BCA

Ask pupils to do **G4.1 Exercise 3** in the class book (p. 21).

Review

Show an alternative approach to the angle sum of a triangle.

Launch **Angles in a triangle**.

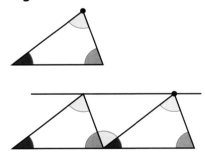

SIM

Drag the red point to the right to translate the triangle in a direction parallel to its base until two identical triangles with touching bases are formed. Point out that corresponding sides of the two triangles are parallel.

Discuss the three angles on the straight line formed by the touching bases. Use these to show that:

⊙ the angle sum of a triangle is 180°;

⊙ the exterior angle is equal to the sum of the two interior opposite angles.

Ask pupils to remember the points on **slide 3.4**.

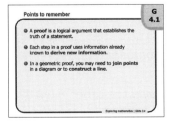

Points to remember

• A **proof** is a logical argument that establishes the truth of a statement.

• Each step in a proof uses information already known to **derive new information**.

• In a geometric proof, you may need to **join points** in a diagram or to **construct a line**.

Homework

Ask pupils to do **G4.1 Task 3** in the home book (p. 7).

4 Understanding congruence

Learning points

- Congruent shapes are exactly the same size and shape.

- In congruent shapes, corresponding angles are equal and corresponding sides are equal.

Starter   Say that this lesson is about congruent shapes.

Say the names of different triangles, quadrilaterals and other polygons. Make sure that pupils can recall what the shapes look like and properties such as equal sides, equal angles, parallel sides, diagonal properties and lines of symmetry. For example:

- **rhombus** — four equal sides, opposite sides parallel, opposite angles equal, diagonals bisect each other at right angles, two lines of symmetry

Ask pupils to work in pairs and to answer questions on their whiteboards.

> Which shapes *always* have parallel sides?
> [square, rhombus, rectangle, parallelogram, trapezium, regular polygons with an even number of sides]
>
> Which shapes *never* have parallel sides?
> [all the triangles, kite, arrowhead, regular polygons with an odd number of sides]
>
> Which shapes *may* have parallel sides?
> [irregular polygons such as a pentagon, hexagon and octagon]

Ask pupils to sketch on their whiteboards a pentagon with no sides parallel, a pentagon with one pair of parallel sides, then a pentagon with two pairs of parallel sides.

Main activity   Give out copies of **G4.1 Resource sheet 4.1**. Ask pupils to use their rulers and to identify pairs of rectangles that are exactly the same [A = G, D = F, E = I].

> How do you know that the rectangles in each pair are exactly the same?

Draw out that the corresponding angles are equal and the lengths of corresponding sides are equal.

Explain that:

- shapes that are exactly the same size and shape are *congruent*, but their position and orientation may be different;

- if two plane shapes are congruent, one will fit exactly over the other, even if it has to be translated, reflected or rotated to do so;

- in order to compare two shapes to see if they are congruent, the dimensions of corresponding sides may have to be changed to the same unit;

- sometimes angles have to be calculated to check whether corresponding angles are equal.

Launch **Congruence**. This shows a series of pairs of shapes. For each pair, ask pupils to state whether or not they are congruent and to explain why they think so. Then click on the 'check' button to animate one of the shapes to see if it will fit exactly over the other. Click on the 'New question' button to reveal the next pair of shapes.

Say that when two shapes are the same shape but different sizes they are said to be *similar*. Illustrate by drawing two circles of different sizes and two squares of different sizes.

Ask pupils to do **G4.1 Exercise 4** in the class book (p. 24). They will need squared paper for questions 2, 3 and 4.

Review

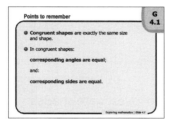

Ask pupils to visualise an isosceles triangle. Ask them to imagine a line of symmetry through the isosceles triangle, dividing it into two congruent parts. Ask them to describe fully the position of the line of symmetry and to identify the two congruent shapes that make up the isosceles triangle.

Repeat for one or two more shapes, such as a regular pentagon and an arrowhead.

Finish by stressing the points on **slide 4.1**.

Homework

Ask pupils to do **G4.1 Task 4** in the home book (p. 8). Pupils will need squared dotty paper.

5 Properties of quadrilaterals

Learning points

- Rectangles, squares, parallelograms, rhombuses, kites and arrowheads are made up from pairs of congruent triangles.

Starter

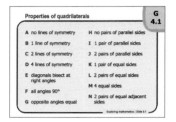

Explain that the focus of this lesson is the properties of quadrilaterals.

Show **slide 5.1**, which lists some properties of quadrilaterals. Ask pupils to discuss in pairs which properties apply to a square and to write the appropriate letters on their whiteboards [D, E, F, G, J, M, N].
Repeat with:

- rectangle [C, F, G, J, L];
- trapezium [A, I];
- parallelogram [A, G, J, L];
- rhombus [C, E, G, J, M, N];
- kite [B, E, G, H, N].

Main activity

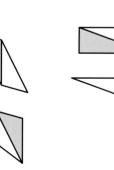

Ask pupils to form groups of four. Tell them that they are to investigate shapes that can be made from a pair of congruent triangles matched edge to edge.

Refer to **G4.1 Exercise 5** (the instructions are repeated on **slide 5.2**). Explain that each group is to explain their findings in the form of a poster or as a slide presentation at the end of the main part of the lesson.

As you circulate, prompt groups with questions such as:

How many different quadrilaterals do two scalene triangles make?
How do you know this shape is a kite?

What different shapes can you make with two right-angled triangles?
Why are they not all quadrilaterals?

What types of quadrilateral do two equilateral triangles make?
How do you know it's a rhombus?

How many different types of quadrilateral does a pair of isosceles triangles make?

Which type of triangle would you need to start with to make a square?

The possible findings are:

Scalene triangles

Right-angled triangles

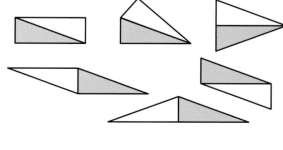

Equilateral triangles

Isosceles triangles

Review

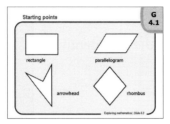

Show **slide 5.3**. Explain that each quadrilateral is made up of two congruent triangles. For each diagram, ask:

Which lengths are equal? How do you know?

Which angles are equal? How do you know?

What type of triangle was the starting point for this quadrilateral?

Could this quadrilateral have been made from a different type of triangle?

You could annotate each diagram with pupils' comments, marking sides that are equal and angles that are equal.

Ensure that pupils identify that:

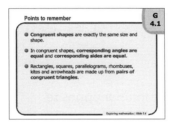

- a rectangle can be formed from two congruent scalene right-angled triangles;
- a parallelogram can be formed by two congruent scalene acute-angled triangles or two congruent scalene obtuse-angled triangles;
- an arrowhead can be formed from two congruent scalene obtuse-angled triangles;
- a rhombus can be formed by two congruent isosceles or equilateral triangles.

Ask pupils to remember the points on **slide 5.4**.

Homework

Ask pupils to do **G4.1 Task 5** in the home book (p. 10)

6 Solving geometrical problems

Learning points

- When you solve geometrical problems, draw a neat diagram.
- Mark on the diagram all the information in the question.
- Include reasons for the statements that you make.

Starter

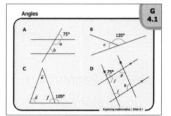

Say that this lesson looks at solving geometrical problems.

Show **slide 6.1**. Say that each figure is made up from straight lines. Point out the pairs of parallel lines in diagrams A and D and that the sizes of some angles are marked.

Ask pupils to answer questions on their whiteboards. Ask them to identify:

- an angle equal to 45°
  [diagram B, c, angles on a straight line]

- an angle equal to 105°
  [diagram A, a, angles on a straight line;
  diagram D, j, angles on a straight line;
  diagram D, h, opposite to angle j in parallelogram]

- an angle equal to 75°
  [diagram A, b, corresponding angle;
  diagram C, f, angles on a straight line;
  diagram C, d, base angle of isosceles triangle;
  diagram D, g, alternate angles;
  diagram D, i, corresponding angles]

- two angles that sum to 105°
  [diagram C, $d + e$, exterior angle equals the sum of the interior opposite angles]

Ask pupils for other possible questions to ask, and the answers (e.g. there are several pairs of angles with a sum of 180°).

Main activity

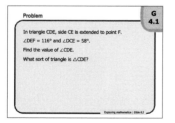

Show the problem on **slide 6.2**.

> In triangle CDE, side CE is extended to point F.
> Angle DEF = 116° and angle DCE = 58°.
> Find the value of angle CDE. What sort of triangle is triangle CDE?

Show pupils how to follow the instructions to draw the diagram. Do this on the board. Point out that the sizes of the angles are not accurate.

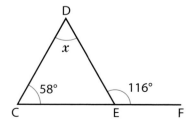

Ask pupils to use their rulers and to draw the diagram for themselves. Then ask them to solve the problem, remembering to give reasons.

Go through the answer, e.g.

Angle CED = 180° − 116° = 64° (angles on a straight line)
Angle CDE = 180° − (58° + 64°) = 58° (angle sum of the triangle is 180°)

or:

Angle CDE = 116° − 58° = 58° (exterior angle = sum of two interior opposite angles)
Triangle CDE is an isosceles triangle (two equal angles).

Ask pupils to do **G4.1 Exercise 6** in the class book (p. 27).

Review

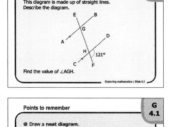

Show **slide 6.3**. Ask pairs to discuss how they would describe the diagram, e.g.

- AB and CD are parallel straight lines.
- Transversal EF cuts AB and CD at G and H respectively.
- Angle DHF is 121 degrees.

Ask pupils to find the value of angle AGH [59°], and to give their reasons.

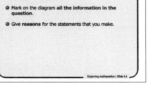

Finish by reminding pupils of the points on **slide 6.4**.

Round off the unit by referring again to the unit objectives. Ask pupils to find time to try the self-assessment problems in **G4.1 How well are you doing?** in the class book (p. 28).

Homework

Ask pupils to do **G4.1 Task 6** in the home book (p. 10).

G4.1 Check up and resource sheets

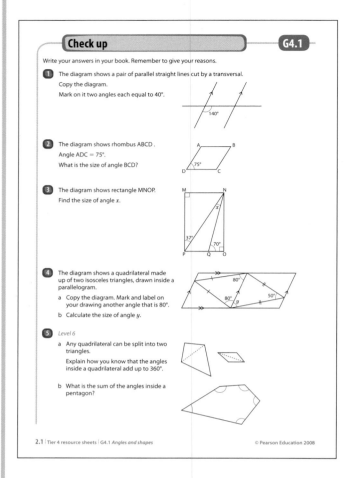

Check up   **G4.1**

Write your answers in your book. Remember to give your reasons.

1. The diagram shows a pair of parallel straight lines cut by a transversal.
   Copy the diagram.
   Mark on it two angles each equal to 40°.

2. The diagram shows rhombus ABCD .
   Angle ADC = 75°.
   What is the size of angle BCD?

3. The diagram shows rectangle MNOP.
   Find the size of angle x.

4. The diagram shows a quadrilateral made up of two isosceles triangles, drawn inside a parallelogram.
   a Copy the diagram. Mark and label on your drawing another angle that is 80°.
   b Calculate the size of angle y.

5. *Level 6*
   a Any quadrilateral can be split into two triangles.
      Explain how you know that the angles inside a quadrilateral add up to 360°.
   b What is the sum of the angles inside a pentagon?

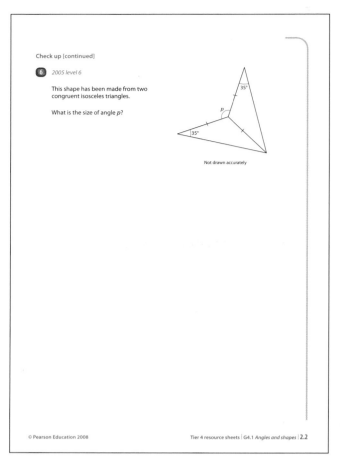

Check up [continued]

6. *2005 level 6*

   This shape has been made from two congruent isosceles triangles.

   What is the size of angle p?

   Not drawn accurately

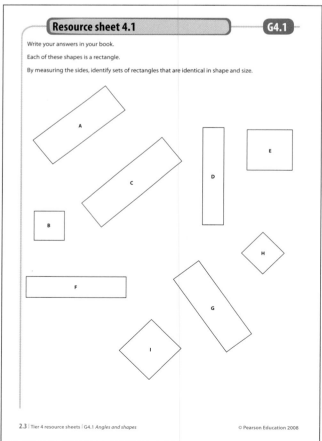

Resource sheet 4.1   **G4.1**

Write your answers in your book.

Each of these shapes is a rectangle.

By measuring the sides, identify sets of rectangles that are identical in shape and size.

G4.1 Answers

Class book

Exercise 1

1 a $s = 57°$ b $t = 123°$

   c $u = 136°$ d $v = 49°$

   (corresponding angles in each case)

2 a $a = 156°, b = 99°$

   b $d = 71°, e = 35°$

   (corresponding angles in each case)

3 a $a = 75°$ (angles on a straight line sum to 180°)

      $b = 75°$ (corresponding angles)

      $c = 105°$ (angles on a straight line sum to 180°)

      $d = 75°$ (vertically opposite angles)

      $e = 105°$ (corresponding angles)

      $f = 105°$ (vertically opposite angles)

      $g = 75°$ (vertically opposite angles)

   b $a = 35°$ (corresponding angles)

      $b = 35°$ (vertically opposite angles)

      $c = 35°$ (corresponding angles)

      $d = 145°$ (angles on a straight line sum to 180°)

      $e = 145°$ (angles on a straight line sum to 180°)

4 $a = e$ (vertically opposite angles)

   $= i = n = f$ (corresponding angles)

   $= d$ (vertically opposite angles)

   $= b$ (corresponding angles)

   $= p$ (corresponding angles)

   $c = o$ (vertically opposite angles)

   $= j = l = h$ (corresponding angles)

   $= g$ (vertically opposite angles)

   $= m$ (corresponding angles)

   $= k$ (corresponding angles)

5 $\angle RZB = 70°$ (vertically opposite angles)

   $a = 70°$ (corresponding angles)

   $d = 110°$ (angles on a straight line sum to 180°)

   $b = 80°$ (vertically opposite angles)

   $\angle AXP = 80°$ (corresponding angles)

   $c = 100°$ (angles on a straight line sum to 180°)

Exercise 2

1 a $a = 120°, b = 120°, c = 60°, d = 60°,$
      $e = 120°, f = 60°, g = 120°$

   b $a = 64°, b = 116°, c = 64°, d = 116°, e = 64°,$
      $f = 64°, g = 116°$

2 $a = c = e = g$ and $b = d = f = h$

3 $a = 37°$ (vertically opposite angles)
   $b = 37°$ (alternate angles)
   $c = 154°$ (vertically opposite angles)
   $d = 154°$ (alternate angles)

4 $b = 110°, d = 139°$
   (alternate angles in each case)

5 a $a = 105°, b = 120°$

   b $c = 127°, d = 83°$
   (alternate angles in each case)

Extension problem

6 AB and CD are not parallel. If they were, the two marked angles would be equal alternate angles

Exercise 3

1 $f = 74°$ (alternate angles)

2 $\angle KIL = 60°$ (alternate angles)
   $a = \angle KIL - 34° = 60° - 34° = 26°$
   $b = \angle KIJ - \angle KIL = 90° - 60° = 30°$

3 $\angle JLK = 64°$ (corresponding angles)
   $m = 180° - 64° = 116°$ (angles on a straight line)
   $\angle EIJ = 81°$ (corresponding angles)
   $n = 180° - 81° = 99°$ (angles on a straight line)

4 $\angle GQP = 36°$ (alternate angles)
   $\angle GQR = \angle HRQ = 28°$
      (alternate angles; vertically opposite angles)
   $\angle PQR = \angle GQP + \angle GQR = 28° + 36° = 64°$

5 $z = 288°$

Extension problem

6 $a = 5b$, so $6b = 180°$ and $b = 30°$
   $c = 180° - 30° - 43° = 107°$

Exercise 4

1 A = K, C = L, F = G

2 a Pupil's two rectangles that are similar but not congruent

   b Pupil's two rhombuses that are similar but not congruent

3 There are six different ways altogether, including the one shown in the class book.

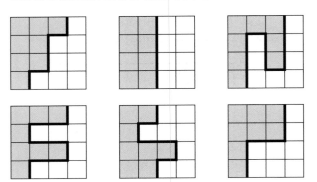

4 There are 15 different ways altogether.

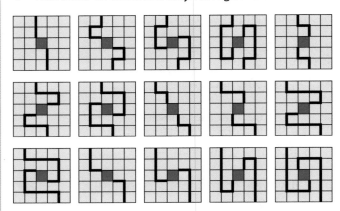

Exercise 6

1 ∠GHD = 144° (corresponding angles; angles in a straight line)

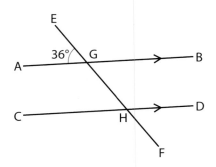

2 ∠WCD = 116° (alternate angles; angles in a straight line)

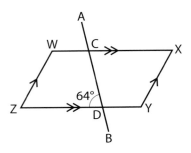

3 a ∠KQP = 55° (corresponding angle)

   b △PKQ is isosceles.

   c ∠NPJ = 110° (exterior angle = sum of opposite two interior angles)

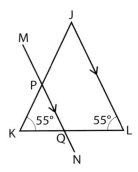

4 ∠SPR = 57° (∠s in a △)
   ∠QPR = 33° (alternate angles)
   ∠PRQ = 57° (∠s in a △)
   △QPR and △SRP are congruent.

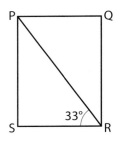

5 ABDC is a parallelogram.
   ∠BCA = 41° (alt. ∠s)
   ∠BCD = 66° (∠s in △)
   so ∠ACD = 107°

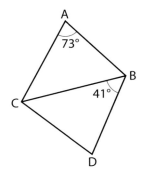

6 Let $\angle FCD = x$ and extend CD to G.
$\angle GDE = x$ (corresponding angles)
$\angle DEF = x$ (alternate angles)
$\angle FCD = \angle FED$

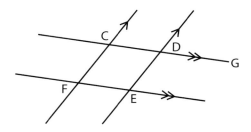

7 $\angle XZW = 155°$
$\angle YWZ = 20°$
(angles in a quadrilateral)

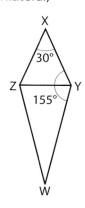

8 $\angle ABD = 70°$ (alternate angles)
$\angle EDB = 75°$ (angles in a triangle)

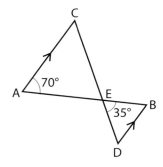

How well are you doing?

1 $a = 50°$ (angles on a straight line)
$b = 60°$ (vertically opposite angles)
$c = 70°$ (angles in a triangle)

2 $\angle DCA = 35°$ (angles in a triangle)
$\angle BCK = 45°$ (angles in a triangle)
$a = 90° - 35° - 45° = 10°$ (right angle)

3 A, F and G are congruent.

4 JK = 5mm, KL = 6mm, LM = 7mm, MJ = 10mm

5 $\angle CJK = 131°$ (angles on a straight line)
$\angle JKF = 131°$ (alternate angles)

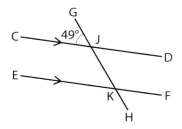

6 $\angle ACD = 21°$ (alternate angles)

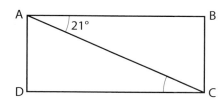

Home book

TASK 1

1 a $b = 39°$ b $x = 149°$
c $m = 159°$ d $p = 77°$
(corresponding angles)

2 $x = 103°$ (alternate angles)
$y = 95°$ (corresponding angles)

3 a $w = 75°$
b $x = 130°, y = 50°$
c $z = 118°$

TASK 2

1 a $j = 45°$ (alternate angles)
b $m = 137°$ (alternate angles)
c $d = 79°$ (alternate angles)
$e = 95°$ (alternate angles)
d $j = 67°$ (alternate angles)
$k = 67°$ (vertically opposite angles)
$l = 67°$ (alternate angles)
$m = 67°$ (alternate angles)
$n = 67°$ (alternate or vertically opposite
angles)

2 $s = 48°, t = 52°$ (alternate angles)

TASK 3

1 $x = 35°$

2 $a = 50°, b = 130°, c = 20°$

3 $a = 115°, b = 155°$

TASK 4

1 A and J, B and H, C and K, F and L

2 **a** 15 extra congruent triangles

   b 15 extra congruent quadrilaterals

TASK 5

1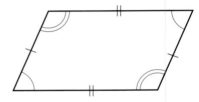

2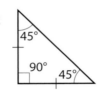

3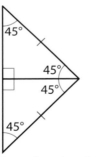

Isosceles triangle

TASK 6

1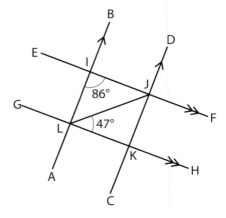

∠IJL = 47° (alternate angles)

∠JKL = 86° (alternate and corresponding angles)

∠KJL = 180° − (47° + 86°) = 47° (angle sum of a triangle is 180°)

∠ILJ = 47° (alternate angles)

△LIJ is isosceles, because ∠IJL = ∠JLI = 47° (two equal angles).

△JKL is isosceles, because ∠KJL = ∠KLJ = 47° (two equal angles).

IJKL is a rhombus as △JKL and △LIJ are congruent isosceles triangles, so all sides of IJKL are equal.

CD-ROM

Check up

1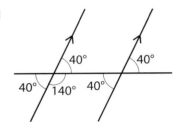

2 ∠BCD = 105°

3 ∠PNO = 37° (alternate angles)
∠QNO = 20° (angle sum of a triangle)
∴ ∠PNQ = 37° − 20° = 17°

4 **a**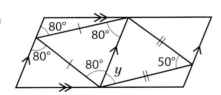

   b $y = (180° − 50°) ÷ 2 = 65°$

5 **a**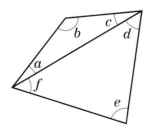

$a + b + c = 180°, d + e + f = 180°$ (angle sum of a triangle)
∴ $a + b + c + d + e + f = 360°$

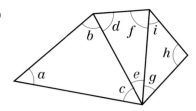

$$a + b + c + d + e + f + g + h + i = 540°$$

6 $p = 2 \times (35° + 35°) = 140°$

A
4.1 Linear sequences

Previous learning

Before they start, pupils should be able to:

- generate terms of a simple sequence given a rule
- generate a sequence given a simple practical context.

Objectives based on NC levels 5 and 6 (mainly level 5)

In this unit, pupils learn to:

- try out and compare mathematical representations
- conjecture and generalise, identifying exceptional cases or counter-examples
- move between the general and the particular to test the logic of an argument
- select appropriate procedures and tools, including ICT
- refine own findings and approaches on the basis of discussion with others
- record methods, solutions and conclusions

and to:

- generate terms of a linear sequence using term-to-term and position-to-term rules, on paper and using a spreadsheet or calculator
- use linear expressions to describe the nth term of an arithmetic sequence, justifying its form by referring to the context from which it was generated.

Lessons
1 **Term-to-term rules**

2 **Position-to-term rules**

3 **Using a spreadsheet to generate sequences**

4 **Exploring patterns**

About this unit
To understand algebra pupils need to make the link between numbers and the use of symbols for numbers. Most pupils are reasonably comfortable with counting up and down in equal steps and looking for patterns in sequences of numbers. This unit formalises that work and introduces n to represent the position of a number in a sequence.

Spreadsheets are used to demonstrate how ICT can be used in mathematics to explore situations and to look at a relationship graphically.

Assessment
This unit includes:

- a self-assessment section (*A4.1 How well are you doing?* class book p. 39);
- a set of questions to replace or supplement questions in the exercises or homework tasks, or to use as an informal test (*A4.1 Check up*, CD-ROM).

Common errors and misconceptions	Look out for pupils who:

Common errors and misconceptions

Look out for pupils who:
- do not understand the use of the letter n;
- confuse n^2 and $2n$;
- confuse term-to-term rules and position-to-term rules;
- use calculators or spreadsheets to avoid using nth terms;
- have difficulty using a spreadsheet.

Key terms and notation

sequence, difference, finite, infinite, increase, decrease, ascending, descending, consecutive, term, term-to-term, position-to-term, rule, nth term

odd, even, square, triangular, multiple, negative

algebra, brackets, symbol, expression, linear, quadratic, variable, relationship

continue, generate, generalise, predict, conjecture, investigate

Practical resources

basic calculators for pupils
individual whiteboards

for lesson 3 per pair of pupils, computers with spreadsheet software or graphics calculators

Exploring maths

Tier 4 teacher's book
Answers for Unit A4.1, pp. 51–53

Tier 4 CD-ROM
PowerPoint files
　　A4.1 Slides for lessons 1 to 4
Excel file
　　A4.1 Sequences for lesson 3
Tools and prepared toolsheets
　　Scatter graph tool
Tier 4 programs
　　Step counter
　　Sequences

Tier 4 class book
A4.1, pp. 30 – 39
A4.1 How well are you doing? p. 39

Tier 4 home book
A4.1, pp. 12 – 15

Tier 4 CD-ROM
A4.1 Check up

Useful websites

Challenging maths problems
www.nrich.maths.org.uk/public/leg.php

Sequences, functions and graphs
www.imathlearning.com/worksheets/3sequence/index.html

Algebra topics
swgfl.skoool.co.uk/keystage3.aspx?id=65#24_30

Number patterns and sequences
www.cimt.plymouth.ac.uk/projects/mepres/book7/y7s7lp.pdf

1 Term-to-term rules

Learning points

◉ A sequence of numbers follows a rule.

◉ You can work out the next term in a sequence if you know the term-to-term rule.

Starter

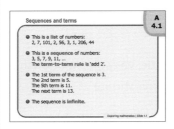

SIM

Say that this lesson is about generating sequences using term-to-term rules. If pupils have covered some of this work previously, use the lesson as revision.

Show **slide 1.1**. Explain that a *list* of numbers can be in any order and can represent anything, e.g. the numbers of football players who scored goals. A *sequence* of numbers is one that obeys some rule. The dots after the last number indicate that the numbers in the sequence continue in the same way as the previous numbers. In this example the *rule* is 'add 2'. Ask pupils to continue the sequence.

Show **slide 1.2**. For each sequence, invite individual pupils to say the rule, then go round the class asking for the next five numbers.

Is the sequence increasing or decreasing?
Is it in ascending or descending order?

Alternatively, launch **Step counter** and practise counting forwards and backwards in steps.

Discuss the idea of sequences having a finite or an infinite number of terms. Introduce the notation for finite sequences, where the final term in the sequence is given after the dots.

◉ The sequence of all odd numbers is *infinite*:
  1, 3, 5, 7, …

◉ The sequence of even numbers between 0 and 80 is *finite*:
  2, 4, 6, …, 78

Ask pupils to decide whether the following sequences are finite or infinite. Invite them to explain their answers.

◉ The sequence of square numbers

◉ The sequence of multiples of 9

◉ The sequence of triangular numbers between 0 and 100

◉ The sequence of negative integers less than -18

◉ The sequence of multiples of 7 less than or equal to 700

Main activity

Revise the word *term*. Each term in a sequence is separated by a comma or by a space.

Write a number sequence on the board such as:

  9, 19, 29, 39, 49, 59, 69, …

What is the 3rd term? What is the 6th term? What is the 7th term?

What is the difference between the 1st and 2nd terms?
Between the 2nd and 3rd terms? 3rd and 4th terms? …

What is the difference between consecutive terms?

What is the next term in the sequence?
How do you know how to find it?

What is the term-to-term rule?

What would be the 10th term?

Alternatively, launch **Sequences** and ask similar questions.

SIM

Say that you know the first term of a sequence and its term-to-term rule. Explain that from this information you can generate as many terms of the sequence as you want.

Ask pupils to generate the first ten terms in these sequences:

- First term 6; term-to-term rule 'add 4'
- First term 10; term-to-term rule 'subtract 5'
- First term 1; term-to-term rule 'multiply by 2'

Where appropriate, challenge pupils:

- First term $\frac{1}{5}$; term-to-term rule is 'multiply by 4'
- First term 243; term-to-term rule 'divide by 3'

Ask pupils to do **A4.1 Exercise 1** in the class book (p. 31).

Review

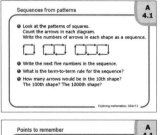

Show **slide 1.3**. Ask pupils to write on their whiteboards the sequence of numbers representing the number of arrows in the squares. Get them to work out the next five numbers in the sequence, the term-to-term rule and the number of arrows in the 10th shape.

Ask pupils how they would work out the number of arrows in the 100th or 1000th shape. Explain that you will be looking at easier and quicker ways of doing this in the next two lessons.

Show **slide 1.4** and sum up the lesson.

Homework

Ask pupils to do **A4.1 Task 1** in the home book (p. 12).

2 Position-to-term rules

Learning points

- You can work out any term in a sequence if you know the formula for the nth term.
- The difference between consecutive terms will help you find the nth term.

Starter Say that this lesson is about using position-to-term rules to generate sequences and finding a formula for the nth term of a sequence.

Explain that in mathematics you use letters to denote numbers. Any letter in the alphabet can be used but in this work the letter n will be used to represent positive integers.

Write the expression $n + 5$ on the board. Explain that n can be any positive integer. The algebraic expression $n + 5$ is an instruction that tells us to add the number 5 to the number n.

If n equals 3, what is the value of the expression $n + 5$?

If n equals 58, what is the value of $n + 5$?

If n equals 107, what is the value of $n + 5$?

Continue for different positive integer values of n.

Write the expression $n - 1$ on the board. Ask pupils to describe the instruction given by the expression. Get them to work out the value of the expression for different positive integer values of n.

Repeat the exercise for the expressions: $5n$, $n \div 2$, $\frac{n}{3}$, $2n + 1$, $3n - 2$. If necessary, continue with further expressions until you are confident that all pupils are able to substitute into the expression and work out its value.

Main activity Ask pupils to give you the first ten multiples of 7 and write them on the board as a sequence of numbers.

What is the 3rd multiple of 7?

What is the 7th multiple of 7?

What is the 10th multiple of 7?

How would you work out the 15th multiple of 7?
[7×15]

How would you work out the 457th multiple of 7?
[7×457]

How would you write the nth multiple of 7?
[$7 \times n$ or $7n$]

Show **slide 2.1**. Establish that the formula for the nth term for the multiples of 5 is $5n$. Show how you can use this knowledge to work out the formula for the nth term of the next sequence as $5n + 2$. Establish that the difference between consecutive terms of the sequence is always 5.

Position-to-term rules — A 4.1

5	10	15	20	...	5n
1st	2nd	3rd	4th	...	nth
5×1	5×2	5×3	5×4	...	5×n

The formula for the nth term is $5n$.

7	12	17	22	...	5n + 2
1st	2nd	3rd	4th	...	nth
5×1+2	5×2+2	5×3+2	5×4+2	...	5×n+2

The formula for the nth term is $5n + 2$.

Ask pupils to give you another sequence based on the multiples of 5 and to work out the *n*th term. Once again establish that the difference between consecutive terms is always 5.

Write the sequence 4, 11, 18, 25, 32, 39, … on the board.

> What is the difference between consecutive terms of this sequence? Is it always the same?
>
> What is the formula for the *n*th term of the sequence?
> $[7n - 3]$

Write the sequence 14, 23, 32, 41, 50, … on the board. Ask pupils to work out the *n*th term of the sequence $[9n + 5]$.

Write the formula $4n + 2$ on the board. Explain that this is the formula for the *n*th term of a sequence. Ask pupils to work out the first ten terms of the sequence [6, 10, 14, 18, 22, 26, 30, 34, 38, 42].

Ask pupils to do **A4.1 Exercise 2** in the class book (p. 22).

Review Show **slide 2.2**.

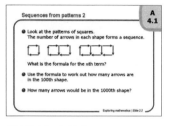

Ask pupils to work out the *n*th term for the sequence. Then ask them to work out the 100th and 1000th terms.

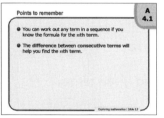

Use **slide 2.3** to summarise the lesson's main points.

Homework Ask pupils to do **A4.1 Task 2** in the home book (p. 13).

Learning points

- ◉ You can use a spreadsheet to explore sequences.

- ◉ Each cell in a spreadsheet is given a name using the column heading and the row heading. For example, the first cell is called A1.

Starter

This lesson preferably needs to take place in a computer room, with access to a spreadsheet program for each computer. You could use graphics calculators as alternatives to computers.

You can do this lesson using a spreadsheet on a computer as a demonstration but it is best done with pupils working in pairs at computers.

Say that this lesson is about using a computer spreadsheet to explore sequences.

Open the Excel file **Sequences**. Use **sheet 1**. Explain that the sequence of numbers has been generated on a computer spreadsheet.

> What is the term-to-term rule for this sequence?

> Find the next five numbers in the sequence.

Demonstrate how to generate the same sequence in column B using the term-to-term rule: enter 3 in cell B2 and in B3 enter the formula **=B2+6**. Show pupils how to copy this down the column by highlighting the column and pressing Ctrl+D. Now ask them to use their own copies of sheet 1 to generate the sequence for themselves in column B.

> Where will you find the 20th term? [in cell B21]
> What is it? [117]

> Find the 365th term. [2187]

Open **sheet 2**. Ask pupils for the term-to-term rule.

Ask them to generate the sequence in column B and to find given terms.

Main activity

Open **sheet 3**. Ask pupils to work out the column of differences and enter them manually in column C. (They are always 5.) Ask pupils how the difference can help them work out the formula for the nth term of the sequence, then ask them to work it out.

Use columns D, E and F to demonstrate how to generate the sequence automatically. In cell D3 enter **=D2+1** and in cell E2 enter **=5*D2+1**. Copy these down columns D and E in turn by highlighting the column and pressing Ctrl+D.

Ask pupils to use the spreadsheet to work out given terms of the sequence such as the 50th term, the 89th term, the 230th term and so on.

Draw a scatter graph using the spreadsheet graphing facility. (To do this, drag over and highlight from cell A2 to B23. Then click on the Chart Wizard on the toolbar, and choose XY (Scatter).)

Ask pupils to describe the graph. Note that the data is discrete and this means that the graph consists of a number of points that cannot be joined by a line or curve. All the points lie on a line, which demonstrates that the sequence is linear. The equation of this line is $y = 5x + 1$.

Open **sheet 4**. Invite pupils to explain what formulae need to be entered to generate in columns D and E the columns of numbers in A and B.

XL

Ask them to work out given terms of the sequence.

Now ask pupils to work out the column of differences automatically. Enter the formula **=D2-E2** in cell F2. Copy this down the column F by highlighting the column and pressing Ctrl+D.

Now ask pupils to work out the nth term of the sequence.

Ask pupils to describe the graph of the relationship. Guide them through drawing the graph using the Chart Wizard.

Ask pupils to do **A4.1 Exercise 3** in the class book (p. 35).

Review Ask pupils to explain how they would generate the following sequences with the information given.

- The first term of a sequence is 7 and the term-to-term rule is 'add 11'.
- The first term of a sequence is 350 and the term-to-term rule is 'subtract 23'.
- The nth term of a sequence is $8n + 15$.
- The nth term of a sequence is $17n - 9$.

You could if you wish use the **Scatter graph tool** to generate the graphs of these, or use the Chart Wizard of a spreadsheet, as above.

TO

Ask pupils to remember the points on **slide 3.1**.

Points to remember

A 4.1

- You can use a spreadsheet to explore sequences.
- Each cell in a spreadsheet is given a name using the column heading and the row heading.

 For example, the first cell is called A1.

Exploring mathematics | Slide 3.1

Homework Ask pupils to do **A4.1 Task 3** in the home book (p. 14).

4 Exploring patterns

Learning points

- Always read the problem carefully.
- Break down the problem into smaller chunks.
- Look for patterns and make a conjecture.
- Predict a new result and test it.
- Make a generalisation.
- Justify or prove your solution.

Starter

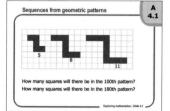

Say that this lesson is about solving problems involving patterns and sequences.

Show **slide 4.1**. Ask pupils to predict how many red squares will be in the next pattern. Invite them to explain what rule they are using.

Establish that the number of red squares follows a sequence where the term-to-term rule is 'add 3'. Ask pupils to justify this pattern by explaining how the pattern grows by adding an extra square to each 'arm' of the pattern.

Ask pupils to work out the nth term of the sequence.

Now ask them to describe the type of sequence (linear) and the graph of the relationship between the position numbers and the terms.

Main activity

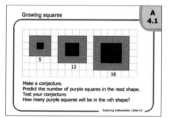

Show **slide 4.2**. Discuss the problem of growing squares. Explain that the problem could represent many different practical situations. For example, it could represent paving a path around a lawn. A gardener may need to know how to calculate the number of paving stones needed for different-sized lawns. It would be useful to have a formula so that the calculation can be done easily.

Note how the problem has been set out by starting with the smallest possible case and building it up systematically. This enables us to look for patterns and, hopefully, find a general rule.

Show pupils how to set out the results in a table with an additional column for the differences between each term. In this case the difference is always 4.

Ask pupils to predict the number of purple squares in the next shape [20] and get them to test it by drawing. Ask them to justify their prediction by referring to the way the pattern is increasing each time.

Ask them to find a formula for the nth term. Depending on their previous knowledge of algebra they could give the answer in the form $4n + 4$ or $4(n + 1)$. Pupils could use a spreadsheet to record their results and use this to determine the nth term.

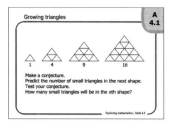

Use **slide 4.3** as extension work to challenge more able pupils. This is a similar problem to growing squares but in this case the pattern is not linear. You can use this just to show the importance of checking the differences or you can challenge pupils by looking at the second differences and noting that the solution is quadratic. They will probably notice that the sequence is that of the square numbers. Use a spreadsheet and generate the graph.

Ask pupils to do **A4.1 Exercise 4** in the class book (p. 37).

Review

Invite pupils to explain their answers to the exercises they have done.

Ask pupils to remember the points on **slide 4.4**.

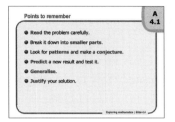

Round off the unit by referring again to the objectives. Ask pupils to find time to try the self-assessment problems in **A4.1 How well are you doing?** in the class book (p. 39).

Homework

Ask pupils to do **A4.1 Task 4** in the home book (p. 15).

Check up   A4.1

Write your answers in your book.

1 Look at this sequence of numbers:
   100, 95, 90, 85, 80, …
   a What is the 4th term?
   b What is the difference between consecutive terms?
   c Is the sequence increasing or decreasing?
   d What is the term-to-term rule?
   e Write the next three terms.

2 Write the term-to-term rule and the next three terms for each of these sequences.
   a 4, 10, 16, 22, 28, …   b 85, 82, 79, 76, …

3 Write down the first five terms of the sequence whose 1st term is 9 and whose term-to-term rule is 'multiply by 2 and add 3'.

4 Write down the nth terms of these number sequences.
   a 7, 14, 21, 28, …   b 5, 8, 11, 14, …   c 2, 8, 14, 20, …

5 Generate the first five terms of the number sequences whose nth terms are given by these formulae.
   a $5n + 3$ b $3n - 1$ c $10n - 6$ d $7n + 0.5$

6 a Draw the next shape in this pattern of tiles.

   b How many tiles would you need for the 5th shape?
   c How many tiles would you need for the nth shape?

Tier 4 resource sheets | A4.1 *Linear sequences* | 3.1

A4.1 Answers

Class book

Exercise 1

1 a 50 b 36
  c 7 d 7
  e 7 f Decreasing
  g Subtract 7 h 15, 8, 1, −6, −13

2 a Add 6
  25, 31, 37, 43, 49
  b Subtract 25
  120, 95, 70, 45, 20
  c Add 19
  67, 86, 105, 124, 143
  d Subtract 5
  −20, −25, −30, −35, −40
  e Add $\frac{1}{5}$
  $\frac{5}{5}, \frac{6}{5}, \frac{7}{5}, \frac{8}{5}, \frac{9}{5}$
  f Subtract $\frac{2}{19}$
  $\frac{10}{19}, \frac{8}{19}, \frac{6}{19}, \frac{4}{19}, \frac{2}{19}$
  g Multiply by 4
  256, 1024, 4096, 16 384, 65 536
  h Divide by 3
  9, 3, 1, $\frac{1}{3}, \frac{1}{9}$

3 a Ascending b Ascending
  c Descending d Ascending
  e Descending f Descending

4 a 0, 15, 30, 45, 60
  b 1000, 978, 956, 934, 912
  c 0, −2, −4, −6, −8
  d −42, −35, −28, −21, −14
  e 4096, 1024, 256, 64, 16
  f 1, 5, 25, 125, 625
  g 0, 7, 21, 49, 105
  h 2, 5, 14, 41, 122
  i −1, −3, −13, −63, −313

5 a 5, 10, 15, 20, 25, 30, 35, …
  b 5, 13, 21, 29, 37, 45, 53, …
  c −27, −18, −9, 0, 9, 18, 27, …
  d 230, 219, 208, 197, 186, 175, …
  e 20, 17.5, 15, 12.5, 10, 7.5, 5, …
  f 1.5, 1.9, 2.3, 2.7, 3.1, 3.5, 3.9, …

g $\frac{1}{5}, \frac{4}{5}, \frac{7}{5}, \frac{10}{5}, \frac{13}{5}, \frac{16}{5}, \frac{19}{5}, \cdots$

h $\frac{100}{25}, \frac{93}{25}, \frac{86}{25}, \frac{79}{25}, \frac{72}{25}, \frac{65}{25}, \frac{58}{25}, \cdots$

i 0, −6, −12, −18, −24, −30, …

j −60, −45, −30, −15, 0, 15, …

Extension problem

6 a Multiply by 2 and add 3
  61, 125, 253
  b Multiply by 3 and add 1
  40, 121, 364
  c Multiply by 5 and subtract 1
  469, 2344, 11 719
  d Multiply by −2
  16, −32, 64

Exercise 2

1 a Multiples of 5 b 20
  c 50 d 85
  e 5×35 f $5n$

2 a $2n$ b $7n$
  c $10n$ d $13n$
  e $8n$ f $25n$

3 a $4n, 4n + 3$ b $11n, 11n − 6$
  c $9n, 9n − 5$ d $20n, 20n − 9$
  e $6n, 6n + 1$ f $15n, 15n + 8$

4 a 21, 28, 35, 42, 49
  b 10, 13, 16, 19, 22
  c 12, 17, 22, 27, 32
  d 34, 43, 52, 61, 70
  e 30, 42, 54, 66, 78
  f 0.8, 1.05, 1.3, 1.55, 1.8
  g 2, 6, 10, 14, 18
  h $1\frac{3}{4}, 2\frac{1}{4}, 2\frac{3}{4}, 3\frac{1}{4}, 3\frac{3}{4}$

5 a 104 b 609 c 595
  d 3992 e 1022 f 100
  g 127.9 h −25

6 a $3n + 5$ b $2n + 7$
  c $5n − 3$ d $6n − 1$
  e $9n + 2$ f $12n − 3$
  g $7n − 2$ h $13n + 1$

Exercise 3

1 a Pupil's spreadsheet
  b A101
  c 302

2 a Pupil's spreadsheet
  b −1310

3 a $4n + 5$; pupil's spreadsheet
  b 1465
  c Computer-generated graph

4 a $9n − 6$; pupil's spreadsheet
  b 3072
  c Computer-generated graph

Extension problem

5 a

Position	Term
1	2
2	5
3	8
4	11
5	14
5	14
6	17
7	20
8	23
9	26
10	29
11	32
12	35

  b $3n − 1$

Exercise 4

1 a $3n$
  b $2n + 1$
  c $n + 2$

2 a $2n + 6$
  b Pupil's investigation.

3 a
  b $3n + 1$
  c Pupil's pattern and formula

4 $n − 1$

Extension problem

5 There are $n − 2$ triangles in an n-sided polygon. So the sum of angles of an n-sided polygon is $(n − 2) \times 180°$.

How well are you doing?

1 30, 37, 44, 51, 58

2 Subtract 11

3 103, 98, **93**, **88**, 83, 78, **73**

4 2, 5, 8, 11, 14

5 a **$4n + 2$**   b $(6n + 6) \times \frac{1}{2}$ or $3n + 3$
  c $2(5n − 3)$

6

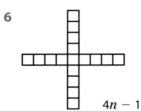

$4n − 1$

Home book

TASK 1

1 a Add 9
    41, 50, 59, 68, 77
  b Subtract 2
    20, 18, 16, 14, 12
  c Add 8
    45, 53, 61, 69, 77
  d Multiply by 2
    32, 64, 128, 256, 512
  e Add 1.5
    6.5, 8, 9.5, 11, 12.5
  f Subtract 0.3
    8.8, 8.5, 8.2, 7.9, 7.6
  g Multiply by 3
    81, 243, 729, 2187, 6561
  h Divide by 2
    12.5, 6.25, 3.125, 1.5625, 0.781 25

2 a 1, 9, 17, 25, 33
  b 500, 478, 456, 434, 412
  c 0, 33, 66, 99, 132
  d 0.6, 0.5, 0.4, 0.3, 0.2
  e 10, 0, −10, −20, −30

   f   1, 5, 13, 29, 61

   g   3, 16, 81, 406, 2031

   h   5, 7, 11, 19, 35

TASK 2

1 a 15, 20, 25, 30

    b 19, 24, 29, 34

    c 13, 18, 23, 28

    d 16, 19, 22, 25

    e 22, 31, 40, 49

    f 5.5, 7.5, 9.5, 11.5

    g 7.5, 8, 8.5, 9

2 a 71   b 79

    c 47   d 275

    e 174   f 373

    g 2561

3 a $3n + 1$ b $2n + 5$

    c $6n - 4$ d $10n - 1$

    e $5n - 4$ f $0.5n + 1.5$

TASK 3

1 a =SUM(A2+4)

    b cell A51

2 a =SUM(A2+1)

    b =A2*3+4

    c B101

TASK 4

1 a 17 octagons

    b

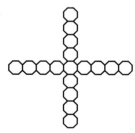

    c $4n - 3$

2 Pupil's pattern and formula

CD-ROM

Check up

1 a 85

    b 5

    c Decreasing

    d Subtract 5

    e 75, 70, 65

2 a Add 6
       34, 40, 46

    b Subtract 3
       73, 70, 67

3 a 9, 21, 45, 93, 189

4 a $7n$

    b $3n + 2$

    c $6n - 4$

5 a 8, 13, 18, 23, 28

    b 2, 5, 8, 11, 14

    c 4, 14, 24, 34, 44

    d 7.5, 14.5, 21.5, 28.5, 35.5

6 a

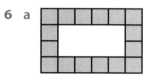

    b 18

    c $2n + 8$

Whole numbers, decimals and fractions

Previous learning

Before they start, pupils should be able to:

- round and order whole numbers and decimals to two places
- use efficient written methods of addition and subtraction and of short multiplication and division of whole numbers
- simplify fractions by cancelling and identify equivalent fractions
- write decimals as fractions, e.g. $0.23 = \frac{23}{100}$
- add and subtract simple fractions with the same denominator
- calculate simple fractions of numbers and quantities.

Objectives based on NC levels 5 and 6 (mainly level 5)

In this unit, pupils learn to:

- identify mathematical features of a context or problem
- use accurate notation
- make connections with related contexts
- manipulate numbers and apply routine algorithms
- calculate accurately, selecting mental methods or a calculator as appropriate
- estimate, approximate and check working, giving accurate solutions appropriate to the context or problem
- evaluate the efficiency of alternative strategies and approaches

and to:

- read and write positive integer powers of 10
- round positive numbers to any given power of 10 and decimals to the nearest whole number or one or two decimal places
- find equivalent fractions and equivalent fractions and decimals
- strengthen and extend mental methods of calculation, working with decimals and fractions
- use efficient written methods to:
  - add and subtract integers and decimals of any size, including numbers with differeing numbers of decimal places
  - multiply and divide 3-digit by 2-digit whole numbers
- add and subtract fractions by writing them with a common denominator
- use a calculator to carry out more difficult calculations, entering numbers, including fractions, using the memory, and interpreting the display in context
- select from a range of checking methods, including estimating in context and using inverse operations
- calculate fractions of quantities.

Lessons
1 **Place value**
2 **Ordering, adding and subtracting decimals**
3 **Multiplication and division calculations**
4 **Using a calculator**
5 **Equivalent fractions and fractions of quantities**
6 **Calculations with fractions**

About this unit
This unit extends pupils' work with whole numbers to decimals and fractions. It helps them to develop their understanding of place value and fluency in calculating mentally, using efficient written methods and using a calculator.

Assessment
This unit includes:
- an optional mental test that could replace part of a lesson (p. 68);
- a self-assessment section (*N4.2 How well are you doing?* class book p. 56);
- a set of questions to replace or supplement questions in the exercises or homework tasks, or to use as an informal test (*N4.2 Check up*, CD-ROM).

Common errors and misconceptions	Look out for pupils who:

Look out for pupils who:

- think that the number of digits after the decimal point determines the size of a decimal number, e.g. 1.25 > 1.9;
- record the answer to 3.98 rounded to one decimal place as 3, not 3.0;
- don't align corresponding digits when setting out calculations in columns, or forget to record carry digits, or record them in the wrong column;
- apply rules of 'to multiply by 10, add a zero' and 'to divide by 10, remove a zero', which don't work with decimals;
- misinterpret fraction, decimal and percentage equivalents, e.g. they wrongly assume that $\frac{1}{4} = 1.4$ and $\frac{1}{3} = 0.3$, or that 5% as a decimal is 0.5 or $\frac{5}{10}$;
- add numerators and denominators when adding fractions: $\frac{2}{3} + \frac{3}{4} = \frac{5}{7}$;
- misinterpret a calculator display in the context of money or measures, e.g. they think that 7.6 means £7 and 6p, or 7 metres and 6 centimetres;
- forget to change measurements to the same units when calculating with them.

Key terms and notation

problem, solution, method, compare, order, solve, predict, explain, justify, systematic

calculate, calculation, calculator, add, subtract, multiply, divide, sum, total, difference, product, quotient, remainder, inverse, round, approximately, estimate

decimal, whole number, multiple, digit, most significant digit, place value, decimal place, units, tenths, hundredths, thousandths, partition, ascending, descending, greater than (>), greater than or equal to (≥), less than (<), less than or equal to (≤)

fraction, numerator, denominator, common denominator, proper fraction, improper fraction, mixed number, cancel, simplify, convert, equivalent, equivalence

Practical resources

number line or counting stick
dice, enough for two per pair of pupils

scientific calculators for pupils
individual whiteboards

Exploring maths

Tier 4 teacher's book
N4.2 Mental test, p. 68
Answers for Unit N4.2, pp. 70–73

Tier 4 CD-ROM
PowerPoint files
   N4.2 Slides for lessons 1 to 5
Tools and prepared toolsheets
   Calculator tool
Tier 4 programs
   Decimal place value – explore
   Decimal place value – build the number
   Decimal place value – spot the mistakes
   Zoom number line
   Adding fractions

Tier 4 class book
N4.2, pp. 40 – 57
N4.2 How well are you doing? p. 56

Tier 4 home book
N4.2, pp. 16 – 21

Tier 4 CD-ROM
N4.2 Check up
N4.2 Pupil resource sheets
   3.1 One per pupil

Useful websites

Builder Ted, Rounding off
www.bbc.co.uk/education/mathsfile/ gameswheel.html
Fraction faxination
nrich.maths.org/public/viewer.php?obj_id=5061
Again and again
www.mathsonline.co.uk/nonmembers/gamesroom/again/index.html

1 Place value

Learning points

- The position of a digit in a number affects its value.
  Each place after the decimal point has a value one tenth of the value of the place to its left.
  Examples: $0.3 = \frac{3}{10}$ $0.03 = \frac{3}{100}$ $0.003 = \frac{3}{1000}$

- To round decimals, look at the first unwanted digit.
  If it is 5 or more, add 1 to the last digit that you keep. Then leave off all the unwanted digits.

- Round up 'halfway' numbers, e.g. 42.5 rounds up to 43; 8750 rounds up to 8800.

- 7.96 rounded to one decimal place is 8.0, not 8.

Starter   Use **slide 1.1** to discuss the objectives for the first four lessons.

Discuss the place value of different digits in whole numbers and decimals. Write a whole number such as 3 417 628 on the board for the class to read aloud in words.

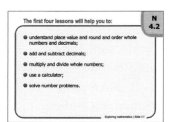

> **What is the value of the digit 1? Of the 3? Of the 4?**
>
> **What number is 10 000 more than this number? 10 000 less?**

Give pupils some numbers to write in figures on their whiteboards, e.g. one hundred and fifty thousand and seventy; seven million, two thousand and five.

Main activity   Write on the board a decimal such as 4.763. Stress that each place after the decimal point has a value one tenth of the value of the place to its left. Show that:

$$4.763 = 4 + 0.7 + 0.06 + 0.003$$
$$= 4 + \frac{7}{10} + \frac{6}{100} + \frac{3}{1000}$$

> **What number is seven hundredths more than this number?**
>
> **Seven hundredths less? Three tenths more? Four thousandths less?**

Launch **Decimal place value – explore**. Use the place value board to build decimal numbers and relate them to their fraction equivalents.

Then use **Decimal place value – build the number** and **spot the mistakes** to set problems for pupils.

Remind pupils about the rules for rounding whole numbers. If the first unwanted digit is 5, 6, 7, 8 or 9, add 1 to the last digit that you keep, otherwise make no changes. Then replace all the unwanted digits by zeros. Give a few large numbers for pupils to round to the nearest ten thousand, hundred thousand or million, e.g.

4 502 611   5 560 097   7 899 911

Remind pupils about the rules for rounding decimals. If the first unwanted digit is 5, 6, 7, 8 or 9, add 1 to the last digit that you keep, otherwise make no changes. Then leave off all the unwanted digits. Discuss some examples, then give a few decimals for pupils to round on their whiteboards.

Select individual work from **N4.2 Exercise 1** in the class book (p. 41).
Pupils will need squared paper for question 11.

Review

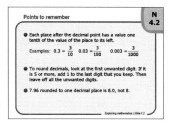

Ask pupils to add or subtract 0.1, 0.01 or 0.001 to or from decimals with up to three places, and to answer on their whiteboards, e.g.

What is 0.01 less than 5? 0.001 more than 2.009?

Subtract 0.1 from 3.07.

Sum up by asking pupils to remember the points on **slide 1.2**.

Homework

Ask pupils to do **N4.2 Task 1** in the home book (p. 16).

2 Ordering, adding and subtracting decimals

Learning points

- When you compare two decimals, compare the sizes of digits in equivalent places.

- For column addition and subtraction of decimals:
  - line up the decimal points and write tenths under tenths, hundredths under hundredths, and so on;
  - fill gaps at the end of the decimal places with zeros (optional);
  - show 'carry' figures clearly;
  - change units of measurement to the same unit.

Starter Say that this lesson is about ordering, adding and subtracting decimals.

Use counting stick.

Tell pupils that one end is the number 0.3 and the other end is the number 0.5. Count on as a class in steps of 0.02, paying special attention to what happens as you count through 0.4. Count back from 0.5 to 0.3. Point at random to different divisions and ask which number it is.

Repeat with a line from 0.07 to 0.09, counting on then back in steps of 0.002.

Launch **Zoom number line**. Use it to identify decimals with up to three places on a number line, using the zoom facility.

Ask pupils to do question 1 of **N4.2 Exercise 2A** in the class book (p. 43).

Main activity Check that pupils remember how to add and subtract whole numbers and decimals in columns with the decimal points aligned. Remind them that if the numbers involve different units of measurement (e.g. pounds and pence, litres and millilitres) they must first be changed to the same unit. Demonstrate a couple of examples:

- Find the total of 2.8 kg, 750 g and 3.625 kg.
- Subtract 456 mm from 2.3 metres.

Explain that padding empty spaces on the far right with zeros makes no difference to the number but can help to keep track of the calculation.

Ask pupils to do question 2 of **N4.2 Exercise 2A** in the class book (p. 43).

SIM

Write a set of numbers on the board, such as: 1.09, 0.19, 0.9, 0.091, 0.109.

Discuss how to decide which number is biggest. (Some pupils find it easier to add zeros so that each number has the same number of decimal places.) Make sure that pupils understand the idea of working from the left until the most significant digit is met. Compare this with the digits in the equivalent places in the other numbers. Continue to order the numbers from largest to smallest.

Remind pupils about the meaning of the symbols $<$ and $>$. Write pairs of numbers on the board, such as 9.54 and 9.45, 0.72 and 0.7, 0.008 and 0.078. Ask pupils to write the number pairs on their whiteboards with $<$ or $>$ between them.

Ask pupils to work in pairs on **N4.2 Exercise 2B** in the class book (p. 43).

Review

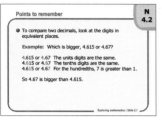

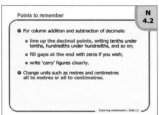

Discuss solutions to the problems in **Exercise 2B**, question 4. Ask pairs to explain how they worked out their answers.

One strategy to find the teams that would produce a dead heat is to calculate the total time for all eight runners, then divide by 2. This gives the time for each team, making it easier to work out how to compose them.

Stress the points on **slides 2.1 and 2.2**.

Homework

Ask pupils to do **N4.2 Task 2** in the home book (p. 17).

3 Multiplication and division calculations

Learning points

- For written methods of multiplication and division in columns:
  - estimate the answer first;
  - line up units under units, tens under tens, and so on;
  - when dividing, add zeros after the decimal point if necessary;
  - show 'carry' figures clearly;
  - use the estimate to make sure that the answer is about the right size and that any decimal point is in the correct place.

- Check answers by using the inverse operation.

Starter

Say that this lesson is about using written methods to multiply and divide whole numbers and solve problems.

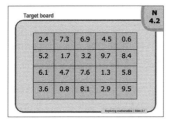

Show **slide 3.1**, a target board. Use it to ask a range of mental questions:

> **What is the largest/smallest number on the board?**

> **What number is nearest to … ?**

> **What is the sum (or difference) of this pair of numbers?**

If necessary, model explanations, e.g. counting up from 2.4 to find 6.1 − 2.4.

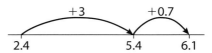

> **What is double (or half of) this number?**

With halving, start with numbers with an even number of tenths, then move on to numbers with an odd number of tenths.

> **Multiply (or divide) this number by 10 (or 100, or 1000).**

Remind pupils that digits move left for multiplication and right for division.

> **What is 5 times this number?**

Discuss how multiplying by 5 is equivalent to multiplying by 10 and then halving.

Main activity

Remind the class how to multiply a 3-digit by a 2-digit number efficiently, e.g. 476 × 57.

First estimate the answer as 500 × 60 = 30 000, and compare the actual answer with the estimate.

Demonstrate another example, such as 509 × 83.

```
          476
      ×    57
        23800   (476 × 50)
         3332   (476 × 7)
        27132
          1 1
```

Answer: 476 × 57 = 27 132

Move on to dividing a 3-digit by a 2-digit number, e.g. 846 ÷ 36. Estimate the answer as 800 ÷ 40 = 20.

Show how to deal with the remaining 18. Explain that this can be divided by 36 to get the fraction $\frac{18}{36}$ or $\frac{1}{2}$.

Alternatively, carry on, put in a decimal point and an extra zero and arrive at the decimal 0.5.

Demonstrate another example, such as 891 ÷ 36, continuing the division to two decimal places.

```
          23.5
    36)846.0
       720.0   (20 × 36)
       ─────
       126.0
       108.0   (3 × 36)
       ─────
        18.0
        18.0   (0.5 × 36)
       ─────
         0.0
```

Answer: 846 ÷ 36 = 23.5

If time allows, give each pair a copy of **N4.2 Resource sheet 3.1**. Refer them to question 1.

> **What information can we write in the table?**

Tell pupils to write the information from the question in the table, so that the second column, the first two cells of the third column, and the last cell in the last column are filled in. Get pupils to explain in which box of the table they should record the answer to each question, then ask them to complete the table. For answers, see p. 00.

Now ask the pairs to complete question 2 on **Resource sheet 3.1**.

Select individual work for pupils to do without a calculator from **N4.2 Exercise 3** in the class book (p. 45).

Review Write on the board: 595 ÷ 35 = 17 and 422 − 58 = 354. (The second calculation is deliberately incorrect.)

> **How can we check that 595 ÷ 35 = 17 is correct?**

Remind pupils that they can use inverse operations and check whether 17 × 35 returns them to the starting number of 595.

> **How can we check whether 422 − 58 = 354?**

The inverse operation is 354 + 58 has an answer of 412, not 422, so the answer to 422 − 58 = 354 is incorrect.

Summarise the lesson with the learning points on **slide 3.2**.

Points to remember
N 4.2

● For written methods of multiplication and division:
  ● estimate the answer;
  ● line up units under units, and so on;
  ● to divide, add zeros after the decimal point if needed;
  ● show 'carry' figures clearly;
  ● use the estimate to check the answer is about the right size and the decimal point is in the correct place.
● You can check answers by using inverse operations.

Exploring mathematics | Slide 3.2

Homework Ask pupils to do **N4.2 Task 3** in the home book (p. 18).

4 Using a calculator

Learning points

When you use a calculator:

- estimate the result of a calculation;
- use the CLEAR-ALL key before each new calculation;
- use the CLEAR key to clear the last entry;
- use the memory to store parts of a calculation or to keep a total;
- think carefully about the meaning of the numbers in the final display;
- round the answer to a sensible number, depending on the context;
- check the answer against the estimate.

Starter

Tell the class that the aim of this lesson is to consolidate and extend their calculator skills.

Pose the first problem on **slide 4.1**.

> **What calculation do we need to do? What is the answer?**

Write on the board 285 ÷ 12. Use the **Calculator tool** to show the answer of 23.75. Explain that this means that 23 fish would be in each pond with some fish left over.

> **If we put 23 fish in each of the 12 ponds, how many fish is that?**

Get pupils to work out 23 × 12 on their calculators. Confirm the answer of 276 fish.

> **How many fish are left over?** [285 − 276 = 9 fish]

> **If the problem were £285 divided between 12 people, what would the answer 23.75 represent?**
> [in a money context, the two digits after the decimal point represent pence; the answer 23.75 means that the 12 people will each get £23.75]

> **If the problem were 285 litres of water divided between 12 water tanks, what would the answer 23.75 represent?**
> [23 litres 750 millilitres of water in each tank]

> **If the problem were 285 minutes divided between 12 lessons, what would the answer 23.75 represent?**
> [23 minutes 45 seconds for each lesson]

Repeat with the second problem on **slide 4.1**. First use the calculator to find the remainder, then discuss different contexts for the calculation 900 ÷ 32 and what the display of 28.125 would mean in each context.

Main activity

Explain the function of the four main memory keys. These vary according to type of calculator so modify the instructions below to suit your calculators.

[M+] This key adds the contents of the display to the contents of the memory.

[M−] This key subtracts the contents of the display from the contents of the memory. This is [SHIFT] [M+] on some calculators.

$\boxed{\text{MR}}$ This key recalls the contents of the memory and puts it in the display. The contents of the display will disappear but may still be involved in the calculation. This is $\boxed{\text{RCL}}$ on some calculators

$\boxed{\text{Min}}$ This key puts the value in the display into the memory and the contents of the memory are lost. This is $\boxed{\text{STO}}$ on some calculators.

Show pupils how to use the memory to work out a calculation such as $\dfrac{78.6 - 47.9}{13.8 - 10.6}$. Remind them to estimate first by rounding each number to the nearest 10. Start by clearing all using the CLEAR-ALL key. Explain that the denominator is worked out first and then stored in the memory, using either the $\boxed{\text{M}+}$ or the $\boxed{\text{STO}}$ key. The display is then cleared and the value of the numerator calculated. After the division sign is pressed, the $\boxed{\text{MR}}$ key is used to recall the value of the denominator.

Using examples such as $12.4 \div (7.3 - 4.26)$ and $\dfrac{42.7 + 86.3}{14.8 - 11.2}$, discuss the advantages of using the memory keys versus the bracket keys. Get pupils to think about the number of key presses needed and what might need to be recorded as interim steps.

Select individual work from **N4.2 Exercise 4** in the class book (p. 47).

Review   Discuss the first problem on **slide 4.2**.

> What calculation do we need to do? What is the answer?

In the first problem, when 1 is divided by 160 the calculator display will show 0.006 25. Discuss whether this is a sensible answer in the context of the question, and round it to 0.006 (to 3 d.p.), or approximately 6 g.

Show the second problem.

> What is the area of a rectangle 2.39 cm by 4.56 cm?

Find the area by multiplying $2.39 \times 4.56 = 10.8984$. Discuss the units for the answer and what would be sensible in the context. Give the answer as 10.9 cm^2 (to 1 d.p.).

Ask pupils to remember the points on **slide 4.3**.

Problems

N 4.2

A machine dispenses 1 kg of sugar equally between 160 cups of tea. How much sugar is put in each cup?

A rectangle measures 2.39 cm by 4.56 cm. What is its area?

Points to remember

N 4.2

When you use a calculator:
● estimate first;
● use CLEAR All or ON before each new calculation;
● use CLEAR to clear the last entry;
● use the memory to store parts of a calculation;
● think carefully about the meaning of the display;
● round the answer to a sensible number;
● check the answer against the estimate.

Homework   Ask pupils to do **N4.2 Task 4** in the home book (p. 19).

5 Equivalent fractions and fractions of quantities

Learning points

- Convert a fraction into an equivalent fraction by multiplying or dividing the numerator and the denominator by the same number.

- Find a fraction of a number by using multiplication and division.

Starter

Use **slide 5.1** to discuss what pupils will learn in this and the next lesson.

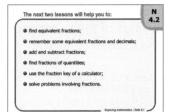

Remind pupils that any fraction can be converted to an equivalent fraction by multiplying or dividing the numerator and denominator by the same number.

Ask some questions such as:

What is the missing number in $\frac{9}{15} = \frac{\square}{5}$? In $\frac{3}{8} = \frac{\square}{24}$?

Write some fractions on the board for pupils to simplify, e.g. $\frac{18}{30}$ $\frac{21}{49}$ $\frac{675}{1000}$.

Main activity

Refer pupils to their calculators. Explain that the fraction key often looks like $\boxed{a^b/_c}$.

Ask them to enter $\boxed{4}\boxed{a^b/_c}\boxed{6}$. The display represents $\frac{4}{6}$ and will look something like:

$$\boxed{4 \lrcorner 6}$$

If they now press $\boxed{=}$ the fraction will be simplified to $\frac{2}{3}$.

Ask pupils to simplify the three fractions on the board using their calculators.

Review the method for changing improper fractions to mixed numbers, and vice versa. Use an example where cancelling is required, reminding pupils that it is sometimes easier to do this after the fraction is converted to a mixed number, as with:

$$\frac{34}{8} = 4\frac{2}{8} = 4\frac{1}{4} \qquad 4\frac{3}{8} = \frac{35}{8}$$

Repeat by changing $2\frac{2}{5}$ and $2\frac{7}{9}$ to improper fractions.

Now ask pupils to use their calculators and to enter $\boxed{3}\boxed{4}\boxed{a^b/_c}\boxed{8}$.

This time, when $\boxed{=}$ is pressed, the display will show:

$$\boxed{3 \lrcorner 2 \lrcorner 5}$$

which represents the fraction $3\frac{2}{5}$.

Next show pupils that the mixed number $3\frac{2}{5}$ is entered as $\boxed{3}\boxed{a^b/_c}\boxed{2}\boxed{a^b/_c}\boxed{5}$.

Select individual work from **N4.2 Exercise 5A** in the class book (p. 50).

Ask pupils to use their calculators and to answer questions on their whiteboards.

What fraction of a metre is 345 cm?
[a metre is 100 cm, so the fraction is $\frac{345}{100}$, which converts to $3\frac{45}{100}$ and cancels to $3\frac{9}{20}$]

What fraction of a kilogram is 2400 grams? [$2\frac{2}{5}$]

Show **slide 5.2**, a target board. Point to 28.

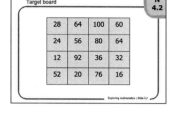

What is three quarters of 28? How did you work it out?

Establish that one way to do it is to divide 28 by 4, then multiply by 3.

Point to another number and ask pupils to find a fraction of it, working mentally. Choose a denominator that is a factor of the number on the board. Repeat a few times.

Repeat with more numbers, this time asking pupils to use their calculators.

Show **slide 5.3**, another target board. Say that these are amounts of money. Point to 9.

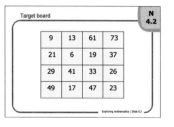

What is three quarters of £9? How did you work it out?

Repeat a few times without calculators, using denominators of 2, 4, 5 or 10. Work slowly enough for pupils to make jottings to work out their answers.

Select further individual work from **N4.2 Exercise 5B** in the class book (p. 51).

Review

Discuss the exercises that pupils have done.

Sort out any difficulties they have experienced, particularly in using their calculators.

Round off the lesson using the points on **slide 5.4**.

Homework

Ask pupils to do **N4.2 Task 5** in the home book (p. 20).

6 Calculations with fractions

Learning points

- Given a fractional part, find the whole by using division then multiplication.
- Add or subtract fractions with different denominators by first changing them to equivalent fractions with a common denominator. Deal with whole numbers first.

Starter   Say that this lesson continues work on calculations with fractions.

Show the class how to find the whole, given a fractional part. For example:

> **Three fifths of a number is 12. What is the number?**
> [find one fifth by dividing 12 by 3 to give 4, then multiply by 5 to get five fifths]

> **A jug that is two thirds full has 500 ml water in it.**
> **How much does a full jug hold?**
> [find one third by dividing by 2 to get 250 ml, then multiply by 3 to get three thirds]

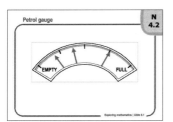

Show **slide 6.1**. Click on the slide to reveal the first arrow.

> **A car's petrol tank holds 60 litres of petrol when it is full.**
> **How much petrol is in the tank now?**

> **What if there is 30 litres in the tank now?**
> **How much does it hold when full?**

Repeat, varying the amounts. Discuss how to set out working, such as:

> Three quarters is 30 litres.
> One quarter is $30 \div 3 = 10$ litres.
> Four quarters is $10 \times 4 = 40$ litres.

Click on the slide to reveal the arrow in a new position. Estimate the proportion of the tank that is filled (e.g. three eighths). Repeat the questions. Click again and repeat.

> Ask pupils to do **N4.2 Exercise 6A** in the class book (p. 53).

Main activity   Show pupils how to add and subtract simple fractions. Stress that both fractions must have the same denominator for the calculation to take place. Demonstrate examples:

- denominators with no common factors (e.g. $\frac{1}{3} + \frac{1}{2}, \frac{3}{8} - \frac{1}{3}$);
- one denominator a multiple of the other (e.g. $\frac{2}{9} + \frac{1}{3}, \frac{5}{12} - \frac{1}{4}$);
- denominators with a factor in common (e.g. $\frac{3}{8} + \frac{5}{12}, \frac{7}{10} - \frac{2}{15}$).

Use **Adding fractions** as support.

Show pupils how to add and subtract mixed numbers by dealing with the whole numbers first and then ensuring that both the fractional parts have the same denominators. Leave both calculations displayed on the board.

Adding mixed numbers	**Subtracting mixed numbers**
$2\frac{5}{8} + 3\frac{7}{12}$	$4\frac{5}{12} - 2\frac{3}{4}$
$= 5\frac{5}{8} + \frac{7}{12}$	$= 2\frac{5}{12} - \frac{3}{4}$
$= 5\frac{15}{24} + \frac{14}{24}$	$= 2\frac{5}{12} - \frac{9}{12}$
$= 5\frac{29}{24}$	$= 1\frac{17}{12} - \frac{9}{12}$
$= 6\frac{5}{24}$	$= 1\frac{8}{12}$
	$= 1\frac{2}{3}$

Tell pupils that they are expected to be able to do simple fraction calculations without a calculator but more complicated problems can be done on a calculator. Guide the class through both the calculations on the board using their calculators.

Select individual work from **N4.2 Exercises 6B** in the class book (p. 55).

Review

Show the problem on **slide 6.2** for pupils to discuss in pairs.

[Since $\frac{1}{4} + \frac{1}{6} + \frac{1}{3} = \frac{18}{24} = \frac{3}{4}$, the 12 coins that the pirate kept were one quarter of the coins. The total number of coins was 48, and the lookout got one third, or 16 coins.]

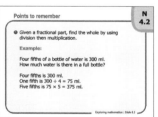

Sum up the lesson using **slides 6.3 and 6.4**.

Round off the unit by referring again to the objectives. Suggest that pupils find time to try the self-assessment problems in **N4.2 How well are you doing?** in the class book (p. 56).

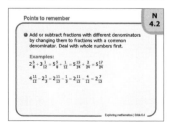

Homework

Ask pupils to do **N4.2 Task 6** in the home book (p. 21).

N4.2 Mental test

Read each question aloud twice.

Allow a suitable pause for pupils to write answers.

1 In a café I buy two cups of coffee and a sandwich.
Altogether I pay three pounds.
The sandwich costs one pound sixty.
What is the cost of one cup of coffee?   *2003 KS3*

2 Write the next number in this counting sequence.
Eight point seven, eight point eight, eight point nine, …   *2003 KS3*

3 Add together nought point two, nought point four and nought point six.   *2005 KS2*

4 What is the sum of eight point five and eight point six?   *2002 KS2*

5 What is four multiplied by three point five?   *2000 KS2*

6 What is four thousand seven hundred and seventy-three rounded to the
nearest hundred?   *2003 KS2*

7 Write two-fifths as a decimal.   *2000 KS3*

8 What number is one hundred less than ten thousand?   *2006 KS2*

9 A city has a population of five million and forty-seven thousand.
Write this number in figures.   *1999 KS3*

10 Multiply eight point seven by two.   *2004 KS3*

11 Calculate ten minus four point three five.   *2005 KS2*

12 What is three point nine divided by two?   *2003 KS3*

Key:

KS3 Key Stage 3 test   KS2 Key Stage 2 test
Question 1 is at level 3; questions 2 to 6 are at level 4;
questions 7 to 11 are at level 5; question 12 is at level 6.

Answers

1	70p or £0.70	**2**	9 or 9.0
3	1.2	**4**	17.1
5	14	**6**	4800
7	0.4	**8**	9900
9	5 047 000	**10**	17.4
11	5.65	**12**	1.95

N4.2 Check up and resource sheets

Check up · N4.2

Write your answers on the sheet.

Whole numbers, decimals and fractions (no calculator)

1. Put a ring around the smallest number.

   0.27   0.207   0.027   2.07   2.7

2. Circle the two numbers that have a total of 10.

   0.01   0.11   1.01   9.09   9.9   9.99

3. Here is a number line. Draw an arrow to show the position of 0.111.

   0.1   0.12

4. Put a ring around the decimal which is equal to one fifth.

   0.1   0.2   0.3   0.4   0.5

5. Complete these fractions to make each equivalent to $\frac{3}{5}$.

   $\frac{\square}{10}$ $\frac{12}{\square}$ $\frac{\square}{15}$

6. Write a decimal which is greater than 0.8 and less than 0.81. ....

7. Find the answers to these calculations. Show your working.

   a $509 \times 24 =$ ....

   b $15.5 - 14.84 =$ ....

   c $924 \div 22 =$ ....

4.1 | Tier 4 resource sheets | N4.2 *Whole numbers, decimals and fractions*   © Pearson Education 2008

Check up [continued]

8. The first two terms in this sequence are 3.2 and 3.3.
   The sequence then follows the rule:
   'to get the next term, add the two previous terms'.
   Write the next two terms.

   3.2   3.3   6.5   9.8   ....

Whole numbers, decimals and fractions (calculator allowed)

9. Use a calculator to work out what number goes in each box.

   a $49.5 \times (2.06 + 8.5) =$ [ ]

   b $100 - (22.75 + 19.08) =$ [ ]

   c $32.45 \times$ [ ] $= 253.11$

10. Every 100 g of brown bread contains 8.2 g of fibre.
    A loaf of bread weighing 400 g is cut into 16 equal
    slices. How much fibre is there in one slice?

    Answer: [ ] grams

11. A machine makes paper clips that go into boxes.
    A full box has 115 paper clips.
    How many full boxes can be made from 100 000
    paper clips?

    Answer: [ ] boxes

© Pearson Education 2008   Tier 4 resource sheets | N4.2 *Whole numbers, decimals and fractions* | 4.2

Resource sheet 3.1 · N4.2

Write your answers on the sheet.

1. Running burns 24 calories each minute.
   Cycling burns 22 calories each minute.
   Swimming burns 18 calories each minute.

   Sam ran for 17 minutes, cycled for 29 minutes and then finished by swimming. Altogether he
   burned 1460 calories.

   Put as much information as you can in the table below. Then use the table to answer these
   questions.

   a How many calories did Sam burn by running?
   b How many calories did Sam burn by cycling?
   c How many calories did Sam burn by swimming?
   d For how long did Sam swim?
   e How long in total did he spend exercising?

Activity	Calories burned each minute	Number of minutes exercising	Calories burned during exercise
Running			
Cycling			
Swimming			
TOTALS			

2. You are going to exercise for 45 minutes.
   Decide for how many minutes you will swim, cycle and run. The total must be 45 minutes. Put
   this information in the table.
   Work out how many calories you will have burned in 45 minutes.

Activity	Calories burned each minute	Number of minutes exercising	Calories burned during exercise
Running	24		
Cycling	22		
Swimming	18		
TOTALS		45	

4.3 | Tier 4 resource sheets | N4.2 *Whole numbers, decimals and fractions*   © Pearson Education 2008

N4.2 Answers

Class book

Exercise 1

1 a 14 009   b 60 600
  c 900 050   d 2 040 020

2 a ninety thousand, one hundred and eight
  b sixty thousand and ten
  c seven million, sixty thousand, eight hundred
  d four hundred and three thousand and forty

3 a two hundredths
  b three tenths
  c seven
  d three thousandths
  e thirty thousand
  f nine hundred thousand
  g six million
  h five hundredths

4 a 2.1   b 6.7
  c 3.75   d 1.1
  e 9.25   f 8.75
  g 1.335   h 4.995
  i 7.275

5 a 710   b 10 500   c 2 501 000

6 a 4300   b 504 800   c 10 000

7 a 6000   b 60 000   c 7 330 000

8 a 706.6   b 60.0   c 1.1

9 a 12.13   b 3.46   c 0.04

10 a 0.020   b 10.000   c 5.000

11 Answers which depend on the constant function
   will depend on the type of calculator used.
   a 3.4 in 8 presses: 2.2 + 1.2 =
   b 3.32 in 9 presses: 1.22 + 2.1 =
   c e.g. 110 in 8 presses: 22 + = = = =
   d e.g. 2.42 in 9 presses: 2.22 + .1 = =
   e e.g. 96 in 9 presses: 12 + 21 = = = =

Exercise 2A

1 a 3.94   3.96   3.98   **4.00**   **4.02**   **4.04**
  b 4.05   4.07   4.09   **4.11**   **4.13**   **4.15**
  c 2.93   2.96   2.99   **3.02**   **3.05**   **3.08**
  d 6.93   6.97   7.01   **7.05**   **7.09**   **7.13**
  e 2.89   2.94   2.99   **3.04**   **3.09**   **3.14**
  f 5.995   5.997   5.999   **6.001** **6.003** **6.005**

2 $12.618 + 3.776 = 16.394$
   $1.097 + 9.77 = 10.867$
   $14.31 - 11.048 = 3.262$
   $0.847 - 0.514 = 0.333$
   $15.88 - 4.109 = 11.771$

Exercise 2B

1 a 2.602, 2.60, 2.162, 2.06
  b 2.34, 1.43, 1.324, 1.234

2 1st Grey, 2nd Green, 3rd Black

3 3.715 cm, 3.39 cm, 3.7 cm

4 a Reds took 51.81 seconds.
     Blacks took 53.03 seconds.
     Reds won by 1.22 seconds.
  b The fastest possible team is Jessica, Meena,
     Megan and Lauren. The time for this team
     would be 49.63 seconds.
  c The race will be a dead heat if Jessica changes
     places with Megan. Each team will then take
     52.42 seconds.
  d The team that will take 53.50 seconds is
     Chloe, Meena, Charlotte and Olivia.

Exercise 3

1 16 full boxes   2 6336 stamps

3 £13.50   4 £9350

5 a **29 × 82** = 2378   b **65 × 58** = 3770
  c **91 × 29** = 2639   d **42 × 65** = 2730
  e **82 × 42** = 3444   f **58 × 82** = 4756
  g 928 ÷ **32** = **29** h **29 × 42** ÷ **58** = 21
  Other answers are possible using equivalent
  facts.

6

×	6	9	8
12	72	**108**	96
19	**114**	171	**152**
11	66	**99**	**88**
14	84	**126**	**112**

Extension problems

7 a $\mathbf{5}3 \times \mathbf{8} = 424$ b $35 \times \mathbf{9} = 315$

   c $24 \times \mathbf{6} = 1\mathbf{4}4$ d $17 \times \mathbf{4}3 = 731$

   e $93 \times \mathbf{76} = 70\mathbf{6}8$ f $\mathbf{7}3 \times \mathbf{5}7 = 41\mathbf{61}$

Exercise 4

1 a £364.50   b 600 people

2 26 lengths; 8 cm left over

3 13 bottles; 125 ml left over

4 49 snacks

5 This is a game.

6 With four digits, the outcome is always 6174, which is known as Kaprekar's constant. The longest chains require seven subtractions to reach Kaprekar's constant, starting with: 1236, 1246, 1279, 1346, 1356, 1389, 1456, 2347, 2357, 2457, 2467, 2567, 3458, 3468, 3568, 3578, 3678, 4569, 4579, 4679 or 4789.

Extension problem

7 a $(56 - 38) \times 62 = 1116$

   b $(2030 \div 35) + 97 = 155$

   c $650 \div (48 - 35) = 50$

   d $27 \times (13 \times 15) = 5265$

Exercise 5A

1 a $\frac{1}{4}$ b $\frac{7}{10}$ c $\frac{4}{9}$

   d $\frac{1}{3}$ e 5 f $3\frac{1}{5}$

2 a $\frac{2}{3} = \frac{48}{72}$ b $\frac{3}{8} = \frac{36}{96}$ c $\frac{5}{9} = \frac{35}{63}$

   d $\frac{9}{5} = \frac{108}{60}$ e $\frac{13}{24} = \frac{52}{96}$ f $\frac{12}{11} = \frac{144}{132}$

3 a $\frac{5}{7}$ b $\frac{4}{9}$ c $\frac{2}{3}$

   d $\frac{8}{11}$ e $\frac{6}{13}$ f $\frac{14}{17}$

4 a $\frac{2}{25}$ b $\frac{7}{40}$ c $\frac{3}{14}$

   d $\frac{5}{12}$ e $\frac{4}{7}$ f $\frac{1}{6}$

Exercise 5B

1 a 149.5   b £345.60

   c 12.5 kg   d 29.75 m

   e 262.5 m²   f 375 litres

   g 52.5 km   h 52.5 minutes

2 This is a game.

Extension problems

3 The fraction was $\frac{1}{49}$.

4 a $\frac{4}{15}$ b 18

5 Parveen is 18 years old and Afzal is 14 years old.

Exercise 6A

1 12 metres

2 1000 metres or 1 kilometre

3 £72

4 625 grams

5 42 minutes

6 1350 cm²

7 320 ml

8 £2.80

Exercise 6B

1 a

+	$\frac{3}{4}$	$\frac{1}{5}$
$\frac{1}{2}$	$1\frac{1}{4}$	$\frac{7}{10}$
$\frac{1}{3}$	$1\frac{1}{12}$	$\frac{8}{15}$

   b

+	$\frac{2}{5}$	$\frac{2}{3}$
$\frac{1}{4}$	$\frac{13}{20}$	$\frac{11}{12}$
$\frac{1}{10}$	$\frac{1}{2}$	$\frac{23}{30}$

   c

+	$\frac{3}{5}$	$\frac{1}{2}$
$\frac{1}{6}$	$\frac{23}{30}$	$\frac{2}{3}$
$\frac{2}{5}$	1	$\frac{9}{10}$

2 a $3\frac{1}{2} + 2\frac{3}{4} = 6\frac{1}{4}$ b $1\frac{5}{6} - 1\frac{2}{3} = \frac{1}{6}$

   c $1\frac{2}{3} + 2\frac{4}{5} = 4\frac{7}{15}$ d $2\frac{3}{4} - 1\frac{2}{3} = 1\frac{1}{12}$

   e $1\frac{5}{6} + 1\frac{2}{3} = 3\frac{1}{2}$ f $2\frac{4}{5} - 1\frac{5}{6} = \frac{29}{30}$

Extension problem

3 a The least score for a path is $1\frac{1}{8}$.

b The path that gives the score of $2\frac{1}{8}$ is IN, right, down, down, right, OUT.

c There are nine different paths through the maze. Six of these pass through the minimum number of cells, which is five.
The path IN, right, down, left, down, right, right, OUT passes through seven cells, as does the path IN, right, right, down, left, down, right, OUT.
The path IN, right, right, down, left, left, down, right, right, OUT passes through all nine cells.

d The path that passes through all nine cells produces the maximum score of $3\frac{7}{8}$.

How well are you doing?

1 a 0.6 **b** $\frac{10}{15}$ and $\frac{6}{9}$

2 a 0.035 **b** 0.65 and 0.35

3 a $\frac{1}{4} + \frac{6}{8} = 1$ **b** $\frac{1}{3} + \frac{8}{12} = 1$

4 a 12 558 **b** 24.669 **c** 26

5 a 18 **b** 9.85 **c** 19.5

6 0.15 g

7 a 135 metres **b** 222 paper clips

Home book

TASK 1

1

Round:	to the nearest 10	to the nearest whole number	to one decimal place	to two decimal places
53.292	50	53	53.3	53.29
8.851	10	9	8.9	8.85
159.444	160	159	159.4	159.44
43.0999	40	43	43.1	43.10

2 Approximately $2 \times 10 \times 30 = 600$ litres of water are used each month to fill the kettle. Other estimates are possible.

3 An estimate of the mass of the cakes is 128 kg, e.g. $40 \times 4 \times 20 \times 40 = 128\,000$ g $= 128$kg. Other estimates are possible.

TASK 2

1 a 0.45 km $= 450\,000$ mm

b 1950 cm^2 $= 0.195$ m^2

c 32 500 mm $= 0.0325$ km

d 0.0065 km^2 $= 65\,000\,000$ cm^2

e 3.6 kg $= 3600$ g

f 17 250 ml $= 17.25$ litres

2 G $2.024 \times 3 = 6.072$
O $6.06 + 0.293 = 6.353$
L $25.42 \div 4 = 6.355$
D $5.01 + 1.39 = 6.4$
M $1.68 \times 4 = 6.72$
I $54 \div 8 = 6.75$
N $8.054 - 1.1 = 6.954$
E $7 - 0.036 = 6.964$

3 Jack's median reaction time is 0.31 seconds.

TASK 3

1 $32 = 4 \times 8$

2 $32 = 2 \times 2 \times 8$

3 $40 = 5 \times 4 \times 2 \times 1$

4 $40 = 5 \times 2 \times 2 \times 2 \times 1$

5 The maximum product for 12 is 81, made from $3 \times 3 \times 3 \times 3$.

6 The maximum product for 13 is 108, made from $4 \times 3 \times 3 \times 3$.
In general, the maximum product:
for a number of the form $3n$ is 3^n
for a number of the form $3n + 1$ is $4 \times 3^{n-1}$
for a number of the form $3n + 2$ is 2×3^n

TASK 4

1 £10.99

2 a $(37 \times 21) + 223 = 1000$
   b $(756 \div 18) \times 29 = 1218$
   c $27 + (36 \times 18) = 675$
   d $31 \times (87 - 19) = 2108$

TASK 5

1 a $\frac{2}{9}$ b $\frac{5}{6}$ c $\frac{3}{8}$ d $\frac{17}{360}$

2 a 225°   b 80°   c 260°   d 228°

3 a 1 h 15 min   b £176.75   c 15.75 kg
   d 25.6 cm   e 187.5 m²   f 20.8 litres

TASK 6

1 The bosun got 12 rubies.

2 2 pirates found both gold coins and rubies.

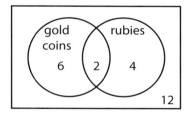

CD-ROM

Check up

1 0.027

2 0.01 and 9.99

3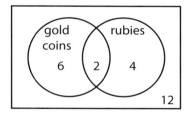

4 0.2

5 $\frac{6}{10}$ $\frac{12}{20}$ $\frac{9}{15}$

6 e.g. 0.805

7 a $509 \times 24 = 12\,216$
   b $15.5 - 14.84 = 0.66$
   c $924 \div 22 = 42$

8 16.3, 26.1

9 a 522.72   b 58.17   c 7.8

10 2.05 grams of fibre

11 869 full boxes of paper clips

Probability

Previous learning

Before they start, pupils should be able to:

- understand and use the probability scale from 0 to 1
- find probabilities based on equally likely outcomes in simple contexts
- estimate probabilities based on experimental data in a frequency table.

Objectives based on NC levels 5 and 6 (mainly level 5)

In this unit, pupils learn to:

- identify the mathematical features of a context or problem
- conjecture and generalise, identifying exceptional cases or counter-examples
- select appropriate procedures and tools, including ICT
- make accurate diagrams and graphs on paper and on screen
- record methods, solutions and conclusions

and to:

- interpret results of an experiment using the language of probability and appreciate
- know that random processes are unpredictable if the probability of an event occurring is p, then the probability of it not occurring is $1 - p$
- use diagrams and tables to record all possible mutually exclusive outcomes for single events and two successive events
- compare estimated experimental probabilities with theoretical probabilities, recognising that:
  - if an experiment is repeated, the outcome may and usually will be different
  - increasing the number of times an experiment is repeated generally leads to better estimates of probability.

Lessons

1 **Theoretical probability**

2 **Events not happening**

3 **The probability of two events**

4 **Experimental probability**

5 **Are you lucky?**

6 **Theory and experiment**

About this unit

This unit includes work on the probability scale, systematically finding all the possible outcomes of events, and estimating probabilities by using data from an experiment and comparing the estimate with the theoretical probability.

Many of the activities are for pairs or groups of pupils in order to support and develop classroom discussion.

Assessment

This unit includes:

- a self-assessment section (*S4.1 How well are you doing?* class book p. 74);
- a set of questions to replace or supplement questions in the exercises or homework tasks, or to use as an informal test (*S4.1 Check up*, CD-ROM).

Common errors and misconceptions

Look out for pupils who:

- make statements of certainty or impossibility that rely on hopes or personal preferences rather than on likelihood;
- use equally likely outcomes to measure probability in situations where outcomes are not equally likely;
- believe that if an experiment is repeated the outcomes will be the same;
- fail to appreciate that experimental probability is an estimate of probability that increases in reliability as the number of trials on which it is based increases;
- are unable to convert between fractions, decimals and percentages and so make limited progress;
- use incorrect measures of probability, for example, 1 in 3 or 1 : 3.

Key terms and notation

likely, unlikely, equally likely, certain, uncertain, probable, improbable, possible, impossible, chance, good chance, poor chance, no chance, fifty-fifty chance, even chance

likelihood, probability, risk, doubt, theoretical probability, experimental probability

fair, unfair, biased, unbiased, random, at random, simulate, simulation

trial, outcome, event, favourable, unfavourable

Practical resources

calculators for pupils
box or bag for counters
50 coloured counters
coloured cubes
dice
coins
playing cards

scissors
envelopes
individual whiteboards
for lesson 6, either computers for pupils and Number spinners, or for each small group of pupils, a pack of four cards numbered 1, 2, 1, 3

Exploring maths

Tier 4 teacher's book
Answers for Unit S4.1, pp. 89–92

Tier 4 CD-ROM
PowerPoint files
　　S4.1 Slides for lessons 1 to 6
Tools and prepared toolsheets
　　Dice tool
　　Coins tool
　　Spinner tool

Tier 4 class book
S4.1, pp. 58–75
S4.1 How well are you doing? p. 74

Tier 4 home book
S4.1, pp. 22–29

Tier 4 CD-ROM
S4.1 Check up
S4.1 Pupil resource sheets
　　3.1 One per pupil
　　4.1 One per pupil
　　5.1 One per pupil
　　6.1 One per pupil

Useful websites

The Game of Pig
cs.gettysburg.edu/projects/pig/piggame.html

Rock, Paper, Scissors
www.worldrps.com

Fish tank
www.bbc.co.uk/education/mathsfile/gameswheel.html

Spinners, Coin tossing
nlvm.usu.edu/en/nav/category_g_3_t_5.html

1 Theoretical probability

Learning points

- Probabilities range from 0 (impossible) to 1 (certain).
  They are written as fractions, decimals or percentages.

- An event can have different outcomes.

- Equally likely outcomes occur in fair trials.

- If the outcomes are equally likely, the theoretical probability of a particular event is:

  $$\frac{\text{number of favourable outcomes}}{\text{total number of possible outcomes}}$$

Starter

Use **slide 1.1** to discuss the objectives for the first three lessons. Say that this lesson is about working out the probability of a single event.

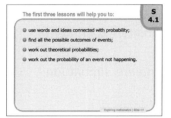

Ask pupils to draw a horizontal line about 20 cm long on their whiteboards. Remind pupils of the probability scale and ask them to place the words 'impossible', 'unlikely', 'even chance', 'likely' and 'certain' on their line.

Ask pupils to suggest examples of events that are certain, impossible or have an even chance of happening. Then ask for examples of events that are not certain but likely, or are not impossible but unlikely.

Explain that, in addition to words, probabilities can be described by a number. Ask pupils to insert values for 'impossible', 'even chance' and 'certain' on their probability scale.

> **What sorts of numbers must be used to describe probability?**
> [fractions, decimals or percentages]

Give some fractions (e.g. $\frac{4}{5}$), decimals (e.g. 0.23) and percentages (e.g. 65%). Ask if they represent the probability of a likely or an unlikely event. Get pupils to justify their answers.

Main activity

Hold up a large die or show a die using the **Dice tool**. Demonstrate the 'trial' of rolling the die and recording its number. Introduce and explain the meaning of the terms *trial*, *outcome* and *event*.

> **How many possible outcomes are there when a die is rolled?**
> **How many outcomes are there favourable to the event 'rolling a 6'?**

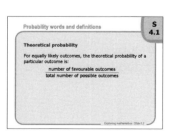

Introduce the idea of *equally likely outcomes*. Outcomes are equally likely when they have an equal chance of occurring.

> **Are the outcomes when a die is rolled equally likely?**
> [yes — if the die is fair]

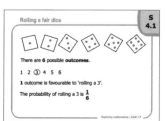

Stress that the terms *at random*, *fair* and *unbiased* indicate that outcomes are equally likely. Revise the definition of *theoretical probability* (**slide 1.2**). Emphasise that this definition is valid only when outcomes are equally likely.

Display **slide 1.3** and take the class through the section on rolling a dice.

> **What is the probability of rolling an even number?**
> **What is the probability of rolling a number less than 5?**

Ask pupils to work in pairs on **S4.1 Exercise 1A** on questions 1 to 3 in the class book (p. 59).

Demonstrate the trial of taking a counter from a box containing 3 red and 2 green counters. Discuss how the trial can be made a fair trial, reinforcing what this means. Shake the box and take a counter without looking and put the counter back in the box before the next trial.

If the trial is fair, how many equally likely outcomes are there?

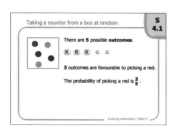

Make sure that pupils understand that there are three possible outcomes for red (three ways a red can be taken) and two for green, giving the possible outcomes: red, red, red, green, green. Explain that sometimes it is necessary to make a list of the equally likely outcomes in an event to help to work out the probability.

Show **slide 1.4**.

What is the probability of picking a green counter from the box?
[there are two equally likely favourable outcomes so the probability is $\frac{2}{5}$]

Select from questions 4 to 6 in **S4.1 Exercise 1B** in the class book (p. 60).

Review

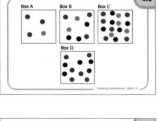

Show the first part of **slide 1.5**. Say that a counter is taken from each box at random. Ask whether these statements are true or false. Pupils should explain their choice.

- For box C, there are 16 equally likely outcomes. [true]

- There are more red counters in box C, so the probability of taking a red counter from box C is greater than the probability of taking a red counter from box A. [false]

- It is more likely that a red counter is taken from box A than box B. [true]

- There is an equal probability of taking a blue counter from each box. [true]

Now display box D (the second part of **slide 1.5**).

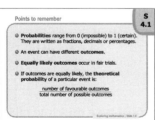

Ask how a different box could be filled with counters so that the probability of picking a black counter is the *same* as that for box D.

Summarise using the points on **slide 1.6**.

Homework

Ask pupils to do **S4.1 Task 1** in the home book (p. 22).

2 Events not happening

Learning points

◉ The probability of an event not happening is 1 minus the probability of the event happening.

Starter

Say that this lesson will focus on the probability of events not happening.

Show **slide 2.1**. Ask pupils to match a decimal or percentage in the top row to a fraction in the bottom row so that they add up to 1.

> **What should be added to 0.5 to make 1?**

Ask a pupil to explain why $0.5 + \frac{1}{2} = 1$ (because $\frac{1}{2} = \frac{5}{10} = 0.5$). Reveal the link on the slide.

Repeat with 70% and 0.25.

Ask pupils to complete the remaining additions in pairs. Check responses using the links on the slide.

Main activity

Draw a box on the board and explain that the probability of picking a red counter at random from the box equals 1. Ask pupils to draw red, blue or green counters in the box so that this is true.

Check that pupil s have placed only red counters in the box.

> **Does the number of red counters matter?**
> [no − only that all the counters are red]

Repeat with these probabilities (the notation P(red) is used for the probability of a red counter being picked).

1 P(red) = 1 [all counters must be red]

2 P(red) = 0 [all counters must be blue or green]

3 P(red) = $\frac{1}{2}$ [there must be an even number of counters, half of which are red and half of which are blue or green]

4 P(not red) = $\frac{1}{2}$ [there must be an even number of counters, half of which are red and half of which are blue or green]

6 P(not red) = $\frac{1}{3}$ [the total number of counters must be a multiple of 3; $\frac{1}{3}$ must be blue or green and $\frac{2}{3}$ red]

7 P(not red) = 4 × P(red) [the total number of counters must be a multiple of 5; there must be four times as many not red as red]

For each box ask questions like:

> **What is the total number of counters in the box?**

> **Is there a different total number of counters that could be in the box?**

> **How did you decide on which counters should go in the box?**

Show **slide 2.2**. Make sure that all pupils know the structure of a standard pack of playing cards.

> **If a card is picked at random from a pack of playing cards, what are the possible outcomes? How many equally likely outcomes are there?**

Take the class through the example of picking a black picture card on **slide 2.2**.
Ask the questions before revealing the answers on the slide.

> What are the possible favourable outcomes for picking a black picture card from a pack of cards?
>
> What is the probability of picking a black picture card from a pack of cards?
>
> What is the probability of not picking a black picture card from a pack of cards?

Repeat with the probability of picking a red king and *not* picking a red king (**slide 2.3**).

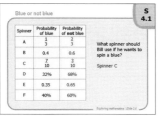

Ask pupils to do questions 1 and 2 from **S4.1 Exercise 2** in the class book (p. 62).

Review the work and ask the class if they can see a quick method of working out the probability of an event *not* happening.

Ask pupils to do the rest of **S4.1 Exercise 2** in the class book (p. 62).

Review Show **slide 2.4**. Ask pupils to work out the missing probabilities in the table. Discuss and display answers on the slide.

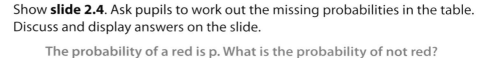

> The probability of a red is p. What is the probability of not red?
> $[1 - p]$
>
> What spinner should you use if you want to spin a red? Why?

Summarise the lesson by stressing the learning points.

Homework Ask pupils to do **S4.1 Task 2** in the home book (p. 24).

3 The probability of two events

Learning points

- When two events occur at the same time or one after the other, you can use a list or table to record the equally likely outcomes.

- Use the list or table to work out a probability from:

$$\frac{\text{number of favourable outcomes}}{\text{total number of possible outcomes}}$$

Starter

Say that this lesson looks at the probability of two events happening at the same time or one after another.

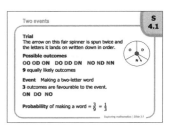

Show **slide 3.1**. Introduce the idea of an experiment made up of two successive trials. Give the class an example of a possible outcome (OO) and ask for others. Discuss ways of making sure that *all* equally outcomes are found, e.g. by writing all outcomes when the first letter is O, then D, then N.

Ask pupils to work in pairs to complete the list. Take feedback. Display the possible outcomes on the slide.

> What is the total number of equally likely outcomes?
>
> How many outcomes make a word?
>
> What is the probability of making a word?
>
> What is the probability of not m ng a word? $[\frac{6}{9} = \frac{2}{3}]$

Select questions from **S4.1 Exercise 3A** in the class book (p. 64).

Main activity

Show **slide 3.2**. Explain that a useful way to show the possible outcomes when two events are combined is to use a table.

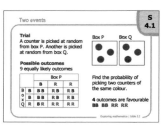

Go through the example on **slide 3.2**. Stress how the table is completed with the outcomes for box P written before those of box Q. Use the information on the slide to show that the probability of picking two counters of the same colour is $\frac{4}{9}$.

RS

Select questions from **S4.1 Exercise 3B** in the class book (p. 65). Pupils will need **S4.1 Resource sheet 3.1** for question 3.

Ask pupils to explain their answers to Exercise 3B. Stress that all the equally likely outcomes must be included in order to work out theoretical probability.

Point out that in some two-event problems the outcome of the two events can be a single value.

Ask pupils what the advantages or disadvantages of using a table or a list are. Draw out that a table makes it easier to check that all outcomes are included.

Review

Introduce this activity.

> A score is recorded when a fair dice is rolled and a fair coin is thrown.
> If the coin lands heads, the score is 1 more than the number on the dice.
> If the coin lands tails, the score is 2 more than the number on the dice.

Give pairs a piece of A3 paper and allow them 3 or 4 minutes to draw up a poster showing all the possible scores using any method they like.

Ask pairs to show their possible outcomes to the class and explain what they have done.

Ask the class to use the possible outcomes to work out the probability of these events:

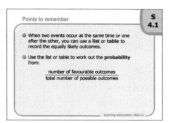

- scoring 3 [$\frac{2}{12}$ or $\frac{1}{6}$];

- scoring an even number [$\frac{6}{12}$ or $\frac{1}{2}$];

- scoring a square number or a cube number [$\frac{3}{12}$ or $\frac{1}{4}$].

Summarise the lesson by stressing the points on **slide 3.3**.

Homework

Ask pupils to do **S4.1 Task 3** in the home book (p. 25)

4 Experimental probability

Learning points

- The experimental probability of an event is:

  $$\frac{\text{number of successful trials}}{\text{total number of trials}}$$

- Different experiments can give different values of experimental probability.

- Experimental probability gives a better estimate of probability as the number of trials increases.

Starter

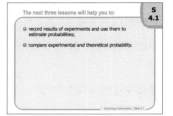

Use **slide 4.1** to discuss the objectives for this and the next two lessons. Say that this lesson is about estimating probabilities using the results of experiments.

Use a bag or open box containing 50 counters in three different colours, with a different number of each colour. Tell the class that you have a number of coloured counters in the box. Ask a pupil to take a counter from the box without looking, to hold it up for the class to see, and to replace it in the box. Record the colour on the board.

> **What colour are the counters in the box?**

Shake the box and repeat the activity about ten times.

Tell the class that there are 50 counters in the box. Ask pupils to write on their whiteboards how many counters of each colour they think are in the box. Discuss how they made their estimates.

Show the class the counters. With the class, work out the probabilities of choosing any of the colours in the box.

Main activity

Explain that the theoretical probability of an event can be worked out because we know the outcomes are equally likely to happen.

Sometimes outcomes are not equally likely, e.g. the outcomes for throwing a biased die. In cases like these, we have to carry out an experiment to estimate the probability of an event happening.

Randomly divide the class into three groups. Count the number in each group and record the numbers on the board.

> **What is the probability of picking a left-handed person?**

> **Can you work this out using equally likely outcomes?**
> [no — the outcomes left-handed and right-handed are not equally likely, so we can't use theoretical probability]

Show **slide 4.2**. Illustrate by working out the experimental probability of picking a left-handed person from each of the groups.

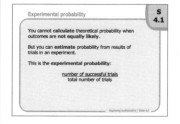

Explain that each separate experiment is known as a *trial*, which in this case is recording whether a person is left- or right-handed. The results of all the trials can be recorded in a frequency table.

Stress that theoretical probability is always the same but experimental probability is likely to change from experiment to experiment.

RS

TO

Ask pupils to work in pairs or groups on experiments from **S4.1 Exercise 4** in the class book (p. 67). Each pair will need two coins for question 1, two 1–6 dice for question 2, and four different coloured cubes in a bag or an envelope for question 3. Pupils will also need copies of **S4.1 Resource sheet 4.1** for questions 2 and 3.

If you wish, the experiments can all be simulated using the **Probability tools**.

Bring the whole class together and compare experimental probabilities. Combine results and work out the experimental probabilities for the whole-class experiment.

Why are the results of different pairs different?
[e.g. with a small number of trials it is just chance]

For which set of results would you expect experimental probability to be closer to the theoretical probability? Why?
[in the whole-class results because there is a larger number of trials]

Review Discuss whether either experimental or theoretical probability should be used to estimate the probabilities of these events.

- The next cow to calve on a farm will have twins.

- It will snow next Boxing Day.

- Two sixes are obtained when a die is rolled twice.

- The next sandwich sold in a sandwich shop is a cheese and tomato.

- The first card dealt at random from a pack of cards is the ace of spades.

- The next car to enter the car park will have a female driver.

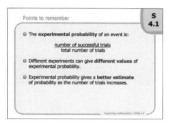

Sum up the lesson by stressing the points on **slide 4.3**.

Homework Ask pupils to do **S4.1 Task 4** in the home book (p. 26).

5 Are you lucky?

Learning points

- Some games involve chance. Some involve skill. Some involve a mixture of both.

- Using ideas of probability can give you the best chance of winning a game.

Starter Say that the lesson is about using ideas of probability to investigate the best strategies for winning a game.

Explain that there are some games (often those played with dice or cards) where chance plays a large part and other games (e.g. chess) that depend mainly on skill. Stress these two points.

- In a fair game that depends only on chance the possible outcomes are always equally likely. Each player has an equal chance of winning.

- Experimental probability and theoretical probability in a fair game of chance should get closer as more games are played.

Explain to the class that they are going to investigate two games to find out how much chance and how much skill are involved.

The first game is 'Noughts and Crosses'. Make sure that everyone knows the rules.

Ask pairs to work on **S4.1 Exercise 5** question 1 in the class book (p. 70).

Compare and discuss the results of 'Noughts and Crosses' by asking pairs for their responses to parts (b) to (e) of question 1. Responses may vary because of differing skill levels. Possible findings are:

- a draw is the most likely result — players of equal skill will nearly always draw, regardless of who goes first;

- going first can be an advantage;

- the game involves chance if both players lack skill.

Main activity Now introduce 'The Game of Pig'; the rules are given before question 2 of **S4.1 Exercise 5** in the class book (p. 71). Play a game, with all pupils playing the same rolls of the die. To do this:

- Use the **Dice tool** to simulate the rolls of a die.

- Ask pupils to stand while they are playing and record the die numbers on their whiteboards. When they 'stick', or when 1 is rolled, they should sit down and work out their score for that turn and their running total.

Continue playing until one of the pupils reaches a score of 100.

Ask pupils to work in groups of two or three on the rest of **S4.1 Exercise 5** in the class book (p. 71). Each group will need a die. Each pupil will need a copy of **S4.1 Resource sheet 5.1**.

RS

Stress that the objective is to find the best strategy for winning the game. Pupils should think about this as they are playing.

Prompt groups as they play with questions like:

On average, how many times is it before you roll a 1? [6]

How many rolls should you aim for before you stick?
[not too few, not too many!]

What score should you aim to get before you stick?

Why is it not a good idea to roll the die too few times? [low score]

Why is it not a good idea to roll the die too many times?
[increased chance of rolling 1]

Review

Discuss and compare the outcomes of the game.

What is the best strategy? Why?

What happens when the best strategy plays the worst?

The game is about balancing the need to score well with the chance of throwing a 1. A good strategy is to roll 4, 5 or 6 times. A safer but less effective strategy is to roll only 1, 2 or 3 times.

Finally, stress the points on **slide 5.1**.

Homework

Ask pupils to do **S4.1 Task 5** in the home book (p. 28).

6 Theory and experiment

Learning points

- When a probability experiment is repeated, the results may be different.

- If a trial is fair, and the number of trials is large, the experimental probability is close to the theoretical probability.

Starter   Say that this lesson is about comparing experimental and theoretical probabilities.

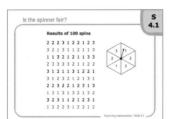

Display **slide 6.1**. Discuss how to decide whether or not the spinner is fair.

- Calculate the experimental probabilities of spinning each number
  [1 → 0.36, 2 → 0.34, 3 → 0.30].

- Compare these with the theoretical probabilities
  [for each number, 0.33 to 2 d.p.].

The spinner is likely to be fair but more results would be useful to confirm this.

Main activity   Using the **Coins tool** toss a coin 20 times, keeping a tally of the heads and tails.

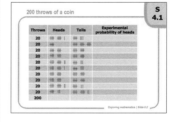

Show **slide 6.2**. Explain that it shows the results of 10 experiments in which the same coin was tossed 20 times. With the class, fill in the blank boxes in the table, including the totals [99 heads; 101 tails; experimental probability of a head 0.495].

Stress that:

- The experimental probabilities differ from experiment to experiment, with some being as expected but others being a long way from the theoretical probability.

- The combined set of 200 trials gives an experimental probability that is very close to the theoretical probability.

Now explain that the class are to do a probability experiment together by doing 40 trials in 10 groups. Results will be combined to create results for 400 trials.

Introduce the experiment in **S4.1 Exercise 6** in the class book (p. 73). Use the **Spinner tool**, choose a four-sided spinner, and set the numbers on it to 1, 2, 1 and 3. Explain that the spinner is to be spun twice and that the pair of numbers generated is to be recorded.

Divide the class into 10 groups of two or three. Groups will need copies of **S4.1 Resource sheet 6.1**. Each group will need a means of simulating the experiment. For example, the group could use the **Spinner tool**, or groups could draw cards at random from a set of four cards numbered 1, 2, 1, 3.

Ask the groups to complete the table on **Resource sheet 6.1** to show all the possible outcomes of a trial and then to complete the rest of **S4.1 Exercise 6** in the class book (p. 73).

Review

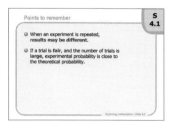

Review the results for all the experiments. Work out the experimental probabilities for the combined results. Discuss differences between the individual sets of 40 trials and compare combined experimental probabilities with theoretical probabilities.

Summarise the lesson by highlighting the points on **slide 6.3**.

Round off the unit by referring again to the objectives. Suggest that pupils find time to try the self-assessment problems in **S4.1 How well are you doing?** in the class book (p. 74).

Homework

Ask pupils to do **S4.1 Task 6** in the home book (p. 29).

Check up
S4.1

Write your answers in your book.

1 Scott picks one of these cards at random.

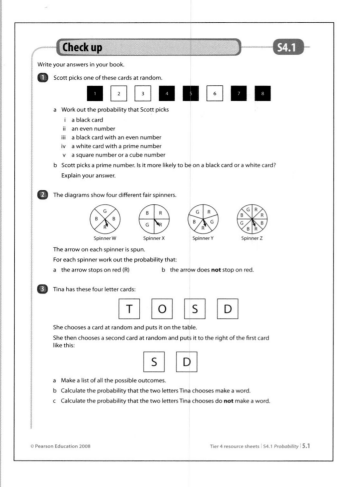

| 1 | 2 | 3 | 4 | 5 | 6 | 7 | 8 |

a Work out the probability that Scott picks
 i a black card
 ii an even number
 iii a black card with an even number
 iv a white card with a prime number
 v a square number or a cube number

b Scott picks a prime number. Is it more likely to be on a black card or a white card?

 Explain your answer.

2 The diagrams show four different fair spinners.

Spinner W   Spinner X   Spinner Y   Spinner Z

The arrow on each spinner is spun.

For each spinner work out the probability that:

a the arrow stops on red (R)   b the arrow does **not** stop on red.

3 Tina has these four letter cards:

T   O   S   D

She chooses a card at random and puts it on the table.

She then chooses a second card at random and puts it to the right of the first card like this:

S   D

a Make a list of all the possible outcomes.

b Calculate the probability that the two letters Tina chooses make a word.

c Calculate the probability that the two letters Tina chooses do **not** make a word.

Check up [continued]

4 The arrow on this fair spinner is spun twice.

The sum of the numbers the arrow points to is recorded.

a Work out the probability that the total score is 4.

b Work out the probability that the total score is **not** 4.

5 Petra and David carry out an experiment using a bag of coloured beads.

They take a bead from the bag at random and record its colour:
red (R), white (W) or blue (B).

They then put the bead back in the bag.

They repeat this a number of times.

Petra's results

| B | R | B | B | R | R | B | B | R | R |
| W | B | B | R | B | W | W | W | B | R |

David's results

R	B	W	R	R	B	R	R	R	B
R	R	R	B	B	B	B	W	R	R
R	W	R	B	W	B	R	R	B	R
R	R	R	W	B	R	W	W	R	R
B	R	R	B	B	B	B	R	R	B
B	R	B	B	R	W	B	W	B	B
W	B	R	W	B	W	R	R	R	W
R	R	R	B	B	W	B	R	B	R
W	B	B	B	B	R	W	W	W	B
B	B	B	R	R	B	R	B	B	R

a Work out the experimental probability of each colour from Petra's experiment.

b Work out the experimental probability of each colour from David's experiment.

c Whose experiment gives a more reliable estimate of probability?
 Explain your answer.

S4.1 Answers

Class book

Exercise 1

1 a ① 2 3 ④ 5 6   probability $\frac{1}{3}$
   b 1 ② 3 ④ 5 ⑥   probability $\frac{1}{2}$
   c 1 2 3 4 ⑤ 6   probability $\frac{1}{6}$
   d 1 2 ③ 4 ⑤ 6   probability $\frac{1}{3}$

2 a **Trial**: Pick a card at random and record the result
   Possible outcomes:
   Red 1, Red 2, Red 3, Red 4, Red 5,
   Blue 1, Blue 2, Blue 3, Blue 4, Blue 5

   b i $\frac{5}{10}$ or $\frac{1}{2}$ ii $\frac{2}{10}$ or $\frac{1}{5}$ iii $\frac{1}{10}$

      iv $\frac{2}{10}$ or $\frac{1}{5}$ v 0   vi 1

      vii $\frac{2}{10}$ or $\frac{1}{5}$ viii $\frac{6}{10}$ or $\frac{3}{5}$

   c There are fewer even-numbered than odd-numbered cards in the possible outcomes.

3 Georgia's necklace is likely to have more white beads. The probability of Georgia picking a white bead ($\frac{3}{4}$) is greater than the probability of Katie picking a white bead ($\frac{2}{3}$).

4 a Either box R or S. The probability of picking a green counter from each of these boxes is $\frac{1}{3}$. This is greater than the probability of picking a green from the other boxes.

   b Box Q and box R have the highest probability of picking a blue ($\frac{1}{2}$).

   c Box R has the lowest probability of picking a red ($\frac{1}{6}$).

   d i Red, Red, Blue, Blue, Green
      ii $\frac{1}{5}$ iii $\frac{3}{5}$ iv $\frac{3}{5}$

5 a Spinner A   1, 1, 2, 3
      Spinner B   1, 1, 1, 2, 3, 3, 3, 3
      The outcomes are equally likely because the spinners are fair and the sectors for each number on each spinner are equal.

   b Ellie; greater probability of scoring 1 on A
   c Ellie; greater probability of scoring 2 on A
   d George, because he is more likely to score 3; Ellie is more likely to score 1.

6 a $\frac{7}{12}$ b $\frac{4}{12}$ or $\frac{1}{3}$ c $\frac{1}{12}$
   d $\frac{5}{12}$ e $\frac{3}{12}$ or $\frac{1}{4}$ f $\frac{3}{12}$ or $\frac{1}{4}$

Exercise 2

1 a i $\frac{7}{15}$ ii $\frac{8}{15}$

   b 1 2 ③ 4 5 ⑥ 7 8
      ⑨ 10 11 ⑫ 13 14 ⑮
      i Probability of occurring: $\frac{5}{15}$ or $\frac{1}{3}$
      ii Probability of not occurring: $\frac{10}{15}$ or $\frac{2}{3}$

   c 1 2 3 4 ⑤ 6 7 8
      9 ⑩ 11 12 13 14 ⑮
      i Probability of occurring: $\frac{3}{15}$ or $\frac{1}{5}$
      ii Probability of not occurring: $\frac{12}{15}$ or $\frac{4}{5}$

   d ① 2 3 ④ 5 6 7 8
      ⑨ 10 11 12 13 14 15
      i Probability of occurring: $\frac{3}{15}$ or $\frac{1}{5}$
      ii Probability of not occurring: $\frac{12}{15}$ or $\frac{4}{5}$

   e ① 2 3 4 5 6 7 ⑧
      9 10 11 12 13 14 15
      i Probability of occurring: $\frac{2}{15}$
      ii Probability of not occurring: $\frac{13}{15}$

2 a $\frac{4}{7}$ b $\frac{3}{7}$ c $\frac{2}{7}$ d $\frac{5}{7}$
   e 0   f $\frac{6}{7}$ g 1   h 0

3 a i 2   ii 50
      iii 16   iv 36
      v 12   vi 40

   b i $\frac{2}{52}$ or $\frac{1}{26}$ ii $\frac{50}{52}$ or $\frac{25}{26}$
      iii $\frac{16}{52}$ or $\frac{4}{13}$ iv $\frac{36}{52}$ or $\frac{9}{13}$
      v $\frac{12}{52}$ or $\frac{3}{13}$ vi $\frac{40}{52}$ or $\frac{10}{13}$

   c i $\frac{39}{52}$ or $\frac{3}{4}$ ii $\frac{36}{52}$ or $\frac{9}{13}$
      iii $\frac{13}{52}$ or $\frac{1}{4}$ iv $\frac{5}{52}$
      v $\frac{5}{52}$ vi $\frac{47}{52}$
      vii $\frac{47}{52}$

4 a Box P: i $\frac{5}{8}$ ii $\frac{3}{8}$
      Box Q: i $\frac{4}{7}$ ii $\frac{3}{7}$
      Box R: i $\frac{1}{7}$ ii $\frac{6}{7}$
      Box S: i $\frac{2}{9}$ ii $\frac{7}{9}$

   b The probability of an event happening added to the probability of an event **not** happening is 1.

Exercise 3A

1 a HH, HT, TH and TT   **b i** $\frac{1}{4}$ **ii** $\frac{3}{4}$

2 a 1 and 1, 1 and 2, 1 and 3,
2 and 1, 2 and 2, 2 and 3,
3 and 1, 3 and 2, 3 and 3

  b i $\frac{2}{9}$ **ii** $\frac{7}{9}$

3 $\frac{3}{4}$

Exercise 3B

1 a No; the outcome R from box 1 is not an equally likely outcome.

  b Yes; it includes all the ways of picking a red from box 1.

  c $\frac{4}{8}$ or $\frac{1}{2}$

  d Yes. Three times more likely.

2 a

		Box 1		
		R	R	B
Box 2	R	RR	RR	BR
	R	RR	RR	BR
	B	RB	RB	BB

  b $\frac{4}{9}$ **c** $\frac{5}{9}$

3 a

		Blue dice					
		1	2	3	4	5	6
Red dice	1	2	3	4	5	6	7
	2	3	4	5	6	7	8
	3	4	5	6	7	8	9
	4	5	6	7	8	9	10
	5	6	7	8	9	10	11
	6	7	8	9	10	11	12

  b There is a very low probability of scoring double six, so if what Connor says is true he is lucky. Usually, however, his luck would even out!

  c There are six ways of scoring 7 and only one way of scoring 12, so a score of 7 is six times more likely.

  d i $\frac{3}{36}$ or $\frac{1}{12}$ **ii** $\frac{1}{36}$

  iii $\frac{10}{36}$ or $\frac{5}{18}$ **iv** $\frac{6}{36}$ or $\frac{1}{6}$

Extension problem

4 The number of outcomes for Chris winning on her turn and Ben winning on his is the same. The number of outcomes for Ben winning on

Chris's turn and Chris winning on Ben's turn is also the same. So the game appears to be fair. However, the probability of losing on any turn is greater than that of winning, so going first gives an advantage. If Chris and Ben play the game an even number of times and take turns to go first the game is fair.

Exercise 4

1 a i $\frac{8}{40}$ or $\frac{1}{5}$ **ii** $\frac{21}{40}$ **iii** $\frac{19}{40}$

  b The same experimental probabilities are unlikely because of the relatively small number of trials.

2 a 7 is most likely to reach a frequency of 10 first because there are more ways to score 7 than any other score

  b 0.22

  c Pupils' results on Resource sheet 4.1

  d The experimental probabilities are likely to be different although the shape of the frequency diagram should be fairly similar.

3 a 1st guess: 0.2
2nd guess: 0.5
3rd guess: 0.6
4th guess: 1

  b The experimental probability of the 4th guess should be 1 because the colour of the last counter in the bag is known.

  c Results are likely to differ because of the small number of trials.

Exercise 5

1 a Pupils' experimental probabilities

  b A draw is the most likely result − players of equal skill will nearly always draw

  c Results would differ against a player of different skill levels.

  d The game involves chance if **both** players lack skill.

  e It is only a fair game if it is played between players of equal skill.

2 a The experimental probability of Leah scoring zero is $\frac{4}{9}$.

  b The experimental probability of Leah rolling 4 is $\frac{3}{31}$.

3 Pupils' results on Resource sheet 3 and experimental probabilities of scoring zero and of rolling 1

4 The best strategy is to try to roll the dice 4, 5 or 6 times and stick at a score of between 20 and 25. It is better to throw too many times than too few.

Exercise 6

1 Possible outcomes:

Second spin		First spin			
		1	**1**	**2**	**3**
	1	1 1	1 1	2 1	3 1
	1	1 1	1 1	2 1	3 1
	2	1 2	1 2	2 2	3 2
	3	1 3	1 3	2 3	3 3

Theoretical probabilities

Outcome	Theoretical probability
1 1	0.25
1 2	0.125
1 3	0.125
2 1	0.125
2 2	0.0625
2 3	0.0625
3 1	0.125
3 2	0.0625
3 3	0.0625

The experimental probabilities from different groups are likely to differ. The experimental probability from the whole-class experiment is likely to be close to the theoretical probabilities.

How well are you doing?

1 0.61

2 0.15

3 a $\frac{3}{10}$ b $\frac{13}{40}$ c $\frac{3}{4}$

4 a

First coin	Second coin
heads	heads
heads	tails
tails	heads
tails	tails

b $\frac{1}{4}$ c $\frac{1}{2}$

5 a $\frac{5}{9}$ b $\frac{1}{3}$

c

		Karen		
×		**2**	**3**	**4**
	2	4	6	8
Huw	**3**	6	9	12
	4	8	12	16

d 16

Home book

TASK 1

1 a   i $\frac{3}{10}$ ii $\frac{1}{10}$ iii $\frac{2}{10}$ or $\frac{1}{5}$ iv $\frac{5}{10}$ or $\frac{1}{2}$

   b   i $\frac{3}{10}$ ii $\frac{5}{10}$ or $\frac{1}{2}$ iii $\frac{3}{10}$ iv $\frac{7}{10}$

2 a It is the box where the probability of picking a red is the greatest.

   b There are two positions Chloe needs to defend: the empty square in the top row and the square in the 1st column of the 3rd row. The latter is the best choice as it also gives Chloe an opportunity to form a winning line.

   c The square in the bottom left corner

TASK 2

1 a $\frac{2}{6}$ or $\frac{1}{3}$ b $\frac{4}{6}$ or $\frac{2}{3}$ c $\frac{4}{6}$ or $\frac{2}{3}$

   d $\frac{2}{6}$ or $\frac{1}{3}$ e $\frac{2}{6}$ or $\frac{1}{3}$ f $\frac{4}{6}$ or $\frac{2}{3}$

2 a $\frac{15}{22}$ b $\frac{7}{22}$ c $\frac{1}{22}$

   d $\frac{21}{22}$ e $\frac{16}{22}$ or $\frac{8}{11}$ f $\frac{6}{22}$ or $\frac{3}{11}$

TASK 3

1

Joan's card		Bill's card			
		C	**D**	**H**	**S**
	C	CC	DC	HC	SC
	D	CD	DD	HD	SD
	H	CH	DH	HH	SH
	S	CS	DS	HS	SS

2 a $\frac{7}{16}$ b $\frac{4}{16}$ or $\frac{1}{4}$

   c $\frac{4}{16}$ or $\frac{1}{4}$ d $\frac{2}{16}$ or $\frac{1}{8}$

TASK 4

1 a $\frac{16}{20}$ or 0.8   b $\frac{29}{50}$ or 0.58

   c Tom's experiment; more spins

2 a 60%   b 43%

TASK 5

1 Possible outcomes (O = odd, E = even):

		1st dice					
		1	2	3	4	5	6
2nd dice	1	O	E	O	E	O	E
	2	E	E	E	E	E	E
	3	O	E	O	E	O	E
	4	E	E	E	E	E	E
	5	O	E	O	E	O	E
	6	E	E	E	E	E	E

Daniel should win the game because the probability of an even score is more likely. Pupils' suggestions for changing the rules to make the game fair.

2 Yes, the game is fair. In ten spins, Jessica would expect to get 12 points (6 lots of 2 points), and Ben 12 points (4 lots of 3 points).

TASK 6

1 0.6

2 Pupils' experimental probabilities.

3 The experimental probability should get closer to the theoretical probabilities as the number of trials increases.

CD-ROM

Check up

1 a
  i $\frac{5}{8}$
  ii $\frac{4}{8}$ or $\frac{1}{2}$
  iii $\frac{2}{8}$ or $\frac{1}{4}$
  iv $\frac{2}{8}$ or $\frac{1}{44}$
  v $\frac{3}{8}$

  b The events are equally likely. The probability of a prime on white equals the probability of a prime on black.

2 Spinner W: a $\frac{1}{4}$ b $\frac{3}{4}$

   Spinner X: a $\frac{2}{4}$ or $\frac{1}{2}$ b $\frac{2}{4}$ or $\frac{1}{2}$

   Spinner Y: a $\frac{2}{5}$ b $\frac{3}{5}$

   Spinner Z: a $\frac{3}{8}$ b $\frac{5}{8}$

3 a TO, TS, TD, OT, OS, OD, ST, SO, SD, DT, DO, and DS

  b $\frac{3}{12}$ or $\frac{1}{4}$

  c $\frac{9}{12}$ or $\frac{3}{4}$

4 a $\frac{8}{25}$ b $\frac{17}{25}$

5 a Petra's experimental probabilities are 0.35 for red, 0.2 for white and 0.45 for blue.
  b David's experimental probabilities are 0.4 for red, 0.18 for white and 0.42 for blue.
  c David's experiment gives a more reliable estimate of probability because of the greater number of trials.

Expressions and formulae

Previous learning

Before they start, pupils should be able to:

- use letter symbols to represent unknown numbers or variables
- simplify linear algebraic expressions by collecting like terms
- multiply a constant over a bracket
- substitute integers into simple linear expressions and formulae, and positive integers into expressions involving small powers, e.g. $3x^2 + 4$ or $2x^5$.

Objectives based on NC levels 5 and 6 (mainly level 5)

In this unit, pupils learn to:

- try out and compare mathematical representations
- use accurate notation
- manipulate algebraic expressions and equations
- explore the effect of varying values
- refine own findings and approaches on the basis of discussion with others

and to:

- understand that algebraic operations, including the use of brackets, follow the rules of arithmetic
- multiply a single term over a bracket
- simplify or transform linear expressions by collecting like terms
- derive and substitute integers into simple formulae and expressions.

Lessons
1 **Simplifying expressions**
2 **Using formulae**
3 **Simplifying expressions with powers**
4 **Using algebraic expressions**

About this unit
The word 'term' in algebra is often used without explanation. It is a word that, like 'power', has several meanings in the English language and a special meaning in algebra. When numbers and/or letters are combined by multiplication or division we have a term. Terms such as 5, $3a$, $2ab$, $7xyz$ and so on are fairly straightforward for pupils to recognise. However, they need to recognise that $2(a + b)$ is a single term, whereas $2a + 2b$ is two terms. They also need to recognise that:

- $3a^2b$ is a single term;
- when they substitute numerical values for letters, each term is evaluated before terms are combined;
- brackets and powers are also calculated before multiplication or division.

These are rules that pupils are already familiar with in number.

Working with algebraic expressions can be meaningless to pupils unless they see how such expressions can relate to real life. This unit includes the use of expressions as formulae in real situations and in strands of mathematics such as geometry or statistics.

Assessment	This unit includes:

Assessment

This unit includes:

- a self-assessment section (*A4.2 How well are you doing?* class book p. 86);
- a set of questions to replace or supplement questions in the exercises or homework tasks, or to use as an informal test (*A4.2 Check up*, CD-ROM).

Common errors and misconceptions

Look out for pupils who:

- add numbers to letters, e.g. $2 + x = 2x$;
- combine letters, e.g. $3ab + c = 3abc$;
- always want to give a numerical answer; for example, a correct answer is $10 + y$ but pupils assign a value such as 5 for y and give the answer 15;
- think that letters always have values according to the alphabet, as in codes, e.g. $a = 1, b = 2, c = 3$ and so on.

Key terms and notation

term, like terms, expression, formula, formulae, index, indices, power, exponent

simplify, substitute, evaluate, multiply out

algebra, algebraic, symbol, operation

Practical resources

scientific calculators for pupils
individual whiteboards

graph plotting and spreadsheet
software for demonstration
cubes of different dimensions

Exploring maths

Tier 4 teacher's book
Answers for Unit A4.2, pp. 105–107

Tier 4 CD-ROM
PowerPoint files
   A4.2 Slides for lessons 1 to 4
Tools and prepared toolsheets
   A4.2 Toolsheet 4.1
   Calculator tool
   Function graph tool
Excel file
   A4.2 Formula

Tier 4 class book
A4.2, pp. 76–87
A4.2 How well are you doing? p. 86

Tier 4 home book
A4.2, pp. 30–33

Tier 4 CD-ROM
A4.2 Check up
A4.2 Pupil resource sheets
   2.1 One per pupil
   3.1 One per pupil

Useful websites

Pyramids
www.nrich.maths.org/public/viewer.php?obj_id=488

Expressions from words
www.emaths.co.uk/InterSoW/background.htm

Challenging maths problems
www.nrich.maths.org/public/leg.php

Sequences, functions and graphs
www.imathlearning.com/worksheets/3sequence/index.html

Algebra topics
swgfl.skoool.co.uk/keystage3.aspx?id=65#24_30

Number patterns and sequences
www.cimt.plymouth.ac.uk/projects/mepres/book7/y7s7lp.pdf

1 Simplifying expressions

Learning points

- A term is one or more numbers and/or letters combined by multiplication or division.
- Like terms have the same combination of letters. $2x$, $5x$ and x are all like terms.
- An expression is one or more terms combined by addition or subtraction.

Starter

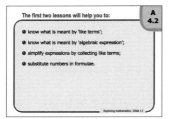

Use **slide 1.1** to discuss what pupils will learn in the next two lessons. Say that this lesson is about simplifying algebraic expressions by collecting like terms.

Remind pupils of the meaning of 'term' and 'like term', or give definitions if pupils have not met them before. Make several cards with a single x, a single y and the number 1, and place them on a table at the front of the class. Explain that x stands for one x.

Get pupils to move the cards from this table to a 'results' table as they add or subtract them. This helps pupils to see that if they place six x cards followed by five y cards, the cards don't change into xy cards.

Ask a pupil to act out the sum $2x + 3x$. They pick up two x cards and place them on the results table. Then they pick up another three x cards and place them on the results table. They look at the results table and see that the answer is $5x$.

Do the same for $y + 2y$, $4x + 5$, $3x + 5y$. Explain that only 'like terms' can be combined.

Show **slide 1.2**. Explain that a *term* is one or more numbers and/or letters combined by multiplication or division. For example, 15, $2a$, $3xy$, $2\frac{p}{q}$ are all terms. Ask pupils to underline the terms in the expressions.

> How do you know that each one of these is a term?

Show **slide 1.3**. Get pupils to underline like terms in different colours. Ask them to simplify the expressions. In the first one, 5 and 21 are like terms, $3a$ and $2a$ are like terms and $4b$ and $6b$ are like terms. When simplified this gives $26 + 5a + 10b$.

Take care over the operations associated with each term. In the second example, the terms $2s$ and 3 are both subtracted.

Main activity

Remind pupils how to multiply numbers using a grid, e.g. 47×6.

×	40	+	7
6	240	+	42

Answer: 282

Then show pupils how to multiply out brackets in expressions such as $3(a + 5)$, $7(x + y)$, $2(3x + 5)$, $6(2a - 3b)$, $4(a + b + c)$. Build on their knowledge of number multiplication by using grid arrays like these:

$\times$	a	$+$	5
3	$3a$	$+$	15

$\times$	$2a$	$-$	$3b$
6	$12a$	$-$	$18b$

Emphasise that in these examples the answers are $3a + 15$ and $12a - 18b$. Numerical answers can only be calculated when we are given values for a and b.

Invite pupils to complete some examples on the board.

When they are confident, move on to show how to multiply out two or more brackets in an expression and then simplify it, e.g.

$4(x + 2) + 5(x + 7)$
$3(2a + 5b) + 9(4a + 7b)$.

Introduce subtraction only if pupils are confident with negative numbers, e.g. $8(x + 3) - 5(x + 4)$ and $7(x + 9) - 2(x - 1)$.

Select individual work from **A4.2 Exercise 1** in the class book (p. 77).

Review Show **slide 1.4**. Say that in a test Roland gave these answers:

$4(2x + 7) = 8x + 7$

$3(5x + 4) = 35x + 34$

$2(3x + 1) - 3(x + 2) = 3x + 8$

Ask pupils to find out what mistakes he had made. Get them to work out the correct answers.

Summarise the lesson using the points on **slide 1.5**.

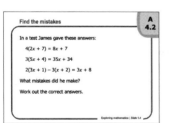

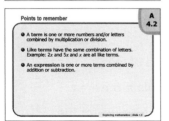

Homework Ask pupils to do **A4.2 Task 1** in the home book (p. 30).

2 Using formulae

Learning points

- A formula is shorthand for a general rule.
  For example, the formula for the area of a rectangle is lw, where l is the length and w the width. Substitute values for l and w to work out the area.

RS

Starter Say that this lesson is about using formulae.

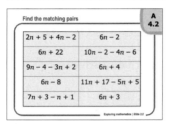

Give out **A4.2 Resource sheet 2.1**. Ask pupils to work in pairs to draw arrows between the matching pairs of algebraic expressions.

Show **slides 2.1** and **2.2**.

Ask pupils to come to the board and draw arrows between the pairs of algebraic expressions using their answers on the resource sheet.

Use any mistakes they make to discuss difficulties, especially with signs.

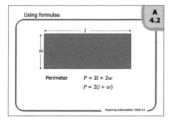

Main activity Explain that algebra is useful for writing rules or formulae in a succinct way using letters instead of words. The letters can be n for the nth term, l for length, t for time, s for speed, and so on. It is good practice to define any letter before using it, like this: 'Let l be the length in centimetres and let w be the width in centimetres'.

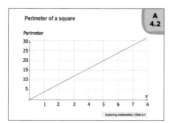

Show **slide 2.3**. Explain how the rule for finding the perimeter of a rectangle can be written in two ways. Say that both the length and the width must be in the same units, such as both in centimetres, or both in metres, and so on.

What units will the perimeter be in?

Assign some values to l and w and ask pupils to work out the perimeter of the rectangle.

What is the formula for the area of this rectangle?

Give units for length and width and ask pupils for the units of area.

Now assign some values to l and w and ask pupils to calculate the area.

Draw on the board a square with side x. Ask pupils for the formula for the perimeter of the square (perimeter $= 4x$).

Show **slide 2.4**. Draw attention to the axes of the graph. Explain that the x-axis represents the length of a side of a square and the y-axis represents the perimeter of a square. The relationship between the length of a side and the perimeter of the square gives a straight line.

Show how you can use the graph to estimate the perimeter of different squares. Ask pupils to use the graph to estimate the perimeter of squares with sides 2.5, 3, 4.2 and so on.

Explain that using the formula perimeter $= 4x$ you can get an accurate answer for the perimeter. Using the graph, you can only estimate the answer. However, the graph gives you a picture of the relationship.

Use **A4.2 Formula spreadsheet**. Point out the column headings and the column entries. Explain that the numbers in cells B2 to B13 are the heights of a group of pupils.

> **What will the number in B14 represent?** [the sum of all the heights]

Show pupils how to enter the sum of the numbers in cells B2 to B13 in cell B14. Click on B14, then enter **=Sum** followed by an opening round bracket **(**. Click on cell B2 and drag down to cell B13 to highlight the cells you want to add. Release the mouse and **B2:B13** will be entered automatically in the formula. Finish by typing the closing round bracket **)**. The complete formula is =Sum(B2:B13).

The sum of all the heights will appear in cell B14.

> **How many heights have been entered?** [12]

> **How can you calculate the mean of the heights?**
> [divide the sum of the heights by 12]

Show how to enter a formula in C14 to get the computer to calculate the mean height [=A14/12].

Ask pupils what changes they would need to make if they included five more heights. Show them how to insert extra rows. For example, click on '9' at the left of the ninth row, pull down the Insert menu and select 'Rows'.

Discuss how algebra is a way of abbreviating an instruction. In this case 'divide the sum of the heights by 12' is replaced with 'A14/12'.

Select individual work from **A4.2 Exercise 2** in the class book (p. 80).

Review

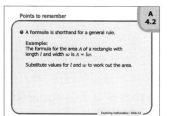

Use questioning to elicit the formulae for odd and even numbers.

> **How can you describe an even number?**
> [it is a multiple of 2; it has 2 as a factor]

> **Let the letter n represent any counting number.**
> **How can we write any even number?** [$2n$]
> **How can we write any odd number?** [$2n + 1$ or $2n - 1$]

Discuss the points to remember on **slide 2.5**.

Homework

Ask pupils to do **A4.2 Task 2** in the home book (p. 31).

3 Simplifying expressions with powers

Learning points

- *Index notation* is used when numbers are multiplied by themselves.
  $3 \times 3 \times 3 \times 3 \times 3 \times 3 = 3^6$

- In algebra, the same notation is used when letters are multiplied by themselves.
  $a \times a \times a \times a \times a \times a = a^6$
  We say 'a raised to the power of six'.

- The numbers and letters are written in *index form*.

- $5x^2y^3$ means $5 \times x \times x \times y \times y \times y$.
  When $x = 2$ and $y = 3$, $5x^2y^3 = 5 \times 2 \times 2 \times 3 \times 3 \times 3 = 540$.

Starter

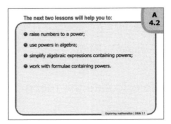

Use **slide 3.1** to discuss what pupils will learn in the next two lessons. Tell pupils that in their number work they have learned how to write a number raised to a power and that this lesson is about using powers in algebra.

Remind pupils about squaring integers, and that the inverse of squaring is finding the square root. Remind them of notation 9^2 and $\sqrt{81} = \pm 9$.

> Why can a square root be positive or negative?

Write 4^3 on the board. Ask pupils how they would work this out ($4 \times 4 \times 4 = 64$). Ask them to work out 3^3, 5^3 and 8^3, using jottings if they need to.

Explain that the inverse of cubing is finding the cube root and remind them of the notation $\sqrt[3]{64}$. Point out that a cube root of a positive number is positive, and that a negative number can have a cube root, which is negative.

Get pupils to work out some simple cube roots such as $\sqrt[3]{27}, \sqrt[3]{1}, \sqrt[3]{-8}$.

Ask pupils to use their calculators to work out some squares and cubes of a range of numbers, such as 12^3 and 2.4^3.

Use the **Calculator tool** to remind pupils how to use the square-root and cube-root keys. If necessary, explain that on some calculators the root key is pressed before the number and on others afterwards, and that most calculators give only the positive square root.

Ask pupils to find roots such as: $\sqrt{289}, \sqrt{6.25}, \sqrt{961}, \sqrt[3]{1331}, \sqrt[3]{3375}$

Main activity

Remind pupils of the work on powers in Unit N4.1. Explain that 5^2 is 'five squared' or 'five raised to the power of two' or 'five to the power of two'.

The number written as a superscript is called the *power* or the *index number* (plural *indices*) or the *exponent*.

Explain that any number raised to the power of 1 is that number, e.g. $3^1 = 3$, $5^1 = 5, 62^1 = 62$, and that any number raised to the power of 0 is one, e.g. $3^0 = 1$, $7^0 = 1, 256^0 = 1$.

Show pupils how to write repeated multiplications as powers. Ask them to use the power key on their calculators to work out values. Power keys on calculators work in different ways. Check that each pupil is able to use their own calculator correctly.

Build up a table of powers like this:

5	5^1	5
5×5	5^2	25
$5 \times 5 \times 5$	5^3	125
$5 \times 5 \times 5 \times 5$	5^4	625
$5 \times 5 \times 5 \times 5 \times 5$	5^5	3125
$5 \times 5 \times 5 \times 5 \times 5 \times 5$	5^6	15 625

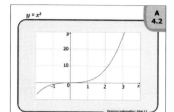

Point out to the class how rapidly the numbers increase.

Show the graph of $y = x^3$ on **slide 3.2**. Draw attention to how the graph rapidly becomes steep. Ask pupils to use their calculators to work out a few numbers between 0 and 4 raised to the power 3. Check their answers against the graph.

Explain that we use the same index notation in algebra with letters. Build up a table for powers of a similar to that for powers of 5. Point out that these expressions can be evaluated only when numbers are substituted for the letters.

Explain that $4a^3$ means $4 \times a^3$. Given a value for a, evaluate a^3 first and then multiply by 4. For example, if $a = 5$, $a^3 = 125$ and $4a^3 = 500$. Ask pupils to evaluate $4a^3$ for other values of a.

Explain that $2x^3$ is not the same as $(2x)^3$ and that $5 + x^2$ is not the same as $(5 + x)^2$, even though they sound the same when spoken.

You may wish to show pupils how to write more complex terms using powers such as a^2b^3 or a^2b^4. Give values for the letters and ask pupils to evaluate the terms.

Select individual work from **A4.2 Exercise 3** in the class book (p. 82). Pairs or groups of pupils will need dice and **A4.2 Resource sheet 3.1** for the game in question 5.

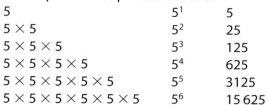

RS

Review Discuss expressions that can get confused, e.g.

'Seven x squared': $7x^2$
'Seven x all squared': $(7x)^2$
'n plus six cubed': $n + 6^3$
'n plus six all cubed': $(n + 6)^3$

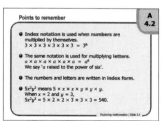

and expressions that may be spoken in the same way, e.g.

'Two b minus three squared': $2b - 3^2$ and $2(b - 3^2)$ and $2(b - 3)^2$ and $(2b - 3)^2$

Sum up the lesson using **slide 3.3**.

Homework Ask pupils to do **A4.2 Task 3** in the home book (p. 32).

4 Using algebraic expressions

Learning points

- A **formula** is an algebraic expression in which the letters represent something in real life. For example, the formula for the area of a square is x^2, where x is the length of each side of the square.

Starter

Say that this lesson looks at formulae that involve powers.

Show **slide 4.1**. Invite pupils to the board to draw arrows between the like terms.

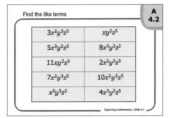

Main activity

Draw a square on the board with side length x. Ask pupils for the formula for the area of the square (area $= x^2$).

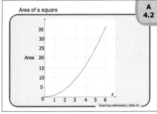

Show **slide 4.2** and ask pupils to look carefully at the axes. Ascertain that the x-axis represents the length of the side of a square and the y-axis represents the area of the square. Ask pupils to use the graph to find values of the area for given values of x.

Explain that a formula enables you to calculate the area accurately while the graph enables you to estimate the area. Discuss the units for area when the side is measured in millimetres, centimetres, metres and so on.

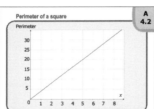

Compare the graph with that for the perimeter of a square on **slide 4.3**. Note the differences between the two graphs, such as one being a straight line and the other a curve. Note how the graph for area increases more rapidly than the graph for perimeter.

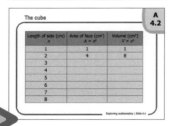

Show pupils cubes of different dimensions. Ask them to give you the formulae for the area of a face and the volume of the cube.

Show the table on **slide 4.4**.

Involve pupils in completing the table.

Use **Toolsheet 4.1** to display and compare the graphs of $A = x^2$ and $V = x^3$. Draw each graph using the **Function graph tool**, selecting free input and inputting $y = x^2$ and $y = x^3$.

Select individual work from **A4.2 Exercise 4** in the class book (p. 84).

Review

Use **slide 4.5**. Ask pupils to predict the maximum number of crossing points for five lines (10).

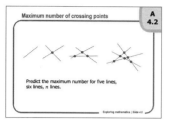

What made you think it was 10?

Can you see a pattern? [the numbers go up by one more each time]

Can you test it and confirm your prediction by drawing? [this gets more difficult as the number of lines increase]

Can you predict the maximum number of crossing points for six and seven lines? [15 and 21 respectively]

Put the results in a table. Ask pupils to work out the differences between each term of the sequence.

Get pupils to work out the formula for the nth term $\left[\dfrac{n(n-1)}{2}\right]$. Invite them to explain their answers by looking at the geometric structure.

Finish the lesson by stressing again the usefulness of formulae for representing relationships between variables.

Round off the unit by referring again to its objectives. Suggest that pupils find time to try the self-assessment problems in **A4.2 How well are you doing?** in the class book (p. 86).

Homework

Ask pupils to do **A4.2 Task 4** in the Tier 4 home book (p. 33).

A4.2 Check up and resource sheets

    A4.2

Write your answers in your book.

1. Simplify this expression by collecting together like terms.

   $4x + 5y + 7x - 5$

2. Multiply out the brackets in these expressions.

   a $5(x + 4)$

   b $7(3x - 6)$

3. Multiply out the brackets and simplify this expression.

   $4(2x + 5) + 3(5x + 7)$

4. Find the value of this formula using the values given.

   $3(5p + 2q)$ $p = 6, q = 9$

5. The formula for the nth term of a number sequence is $6(2n - 1)$.

   Work out the 28th term of the sequence.

6. Write this expression in index form.

   $5 \times a \times a \times a \times a \times b \times b$

7. Work out the value of the expression $7x^3y^4$ when $x = 4$ and $y = 2$.

8. The nth term of a number sequence is $\frac{n(n + 1)}{2}$.

   Find the 15th term.

    A4.2

Write your answers in your book.

1. Find the matching pairs.

$3(2a + 4)$	$6a + 18$
$6a + 3$	$2(3a + 12)$
$6(a + 3)$	$6a + 8$
$3(2a + 1)$	$6a + 12$
$6a + 24$	$2(3a + 4)$

2. Find the matching pairs.

$2n + 5 + 4n - 2$	$6n - 2$
$6n + 22$	$10n - 2 - 4n - 6$
$9n - 4 - 3n + 2$	$6n + 4$
$6n - 8$	$11n + 17 - 5n + 5$
$7n + 3 - n + 1$	$6n + 3$

    A4.2

$3x + 5$	x^2	$2(x + 1)$	$2x^2 - 7$
$2(x^2 - 9)$	$5x - 7$	$4(x - 1)$	x^3
$x + 9$	$x^2 - 3$	$x^3 - 8$	$7x - 5$
$9x + 1$	$x^3 - x^2$	$x(3x - 2)$	$9(6 - x)$
$3(x^2 - 5)$	$x^2 - x$	$2x + 7$	$6x + 0.5x$

A4.2 Answers

Class book

Exercise 1

1 a $\underline{2x} + \underline{3xy} - \underline{5y} - \underline{7xyz}$

   b $\underline{5mn} + \underline{6mst} - \underline{nst} + \underline{ms} - \underline{4}$

   c $\underline{9pq} - \underline{4p} + \underline{3q} - \underline{2r} + \underline{pr}$

   d $\underline{13} + \underline{2w} - \underline{3x} - y + \underline{2xy}$

2 a $6x$ b $13y$

   c $16p$ d $18 + 6q$

   e $13x + 10y$ f $8 + 9n$

   g $3x + 9y$ h $8p + 7$

   i $3t + 2s$ j $3x + 5y$

   k $5w + 2l + 4$ l $7ab + a - 2b$

3 a 212   b 201

   c 434   d 432

   e 882   f 639

4 a $12 + 3x$ b $5y + 35$

   c $6x + 6y$ d $2x + 2y + 6$

   e $6x + 12$ f $20a + 15b$

   g $21 - 14t$ h $12x - 20$

   i $12a + 18b - 30c$ j $36p - 27q + 9r$

5 a $5x + 21$ b $11y + 46$

   c $14s + 71$ d $14p + 62$

   e $22a + 2$ f $45x + 38$

   g $46t - 119$ h $58b + 1$

   i $93x + 60$ j $140y - 104$

6 $2(x + 4) + 6(x + 5)$ and $8x + 38$

   $9(x + 2) - (x + 7)$ and $8x + 11$

   $3(2x + 1) + 2(x + 9)$ and $8x + 21$

   $6(x + 7) + 2(x - 3)$ and $8x + 36$

   $7(2x + 1) - 3(2x - 4)$ and $8x + 19$

7 a

	$4p + q + r$	
$2p + q$		$2p + r$
$p + q$	p	$p + r$

   b

	$12x - 5y$	
$7x - 2y$		$5x - 3y$
$2x - 2y$	$5x$	$-3y$

8

$a - b$	$a + b - c$	$a + c$
$a + b + c$	a	$a - b - c$
$a - c$	$a - b + c$	$a + b$

Extension problems

9 a $2t + 22$ b $2x + 18$

   c $6m + 46$ d $6w + 3$

   e $26x + 34$ f $17q - 8$

   g $6r + 1$ h $58s + 11$

   i $93x - 75$ j $10y - 18$

10 a $6(x + 7)$ b $4(2x + 9)$

   c $3(4x + 7)$ d $5(3x + 5)$

   e $3(8x + 11)$ f $13(2x - 3)$

   g $12(4x - 5)$ h $5(6x + 11)$

   i $19(2x - 5)$ j $17(2x - 7)$

Exercise 2

1

	Perimeter P	Area A
a	34 cm	60 cm^2
b	42 cm	68 cm^2
c	94 cm	280 cm^2
d	22 cm	24 cm^2
e	160 cm	1500 cm^2

2

	Area A
a	24 cm^2
b	22.5 cm^2
c	42 cm^2
d	140 cm^2
e	75 cm^2
f	14 cm^2
g	0.5 cm^2

3 a 24 cm   b 14.4 cm

    c 43.8 cm   d 150 cm

    e 9 cm   f 87.6 cm

    g 114 cm   h 4.5 cm

4 a 7cm   b 2.8 cm

    c 3.6 cm   d 4 cm

    e 5 cm   f 7 cm

5 a $4n$ b $n + 20$

    c $n \div 4$ d $4n - 6$

    e $2n + 40$ f $n \div 8$

    g $28n$

Extension problems

6 a 1103

    b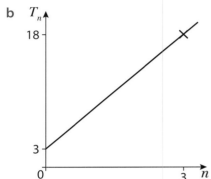

    c A straight line passing through (0, 3) and (3, 18) or two other valid points.

Exercise 3

1 a 64   b 64

    c 27   d 625

    e 16 384   f 216

    g 16 807   h 6561

2 a $2^3 \times 3^2 \times 5$ b $2^2 \times 3^3 \times 5^2$

    c $5^2 \times 7^3$ d $2 \times 3^4 \times 7$

    e $3 \times 5^2 \times 7 \times 11$ f $2^4 \times 3^2 \times 5 \times 7$

3 a x^5 b y^7

    c p^3q^2 d m^4n^3

    e xy^2z^3 f $3pq^2r^2$

4 a 117   b 216

    c 980   d 16 050

    e 900   f 1736

5 This is a game.

6 a 72   b 2352

    c 500   d 12 544

    e 19 683   f 10 240

    g 2430   h 1.875

Exercise 4

1

x	$5(x + 2)^2$	$5(x + 2^2)$	$(5x + 2)^2$	$5x + 2^2$
3	125	35	289	19
2	80	30	144	14
1	45	25	49	9
0	20	20	4	4
−1	5	15	9	−1
−2	0	10	64	−6
−3	5	5	169	−11

2 a 49 cm²   b 13 cm

3 a 125 cm³   b 6 cm   c 100 cm

4 a 192 cm²   b 6 cm

Extension problem

5 a 7   b $2^n - 1$

How well are you doing?

1 a **D** $4a + 3$ b $8b + 3$

2 a 18   b 2   c **C** $y = x^2$

3 It should read $6a + 3$. Jenny did not multiply both terms by 3

4 $8x + 31$

5 7.48 cm² (2 d.p.)

6 5

Home book

TASK 1

1 a $8x + 10y$ b $17 + 8p + 7q$

    c $9n - 11$ d x

    e $3y + 5x + 14$ f $16n + 8 + 19m$

2 a $3x + 15$　　b $7y + 56$
　 c $9x - 18$　　d $8x - 6$
　 e $15x - 45$　　f $70x + 60$

3 a $21x + 32$　　b $44x + 46$
　 c $135x - 5$　　d $115x + 10$
　 e $59x - 81$　　f $68x - 27$

TASK 2

1 a 30　　　　　b 280
　 c 39　　　　　d 42
　 e 140　　　　f 36
　 g 200

2 a 33 cm^2　　b 5 cm

3 a 1015　　　　b 25th

TASK 3

1 a n^4　　　　b p^3
　 c $3x^4$　　　d $5x^2y^3$

2 a 200　　　　b 81
　 c 2560　　　d 13 440
　 e 23 328　　f 27 783
　 g 250　　　　h 43 200

3 a 112　　　　b 2450
　 c 75　　　　　d 2187

TASK 4

1 a 225 cm^2　　b 64 cm^3　　c 150 cm^2

2 $\dfrac{n(n - 3)}{2}$

CD-ROM

Check up

1 $11x + 5y - 5$

2 a $5x + 20$
　 b $21x - 42$

3 $23x + 41$

4 144

5 330

6 $5a^4b^2$

7 7168

8 120

Measures and mensuration

Previous learning

Before they start, pupils should be able to:

- convert one metric unit of length, mass or capacity to another
- interpret scales on a range of measuring instruments
- understand and use the formula for the area of a rectangle
- calculate perimeters and areas of shapes made from rectangles.

Objectives based on NC levels 5 and 6 (mainly level 5)

In this unit, pupils learn to:

- identify mathematical features of a context or problem
- move between the general and the particular to test the logic of an argument
- calculate accurately, selecting mental methods or a calculator as appropriate
- select appropriate procedures and tools
- estimate, approximate and check working, giving accurate solutions appropriate to the context or problem
- refine own findings and approaches on the basis of discussion with others

and to:

- choose and use units of measurement to measure, estimate, calculate and solve problems in a range of contexts
- know rough metric equivalents of imperial measures in common use
- visualise 3D shapes from their sets, and use geometric properties of cuboids and shapes made from cuboids
- recognise simple plans and elevations
- derive and use formulae for the area of a triangle, parallelogram and trapezium and the volume of a cuboid
- calculate areas of compound shapes and volumes and surface areas of cuboids and shapes made from cuboids.

Lessons
1 **Converting between units**
2 **Perimeter and area of triangles**
3 **Perimeter and area of quadrilaterals**
4 **Volume of cuboids**
5 **Surface area of cuboids**

About this unit
Pupils need to be confident about converting between metric units for length, area, volume, mass and capacity. They also need to know the rough metric equivalents for commonly used imperial measurements.

This unit reviews what pupils already know about perimeters of plane shapes such as rectangles, triangles and regular polygons. It builds on their knowledge of the area of a rectangle and develops methods for finding the areas of a triangle, parallelogram and trapezium.

Pupils need to know the difference between the volume and surface area of a cuboid and be able to calculate the volume of a cuboid. They then apply their knowledge to shapes made from cubes and cuboids.

Assessment
This unit includes:

- a self-assessment section (*G4.2 How well are you doing?* class book p. 105);
- a set of questions to replace or supplement questions in the exercises or homework tasks, or to use as an informal test (*G4.2 Check up*, CD-ROM)

<table>
<tr><td>**Common errors and misconceptions**</td><td>Look out for pupils who:</td></tr>
</table>

Common errors and misconceptions

Look out for pupils who:

- cannot distinguish between commonly used imperial units and metric units;
- confuse relationships between units, e.g. forget that $1\,m^2 = 10\,000\,cm^2$ (not $100\,cm^2$);
- don't realise that a square is a particular rectangle, and a rectangle is a particular parallelogram, or that a cube is a particular cuboid with all its edges equal;
- use a slant height rather than the perpendicular height when they find the area of a triangle or parallelogram;
- confuse surface area with volume or use cubic units for surface area;
- don't include the areas of all the faces when they find the surface area of a cuboid.

Key terms and notation

approximately equal to ($\approx$)

units, millimetre (mm), centimetre (cm), metre (m), kilometre (km), millilitre (ml), litres (l), gram (g), kilogram (kg)

inch, feet/foot (ft), yard, mile, fluid ounce, cup, pint, gallon, ounce (oz), pound (lb), stone

square millimetre (mm^2), square centimetre (cm^2), square metre (m^2), square kilometre (km^2)

cubic millimetre (mm^3), cubic centimetre (cm^3), cubic metre (m^3)

compound, area, perimeter, parallelogram, trapezium, cube, cuboid, prism, face, surface area, volume

Practical resources

individual whiteboards	A4 paper and scissors
calculators	empty shoe box, or similar
centimetre squared paper or	a cuboid to demonstrate surface area
centimetre square dotty paper	in lesson 6

Exploring maths

Tier 4 teacher's book
Answers for G4.2, pp. 121–123

Tier 4 CD-ROM
PowerPoint files
    G4.2 Slides for lessons 1 to 5
Tier 4 programs
    Metric units quiz
    Unit equivalents
    Perimeter and area quiz
    Triangle area
    Parallelogram area

Tier 4 class book
G4.2, pp. 88–106
G4.2 How well are you doing? p. 105

Tier 4 home book
G4.2, pp. 34–39

Tier 4 CD-ROM
G4.2 Check up
G4.2 Pupil resource sheets
    2.1 One per pupil
    3.1 One per pupil

Useful websites

Imperial units
en.wikipedia.org/wiki/Imperial_unit

Animal weigh in
www.bbc.co.uk/education/mathsfile/gameswheel.html

Painted cube
www.nrich.maths.org/public/viewer.php?obj_id=2322

Nine colours
www.nrich.maths.org/public/viewer.php?obj_id=768

1 Converting between units

Learning points

- Converting between metric units involves multiplying or dividing by a power of 10.
- Conversions between metric units are exact.
- Conversions between metric and imperial units are approximate.
- $1\,m \approx 3\,ft$
- $1\,kg \approx 2.2\,lb$
- 1 litre $\approx$ 2 pints
- $8\,km \approx 5\,miles$

Starter Say that this lesson is about converting between units of measurement.

> **What are the metric units for length? For mass? For capacity?**

Launch **Metric units quiz**. This asks pupils to choose a suitable metric unit to measure different items. Use 'Next' and 'Back' to move on and back through the questions at a suitable pace.

Pupils can either answer on their whiteboards, or write answers in an exercise book, checking their work as they go along.

Main activity Ask pupils to convert some measurements by multiplying or dividing by 1, 10 or 100, as appropriate. Ask them to answer on their whiteboards.

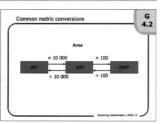

> **What is 2 metres in centimetres? 2 litres in millilitres?**
> **5 kilometres in metres? 6000 grams in kilograms?**

Extend to include decimals.

> **What is 3.4 kilometres in metres? 450 grams in kilograms?**
> **356 millimetres in centimetres? 1.8 kilograms in grams?**

Show **slide 1.1** to remind pupils how to convert metric measurements. Ask them to use the information to change 0.89 km to metres [890 m] and then millimetres [890 000 mm].

Show **slide 1.2**. Discuss measures of area. Explain that one square centimetre is the flat space or area occupied by a square of side one centimetre. Remind pupils that as there are ten millimetres in one centimetre, there will be $10 \times 10 = 100$ square millimetres in one square centimetre. Explain similarly that there are $100 \times 100 = 10\,000$ square centimetres in 1 square metre.

Stress that the units of area are abbreviated to, say, cm^2, not sq. cm.

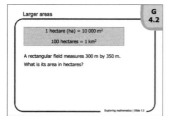

Explain that the hectare is another metric unit for area. The *hectare* is the area of a square with side 100 metres.

Show **slide 1.3**. Ask pupils to solve the problem.

> Select questions from **G4.2 Exercise 1A** in the class book (p. 89).

Ask questions for the class to answer on whiteboards. Accept answers in metric or imperial units.

How tall am I? [Indicate your height.]

How thick is this exercise book? [Hold up an exercise book.]

How far is it from … to …
[Select two places, known by pupils, a few miles apart.]

How wide is the classroom? [Indicate which direction is the width.]

How big is this room? What units would you use?
[Suggest length and width; discuss finding the floor area.]

What units do you use to measure your weight?

How much water is there in a bottle of water?

Explain that both imperial and metric units are used in the UK every day, although only a few, such as the pint and the mile, are 'official'.

Ask pupils to turn to the table before Exercise 1B in the class book (p. 90), and to look at the metric units and their rough imperial equivalents. Explain that the notation ≈ means 'is approximately equal to'.

Write on the board a problem for pupils to work on in pairs.

Joe is 6 feet 5 inches tall. Can he walk through a 2 m door without ducking?

Take feedback and discuss methods, e.g. convert 6 feet into centimetres ($6 \times 30 = 180$ cm), then add 5 inches converted to centimetres ($5 \times 2.54 = 12.7$ cm), giving a total of 192.7 cm. So Joe can walk through the door.

Select questions from **G4.2 Exercise 1B** in the class book (p. 91).

Review

Launch **Unit equivalents**. Click on the 15 cm ruler to select a starting centimetre measurement. (Click on Starting units to change the scale through cm, m, km and mm.)

SIM

What is this measurement in millimetres?

Click on the mm input box and use the keypad to input the value in mm. Click 'Check'.

What is this measurement in metres?

Click on the units on the scale to change the units of the scale to m. Use the keypad to input the value in mm. Click 'Check'.

Repeat for different starting units, using the arrows on the control bar. Repeat for 'Weight' and 'Capacity', setting the starting unit and inputting the starting value either using the keypad or by dragging the pointer or water depth.

Sum up by emphasising the points on **slide 1.4**.

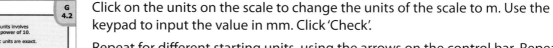

Points to remember

G
4.2

- Converting between metric units involves multiplying or dividing by a power of 10.
- Conversions between metric units are exact.
- Conversions between metric and imperial units are **approximate**.
- 1 m ≈ 3 ft
- 1 kg ≈ 2.2 lb
- 1 litre ≈ 2 pints
- 8 km ≈ 5 miles

Exploring mathematics | Slide 1.4

Homework

Ask pupils to do **G4.2 Task 1** in the home book (p. 84).

2 Perimeter and area of triangles

Learning points

- Area of a triangle $= \frac{1}{2} \times$ base $\times$ perpendicular height
- The height is always perpendicular to the base.
- The units are always square units.

Starter

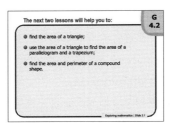

Show **slide 2.1** to discuss the objectives for this and the next lesson. Say that this lesson is about finding the area and perimeter of shapes made from triangles and rectangles.

> What is the formula for the area (A) of a rectangle with width w and length l?

> How do you work out the perimeter of a rectangle?
> [an efficient method is $2 \times (l + w)$]

Launch **Perimeter and area quiz**, which shows shapes on a grid. Questions 1 to 8 involve the perimeter and questions 9 to 15 the area of rectangles or shapes made from rectangles. Use 'Next' and 'Back' to move through the questions. Emphasise the importance of using the correct units.

Ask pupils to answer on their whiteboards. Use their responses to review their understanding of the area and perimeter of rectangles.

Main activity

Draw a triangle on the board, labelling the sides 4 cm, 5 cm and 6 cm. Ask for the perimeter of this triangle.

Replace the measurements with the labels a, b and c. Ask the class to give the perimeter (P) of this triangle. Establish that:

$$P = a + b + c$$

Ask for suggestions for a formula for the perimeter of a regular hexagon of side a, and then of a rectangle with sides a and b. Confirm with diagrams.

Say that you will now look at the area of a triangle. Give out A4 paper. Ask pupils to cut out two identical triangles. Then ask them to cut each triangle into two and to arrange the four triangles to form a rectangle.

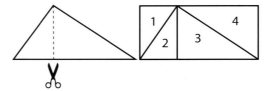
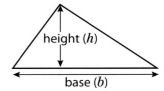

This shows that the area of the triangle (A) with base (b) and perpendicular height (h) has the same area as half a rectangle with the same base and height.

> area of a triangle $= \frac{1}{2} \times$ base $\times$ height, or $A = \frac{1}{2} \times b \times h = \frac{1}{2}bh$

Stress that the height of the triangle is the perpendicular height of the top vertex from the base.

Work an example with $b = 8$ cm and $h = 5$ cm.

Launch **Triangle area**. This shows a rectangle being dissected to form two identical triangles, again showing that the area of the triangle is half the area of the rectangle. Click 'Play' to start, and 'Pause' to stop.

SIM

What happens to the rectangle? What is the new shape formed?

What does this tell us about the area of a triangle?

Select questions from **G4.2 Exercise 2A** in the class book (p. 92).

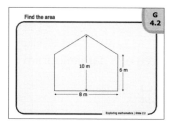

Show the diagram on **slide 2.2**. Ask pupils to work out the area of the compound shape using what they know about the areas of triangles and rectangles.

Take feedback. Encourage pupils to draw any construction lines on the board.

One approach is to divide the area into a rectangle, 6 cm by 8 cm, and a triangle, base 8 cm and height 4 cm, giving an area of $48 + 16 = 64\,cm^2$.

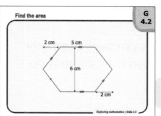

Repeat with the problem on **slide 2.3**. Establish that the area is $42\,cm^2$ and that there are two ways to find it. The first is to calculate the area of the central rectangle and add the two triangles. The second is to calculate the area of the enclosing rectangle and subtract the four small triangles.

Ask pupils to do **G4.2 Exercise 2B** in the class book (p. 94).

Review

Remind pupils that knowing the formula for the area of a triangle allows them to find the areas of shapes made up from triangles.

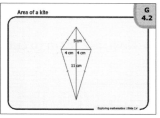

Show the kite on **slide 2.4**. Ask pupils in pairs to work out its area [$64\,cm^2$]. Take feedback from one or two pairs on their method of solution.

As an extension, ask pupils to calculate the product of the diagonals [$16 \times 8 = 128$]. Ask them what they notice about that product and the area of the kite.

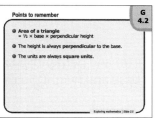

Finish by reinforcing the points on **slide 2.5**.

Homework

Ask pupils to do **G4.2 Task 2** in the home book (p. 35).

3 Perimeter and area of quadrilaterals

Learning points

- Area of a triangle $= \frac{1}{2} \times$ base $\times$ perpendicular height
- Area of a parallelogram $=$ base $\times$ perpendicular height
- Area of a trapezium $= \frac{1}{2} \times$ (sum of parallel sides) $\times$ perpendicular height
- The height is always perpendicular to the base.
- The units are always square units.

Starter

Say that this lesson looks at the formulae for finding the area of a parallelogram and a trapezium.

Ask pupils to imagine a square with its two diagonals drawn in.

Describe the shapes that are formed inside the square.
[four congruent right-angled isosceles triangles]

Repeat with a rectangle [two pairs of congruent isosceles triangles], then a parallelogram [two pairs of congruent scalene triangles] and then a kite [two pairs of congruent right-angled triangles].

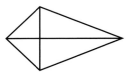

Main activity

Give out A4 paper. Ask the class to cut out a parallelogram. Next, ask them to cut off a right-angled triangle and place it at the opposite side.

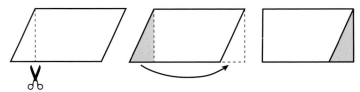

This shows that the area of the parallelogram (A) with base (b) and perpendicular height (h) has the same area as a rectangle with the same base and height. So the area of a parallelogram is given by the formula:

area of a parallelogram $=$ base $\times$ perpendicular height, or $A = b \times h = bh$

Work out an example with $b = 6\,\text{cm}$ and $h = 4\,\text{cm}$ [$A = 24\,\text{cm}^2$].

Launch **Parallelogram area**. This shows a rectangle being dissected to form a triangle and a trapezium, which are reassembled to form a parallelogram. Click 'Play' to start, and 'Pause' to stop.

What happens to the rectangle? What is the new shape formed?

What does this tell us about the area of a parallelogram?

SIM

Ask the class to cut out two identical trapeziums from A4 paper and arrange them to form a parallelogram by rotating one of them by half a turn. This shows that the area of the trapezium is half the area of the parallelogram that can be made from two of them.

 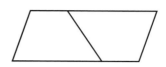 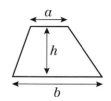

So the area A of a trapezium with parallel sides a and b is:

sum of the lengths of the parallel sides $\times$ perpendicular height

or $A = \frac{1}{2} \times (a + b) \times h = \frac{1}{2}h(a + b)$

Work out an example with $a = 4\,\text{cm}$, $b = 8\,\text{cm}$ and $h = 5\,\text{cm}$ [$A = 30\,\text{cm}^2$].

Ask pupils to do **G4.2 Exercise 3** in the class book (p. 96).

Review

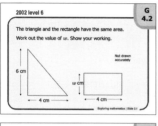

Show **slide 3.1**. Ask pupils in pairs to produce a solution. Discuss different approaches and agree the answer [$w = 3\,\text{cm}$].

Sum up by asking pupils to remember the points on **slide 3.2**.

Homework Ask pupils to do **G4.2 Task 3** in the home book (p. 36).

4 Volume of cuboids

Learning points

- The volume of a cuboid is length × width × height, or area of base × height.

- Volume is measured in cubic units, such as cubic millimetres (mm³), cubic centimetres (cm³) or cubic metres (m³).

- When you find the volume of a cuboid, the edges must all be in the same units.

- To find the volume of a shape made from cuboids, divide the shape up into cuboids and add the volumes together.

Starter

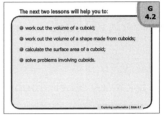

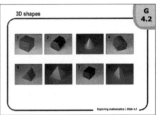

Use **slide 4.1** to discuss the objectives for the next two lessons. Say that this lesson is about finding the volume of cuboids and shapes made from cuboids.

Show **slide 4.2**, a selection of 3D shapes. Ask pupils to answer your questions on their whiteboards by writing the number for the correct shape.

Which shape is a cuboid?
[shape 1 or 7 — establish that a cube is a special cuboid]

Which shape is a cone? [shape 3]

Which shape is a triangular prism? [shape 5]

Which shape is a square-based pyramid? [shape 6]

Which shape is a hexagonal prism? [shape 2]

Which shape has eight faces? [shape 2] **Four faces?** [shape 8]

Which shape has nine edges? [shape 5] **Twelve edges?** [shape 7 or 1]

Which shape has five vertices? [shape 6] **Twelve vertices?** [shape 2]

Main activity

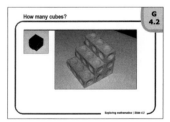

Show **slide 4.3**.

How many unit cubes are needed to make each of these shapes?

Reveal the shapes one at a time — there are four of them — asking for explanations.

Explain that one way is to work out the number of unit squares in one face and multiply this by the number of layers. Establish that the number of unit cubes in each cuboid is the volume of the shape and that it is usually measured in cubic millimetres (mm³), cubic centimetres (cm³) and cubic metres (m³). Indicate the size of each unit.

Establish that the formula for the volume of a cuboid is:

volume of a cuboid = length × width × height

and that it could also be written as:

volume of a cuboid = area of base × height

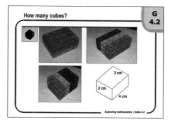

Use **slide 4.4**, a cuboid with two coloured layers. Ask pupils to work out the area of one coloured face [3 × 4 = 12 square units], and then the volume [12 × 2 = 24 cubic units].

Show the next two screens of the slide and repeat. Point out that whichever way you work out the volume the answer is always the same [2 × 3 × 4 = 24 cubic units]. Show the fourth screen of the slide and ask:

> How would you calculate the volume of this cuboid?

> What are the units for the volume of this cuboid?

> What information do you need to calculate the volume of any cuboid?

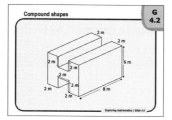

Show **slide 4.5**. Ask pupils to discuss in pairs how they would work out the volume of the shape. Establish that it is made from cuboids.

Allow a couple of minutes for the pairs to discuss their approach, then double up the pairs into groups of four to agree a joint answer.

Take feedback. Annotate the slide as necessary to show how the groups have divided up the shape. After the first group has responded, ask if any other groups have divided the shape in a different way. Establish that there are different ways to divide the shape into cuboids but the aim is to use as few divisions as possible. The volume is 224 m³.

Discuss the shape and establish that it has a constant cross-section. Wherever it is cut perpendicular to its length, the cross-section is the same. Show that the volume of the shape can be calculated by finding the cross-sectional area and multiplying this by the length of the shape, and that this also gives the volume as 224 m³.

> Select individual work from **G4.2 Exercise 4** in the class book (p. 99).

Review Show **slide 4.6**. Ask pupils to solve the problem in pairs. Discuss approaches.

Sum up with the points on **slide 4.7**.

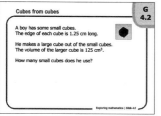

Homework Ask pupils to do **G4.2 Task 4** in the home book (p. 37).

5 Surface area of cuboids

Learning points

- Surface area is measured in square units, such as square millimetres (mm²), square centimetres (cm²) or square metres (m²).

- To find the surface area of a solid, find the sum of the areas of each face.

- In problems involving area and volume, the units of the sides or edges of shapes must be the same.

Starter

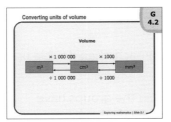

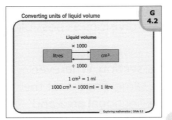

Say that this lesson is about finding the surface area of a cuboid and solving problems involving surface area and volume.

Show **slides 5.1 and 5.2**. Discuss measures of volume. Remind pupils that as there are ten millimetres in one centimetre, there will be $10 \times 10 \times 10 = 1000$ cubic millimetres in one cubic centimetre. Explain similarly that there are $100 \times 100 \times 100 = 1\,000\,000$ cubic centimetres in 1 cubic metre.

Show a shoe box or similar.

> **Estimate the size of this box. What units would you use?**

Discuss its dimensions and finding the volume in cubic centimetres, cubic millimetres and cubic metres.

Discuss the relationship between litres (capacity) and cubic centimetres (volume), explaining that 1 ml is equivalent to 1 cm³.

Refer pupils to **G4.2 Exercise 5A** in the class book (p. 102). Working with the whole class, choose a few questions and go through them on the board.

Main activity

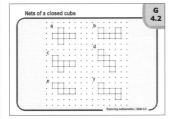

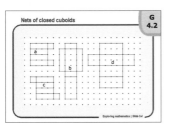

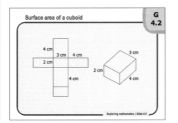

Show **slide 5.3**. Make sure that pupils recall that the net of a solid is the two-dimensional shape that can be folded to make the three-dimensional solid. Ask:

> **Which of these nets will create a closed cube?**

Allow a minute for discussion in pairs and then take some feedback. Discuss why some of the arrangements would form a cube and others would not.

Repeat with **slide 5.4**. Ask:

> **Which of these nets will create a closed cuboid?**

Show the first screen of **slide 5.5**. Ask:

> **Does this net make a cuboid?**

> **What is the total area of the net?**

Allow time for pupils to work out the area [52 cm²]. Explain that when the net is folded to form a cuboid, the area of the net becomes the surface area of the cuboid.

Show the second screen of **slide 5.5**, a cuboid made from the net with the measurements attached. Ask the class:

> **What calculations would you need to do to find the surface area of this cuboid, given just the dimensions?**

Allow discussion time and take feedback. Establish that the surface area of a cuboid can be calculated by adding the areas of all *six* faces together. Encourage a discussion that leads to an efficient method of calculation, such as finding the area of the three different faces shown and then doubling the answer.

Ask pupils to sketch a cuboid and label the dimensions l, w and h. Ask pairs to:

> Write an expression for the surface area of the cuboid, using the dimensions l, w and h.

Take feedback. Explain that there are different correct ways of writing the expression, all of which will give a correct numerical response, but some are more efficient than others. One efficient method is the correct use of notation so:

> surface area $= 2 \times l \times w + 2 \times l \times h + 2 \times w \times h$

becomes:

> surface area $= 2lw + 2lh + 2wh$

Ask the class to work in pairs to explain why the surface area S of a cube with edge l is $S = 6l^2$.

Ask pupils to do **G4.2 Exercise 5B** in the class book (p. 103).

Review

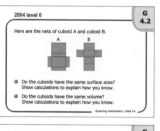

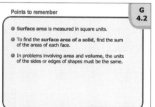

Show **slide 5.6**. Ask pupils to work on the problem in pairs. Use this to confirm their understanding of surface area and volume.

> What units are used for surface area?

> What units are used for volume?

Ask pupils to remember the points on **slide 5.7**.

Round off the unit by referring again to the objectives. Suggest that pupils find time to try the self-assessment problems in **G4.2 How well are you doing?** in the class book (p. 105).

Homework

Ask pupils to do **G4.2 Task 5** in the home book (p. 39)

Check up   G4.2

Write your answers in your book.
You will need centimetre squared paper and a ruler for the first two questions.

1 On centimetre squared paper, draw a triangle that has an area of 8 cm².

2 Copy the line below on centimetre squared paper.
Draw three more lines to make a parallelogram with an area of 10 cm².

3 *Level 4*
This cuboid is made from 12 small cubes.

a How many small cubes are there in this cuboid?

b This shape is made with two cuboids.
How many small cubes are there in this shape?

4 *2004 level 5*
A box contains bags of crisps.
Each bag of crisps weighs 25 grams.
Altogether, the bags of crisps inside the box weigh 1 kilogram.
How many bags of crisps are inside the box?

CRISPS
25g

Check up [continued]

5 *2002 level 5*
A scale measures in grams and in ounces.

grams   0   100   200   300   400

ounces   0   4   8   12   16

About how many ounces is 1 kilogram? Explain your answer.

6 This shape is made from four centimetre cubes.
a What is the volume of the shape?
b What is the surface area of the shape?

7 The drawing shows two cuboids.

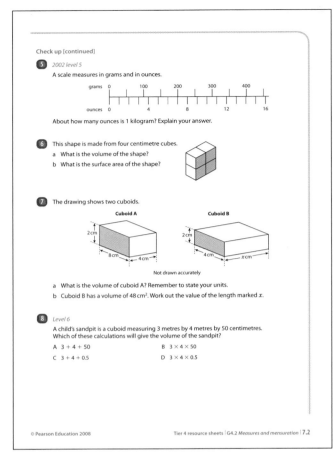

Cuboid A   Cuboid B

2 cm   2 cm

8 cm   4 cm   4 cm   *x* cm

Not drawn accurately

a What is the volume of cuboid A? Remember to state your units.
b Cuboid B has a volume of 48 cm². Work out the value of the length marked *x*.

8 *Level 6*
A child's sandpit is a cuboid measuring 3 metres by 4 metres by 50 centimetres.
Which of these calculations will give the volume of the sandpit?

A 3 + 4 + 50   B 3 × 4 × 50
C 3 + 4 + 0.5   D 3 × 4 × 0.5

G4.2 Answers

Exercise 1A

1. a 0.36 m   b 4600 mm
   c 4 kg   d 630 ml
   e 3400 m   f 0.023 km
   g 340 g   h 210 km

2. a 70 000 000 cm^2 b 4 500 000 mm^2
   c 2 000 000 mm^2 d 0.09 m^2
   e 60 cm^2 f 0.15 m^2

3. 480 000 ml

4. 100 g

5. 22 500 cm^2

6. 38 tonnes

7. 7.5 hectares

8. 24 290 000 hectares

9. 72 tonnes

Extension problem

10. 61 126 221 km^2

Exercise 1B

1. About 64 km

2. About 12 miles

3. William

4. Jade

5. 20 gallons is approximately equal to 18.2 buckets, so 19 buckets will fill the pool.

6. About 336 m

7. About 12 gallons

8. 18 glasses

9. About 2320 km

10. About 148 800 000 km

Extension problems

11. Miklos Nemeth (94.65 m)

12. 252.7 m^2

Exercise 2A

1. a 30 cm   b 28 mm   c 61 mm

2. a $a + b + c$ b $P = a + b + c$
   c $P = 2a + b$ d $P = 3a$

3. a 14 cm   b $P = 2l + 2h$

4. a 40 mm   b $P = w + x + y + z$

5. a 63 mm^2 b 30 cm^2
   c 30.8 m^2 d 30 square inches
   e 50 cm^2 f 182 mm^2 (1.82 cm^2)

6. a 41 cm   b 94 mm   c 27.9 m

7. 14 cm^2

Extension problems

8. 4 cm

9. 7 feet

10. 2.4 m

Exercise 2B

1. a 108 cm^2
   b 198 mm^2
   c 72 cm^2

2. 15 cm^2

3. a 21 m^2 b 18 m

Extension problem

4. 8 mm

Exercise 3

1. a 20 cm^2
   b 20 cm^2
   c 48 square inches
   d 2170 mm^2

2 12 m

3 3 cm

4 a 9 cm²

   b 8 square feet

   c 9 square inches

   d 8.5 m²

   e 6.825 m²

5 16 cm

6 5 mm

Extension problems

7 a 2 cm   b 3 cm

8 $a = 3$ cm, $b = 20$ cm, $c = 8$ cm

Exercise 4

1 a 32 unit cubes

   b 18 unit cubes

   c 14 unit cubes

2 a 42 unit cubes

   b 20 unit cubes

   c 26 unit cubes

3 a 20 cm³   b 80 mm³

   c 24 cm³   d 0.75 m³

4 30 cm³

5 72 mm³

6 3 m

7 a 18 000 mm³

   b 52.728 cm³

8 Any pair of numbers that multiply to give 24

Extension problems

9 16, 12, 8

10 10 boxes

11 7 cuboids: $1 \times 1 \times 100$, $1 \times 2 \times 50$, $1 \times 4 \times 25$, $1 \times 5 \times 20$, $1 \times 10 \times 10$, $2 \times 2 \times 25$, $2 \times 5 \times 10$

Exercise 5A

1 a 2000 cm³   b 500 cm³

   c 700 cm³   d 5000 cm³

2 a 0.460 m³   b 63 litres   c 1.896 litres

3 2 500 m³

Exercise 5B

1 a 24   b 72   c 54

2 a 54 cm²   b 46 m²

   c 188 mm²   d 262 square feet

3 2 cm

4 a 8 cm   b 512 cm³

5 a 5 cm, 8 cm, 10 cm

   b 400 cm³

6 See table below. There are others where length × width = 12 mm².

Height (mm)	Length (mm)	Width (mm)	Surface area (mm²)
3	1	12	102
3	2	6	72
3	3	4	66
3	4	3	66
3	6	2	72
3	12	1	102

How well are you doing?

1 a A   b 250 ml

2 a 12 cm   b 1.2 m   c 0.12 km

3 40 bags

4 35 cm²

5 Area = 12 cm² so $w = 3$ cm

6 a 60cm³   b $x = 6$

   c 94 cm²   d 104 cm³

Home book

TASK 1

1. a 90 000 m   b 4600 mm
   c 0.035 kg   d 700 ml
   e 560 g   f 90 km

2. 0.45 ha

3. 1622 kg

4. 8 tonnes or 8000 kg

5. About 6 miles

6. About 36 900 pints

7. About 225 g

8. About 162 000 000 litres per minute

TASK 2

1. a 60 cm^2
   b 108 mm^2
   c 30 square inches
   d 2.5 m^2

2. 6 m

3. 6 inches

4. a 40 cm
   b 7.1 cm to 1 d.p.(120 ÷ 17)

TASK 3

1. a 54 cm^2
   b 4 m^2

2. a 30 mm^2
   b 9 cm^2
   c 15 square inches

3. 50 square feet

4. 8 cm

TASK 4

1. a 8 cubes   b 24 cubes
   c 48 cubes   d 42 cubes

2. a 28 cubes   b 39 cubes
   c 72 cubes   d 32 cubes

3. a 150 mm^3 b 2240 m^3

4. 4 cm

5. 108 cm^3

TASK 5

1. a 25 000 cm^2 b 1200 mm^2
   c 0.7 m^3 d 175 cm^3

2. a 118 cm^2 b 72.78 m^2

3. a 3 cm by 4 cm by 9 cm
   b 150 cm^3

4. 0.1 m or 10 cm

CD-ROM

Check up

1. Pupil's triangle with an area of 8 cm^2

2. Pupil's parallelogram with an area of 10 cm^2

3. a 30 small cubes
   b 24 small cubes

4. 40 bags

5. 200 g is about 7 ounces, so 1 kg is about 35 ounces.

6. a 4 cm^3 b 16 cm^2

7. a 64 cm^3 b $x = 6$

8. D

Fractions, decimals and percentages

Previous learning

Before they start, pupils should be able to:

- convert one metric unit to another
- convert fractions to decimals by using a calculator
- add and subtract simple fractions and multiply a fraction by an integer
- understand percentage as the 'number of parts per 100' and calculate simple fractions and percentages of numbers and quantities
- carry out calculations with more than one step using brackets and the memory of a calculator.

Objectives based on NC levels 5 and 6 (mainly level 5)

In this unit, pupils learn to:

- identify the mathematical features of a context or problem
- make connections between related problems
- use accurate notation
- calculate accurately, selecting mental methods or a calculator as appropriate
- give accurate solutions appropriate to the context or problem
- evaluate the efficiency of alternative strategies and approaches

and to:

- multiply and divide integers and decimals by 0.1 or 0.01, and derive products such as 6×0.7, 8×0.03
- use division to convert a fraction to a decimal and recognise that a recurring decimal is a fraction
- order fractions by writing them with a common denominator or by converting them to decimals
- express one given number as a percentage of another
- strengthen and extend mental methods of calculation, working with decimals, fractions and percentages
- use efficient written methods to:
  - multiply and divide decimals, understanding where to position the decimal point by considering equivalent calculations
  - add and subtract fractions
  - multiply and divide a fraction by an integer
  - calculate percentages and find the outcome of a given percentage increase or decrease
- use a calculator to carry out more difficult calculations, entering numbers, and interpreting the display in context
- select from a range of checking methods, including estimating in context and using inverse operations.

Lessons

1 **Ordering fractions**
2 **Calculating with fractions**
3 **Multiplying and dividing decimals 1**
4 **Multiplying and dividing decimals 2**
5 **Calculating percentages**
6 **Percentage increases and decreases**

About this unit

The ability to calculate mentally with fractions, decimals or percentages is a useful skill. This unit covers mental and written calculations with fractions, decimals and percentages. Pupils develop confidence at finding equivalent fractions, decimals and percentages so that they can move from one representation to another as they need to. They also learn how to use a calculator for harder calculations with these numbers.

Assessment	This unit includes:

Assessment

This unit includes:
- an optional mental test that could replace part of a lesson (p. 136);
- a self-assessment section (*N4.3 How well are you doing?* class book p. 124);
- a set of questions to replace or supplement questions in the exercises or homework tasks, or to use as an informal test (*N4.3 Check up*, CD-ROM).

Common errors and misconceptions

Look out for pupils who:
- add numerators and denominators when adding fractions: $\frac{2}{3} + \frac{3}{4} = \frac{5}{7}$;
- misinterpret fraction, decimal and percentage equivalents, e.g. think that because 10% is $\frac{1}{10}$ or 0.1, 5% as a fraction is $\frac{1}{5}$ or 0.5;
- think that it is impossible to have more than 100%.

Key terms and notation

problem, solution, method, pattern, relationship, classify, compare, order, predict, represent, solve, explain, justify

calculate, calculation, calculator, add, subtract, multiply, divide, sum, total, difference, product, quotient, remainder, multiple

fraction, numerator, denominator, common denominator, proper fraction, improper fraction, mixed number, cancel, simplify, convert, equivalent, equivalence

decimal, whole number, decimal place, units, tenths, hundredths, thousandths, terminating decimal, recurring decimal and notation such as $0.\dot{3}$

per cent (%), percentage, discount, reduction, reduce, increase, decrease

Practical resources

scientific calculators for pupils	counters in two colours (half a dozen in each colour for each pair of pupils)
individual whiteboards	
squared paper	dice (two per pair of pupils)

Exploring maths

Tier 4 teacher's book
N4.3 Mental test, p. 136
Answers for Unit N4.3, pp. 141–143

Tier 4 CD-ROM
PowerPoint files
  N4.3 Slides for lessons 1 to 6
Excel files
  N4.3 Discount
Tools and prepared toolsheets
  Calculator tool
Tier 4 programs
  Multiplying a fraction
  Dividing a fraction
  Calculate percentages

Tier 4 class book
N4.3, pp. 107 – 125
N4.3 How well are you doing? p. 124

Tier 4 home book
N4.3, pp. 40 – 46

Tier 4 CD-ROM
N4.3 Check up
N4.3 Pupil resource sheets
  1.1 One per pupil
  1.2 One per pair
  2.1 One per pair
  4.1 One per pupil
  5.1 One per pair
  6.1 One set per group, cut up

Useful websites

Fractions – adding, Number line bars – fractions (division of fractions)
nlvm.usu.edu/en/nav/vlibrary.html
Saloon snap
www.bbc.co.uk/education/mathsfile/shockwave/games/saloonsnap.html
Matching fractions, decimals and percentages
nrich.maths.org/public/viewer.php?obj_id=1249

1 Ordering fractions

Learning points

◎ To convert a fraction to a decimal, divide the numerator by the denominator. You can use a calculator to do this.

◎ To put fractions in order, either convert them to decimals and compare the decimals, or change all the fractions to a common denominator.

Starter Use **slide 1.1** to discuss the objectives for the first three lessons. Say that this lesson looks at recurring decimals and putting fractions in order.

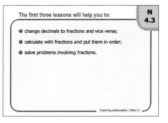

Use **slide 1.2** to remind pupils how to change decimals to fractions, e.g.

0.5 is 5 tenths, which simplifies to $\frac{1}{2}$.

0.35 is 3 tenths and 5 hundredths, or 35 hundredths, which simplifies to $\frac{7}{20}$.

Repeat with: $0.625 = 6$ tenths, 2 hundredths and 5 thousandths, or 625 thousandths, which simplifies to $\frac{5}{8}$.

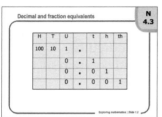

Main activity Use the **Calculator tool** to remind pupils how to change a fraction to a decimal using their calculators. For example, to convert $\frac{4}{6}$ to a decimal, either enter

4 ÷ 6 = , giving a display of 0.66666666, or use the fraction key to enter

4 aᵇ/c 6 = , producing the display:

$$2 \lrcorner 3$$

Press the fraction key to toggle between decimal and fraction forms of the fraction.

Remind pupils about recurring decimals. Ask them to use their calculators to find the decimal equivalent of $\frac{2}{11}$ [0.181 818 181 …]. Explain the recurring decimal notation.

Say that if no calculator is available a fraction such as $\frac{5}{7}$ can be converted to a fraction using division. Zeros can be added after the decimal point so that the division can continue. The answer can be rounded to one or two decimal places.

Repeat, showing that two thirds is 0.666… or 0.ċ6 (zero point six recurring), or 0.67 to two decimal places.

$$
\begin{array}{r}
0.714 \\
7\overline{)5.00} \\
\underline{4.900} \quad 0.7 \times 7 \\
0.100 \\
\underline{0.070} \quad 0.01 \times 7 \\
0.030 \\
\underline{0.028} \quad 0.004 \times 7 \\
0.002 \\
\end{array}
$$

Answer: 0.71 to 1 d.p.

TO

Draw a line on the board. Mark one end 0 and the other end 1. Ask the class where one half is on the line. Then ask for the approximate positions of a range of unit fractions, such as one quarter, one third, one tenth.

> **The numerator is always 1, but what do you notice about the position of fractions as the denominator gets larger?**
> [the fraction gets smaller and closer to 0]

Repeat with two thirds, two quarters, two fifths, two sixths, … Encourage pupils to think where, say, one fifth is, to help them to estimate the position of two fifths.

> **Which would be closer to 1, three fifths or five eighths?**
> **How might we tell?**

Discuss responses. Draw out that both fractions could be changed to decimals and then compared, or both fractions could be changed to equivalent fractions with the same denominator and then compared. If a calculator is available, the first method is generally easier. Use this method to practise comparing a few more fractions.

Select further individual work from **N4.3 Exercises 1A and 1B** in the class book (p. 108–110). Pupils will need **N4.3 Resource sheet 1.1** for questions 1 to 3 in Exercise 1A. They will need **N4.3 Resource sheet 1.2** and counters in two colours for the game in Exercise 1B.

RS

Review

> **Which is greater, two thirds or three quarters? Explain how you know.**

Remind pupils that there are two ways to compare fractions: change both to decimals or change both to fractions with the same denominator. Explain that when working mentally it is usually easier to change both to fractions with the same denominator. When a calculator can be used, it may be easier to change the fractions to decimals.

Finish with the reminders on **slide 1.3**.

Homework

Ask pupils to do **N4.3 Task 1** in the home book (p. 40).

2 Calculating with fractions

Learning points

- To add and subtract fractions without a calculator, change them to the same denominator.
- We can think of a fraction such as $\frac{8}{3}$ as eight thirds, or as one third of 8, or as 8 divided by 3.
- To multiply proper fractions, cancel first, then multiply the numerators and multiply the denominators.

Starter Say that this lesson is about calculating with fractions. Remind pupils how to add and subtract fractions, changing them to a common denominator, e.g.

$$\frac{4}{9} + 2\frac{1}{6}, 3\frac{7}{12} - \frac{3}{8}.$$

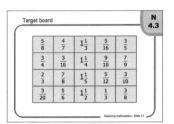

Show the target board on **slide 2.1**. Point to different numbers, asking questions for pupils to answer on whiteboards, using jottings if they need to.

> What is the sum of one half and this fraction?
>
> What is double this fraction? What is half of this fraction?
>
> What is the sum/difference of this pair of fractions?

Main activity Remind the class of the equivalence of 'of' and 'multiply'. For example, show by halving and halving again that $\frac{1}{4}$ of 8 is 2, then show that $\frac{1}{4} \times 8$ is eight steps of one quarter along the number line, which is also 2.

Launch **Multiplying a fraction** to illustrate this idea using areas. Show also that:

$$\frac{4}{5} \times 3 = \frac{4}{5} + \frac{4}{5} + \frac{4}{5} = \frac{4 \times 3}{5} = \frac{12}{5} = 2\frac{2}{5}$$

Next, demonstrate how to multiply a mixed number by an integer by first changing the mixed number to an improper fraction.

Refer again to **slide 2.1**. Point to proper fractions and ask pupils to multiply them by integers on their whiteboards. Repeat with one or two mixed numbers.

Move on to finding the product of two proper fractions using areas.

The diagram shows that $\frac{2}{3}$ of $\frac{4}{5}$ is $\frac{8}{15}$,

or $\frac{2}{3} \times \frac{4}{5} = \frac{8}{15}$, and that:

$$\frac{2}{3} \times \frac{4}{5} = \frac{2 \times 4}{3 \times 5} = \frac{8}{15}$$

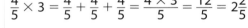

Demonstrate more examples, stressing that the numerators are multiplied and the denominators are multiplied to create the product.

Extend to include cancelling, e.g.

$$\frac{14}{15} \times \frac{3}{4} = \frac{{}^{7}\cancel{14}}{{}^{5}\cancel{15}} \times \frac{\cancel{3}^{1}}{\cancel{4}^{2}} = \frac{7 \times 1}{5 \times 2} = \frac{7}{10}$$

Use the **Calculator tool** to demonstrate how to use a calculator to multiply fractions.

Refer pupils to the first game in **N4.3 Exercise 2A** in the class book (p. 110). Give out dice, two per pair of pupils, and ask the pairs to play the game. Stress that equivalent fractions don't count as being 'different'.

Bring the whole class together again, and move on to showing that $\frac{3}{5} \div 4$ is equivalent to $\frac{3}{5} \times \frac{1}{4}$.

Launch **Dividing a fraction** to illustrate this idea using areas. Show, for example, that $\frac{3}{5} \div 4 = \frac{3}{20}$. Then show that $\frac{3}{5} \times \frac{1}{4}$ is also $\frac{3}{20}$, so $\frac{3}{5} \div 4 = \frac{3}{5} \times \frac{1}{4}$.

Demonstrate how to use a calculator to divide a fraction by an integer.

Refer the pairs to the second game in **N4.3 Exercise 2A** in the class book (p. 111). Give each pair a copy of **N4.3 Resource sheet 2.1** and counters in two colours.

As an alternative to one or both games in Exercise 2A, select individual work from **N4.3 Exercise 2B** in the class book (p. 112).

Review

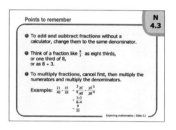

Remind the class that the theme of the lesson is multiplying and dividing fractions. Ask them which aspects they found easy and which they found difficult. Use their ideas to review errors and misunderstandings.

Sum up the lesson using the points on **slide 2.2**.

Homework Ask pupils to do **N4.3 Task 2** in the home book (p. 41).

3 Multiplying and dividing decimals 1

Learning points

- Multiplying by 0.1 is equivalent to dividing by 10;
  dividing by 0.1 is equivalent to multiplying by 10.

- Multiplying by 0.01 is equivalent to dividing by 100;
  dividing by 0.01 is equivalent to multiplying by 100.

- The calculation 0.7×0.04 is equivalent to $\frac{7}{10} \times \frac{4}{100} = \frac{28}{1000}$, or 0.028.

  The answer has the same number of decimal places as the product.

- The calculation $3.5 \div 0.7$ is equivalent to $\frac{3.5 \times 10}{0.7 \times 10} = \frac{35}{7} = 5$.

  Both numbers are multiplied by the same power of 10 to make the divisor an integer.

Starter

Use **slide 3.1** to discuss the objectives for this and the next lesson.

Show **slide 3.2**. Point to numbers for pupils to multiply or divide by 10, 100 or 1000. Stress that digits move left or right.

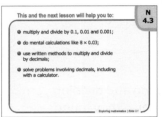

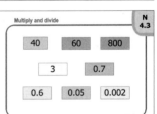

Discuss multiplying and dividing by 0.1, 0.01 and 0.001. Build up a table.

	Equivalent to	Digits move right		Equivalent to	Digits move left
× 0.1	$\times \frac{1}{10}$ or ÷ 10	1 place	÷ 0.1	$\div \frac{1}{10}$ or × 10	1 place
× 0.01	$\times \frac{1}{100}$ or ÷ 100	2 places	÷ 0.01	$\div \frac{1}{100}$ or × 100	2 places
× 0.001	$\times \frac{1}{1000}$ or ÷ 1000	3 places	÷ 0.001	$\div \frac{1}{1000}$ or × 1000	3 places

Refer again to **slide 3.2**. Point to various numbers on the slide and ask pupils to multiply or divide them by 0.1, 0.01 or 0.001, writing the answers on their whiteboards.

Ask pupils to do **N4.3 Exercise 3A** in the class book (p. 113).

Main activity

Explain that a calculation such as 0.7×0.3 can be thought of as $\frac{7}{10} \times \frac{3}{10} = \frac{21}{100}$ or 0.21.

Point out that the product and answer have the same number of decimal places.

> What is 0.6×0.4? And 0.9×0.3?
> And 0.2×0.7?

Continue with examples such as 0.7×0.04, showing that this is equivalent to $\frac{7}{10} \times \frac{4}{100} = \frac{28}{1000}$, or 0.028. Point out again that the product and answer have the same number of decimal places.

Work through $0.05 \times 0.8 = 0.040$. Explain that in this case the zero at the end need not be included in the final answer of 0.04.

Now ask for the product of 7000 and 0.6. Show how we can think of this as:

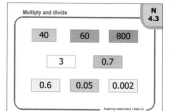

$$7000 \times \frac{6}{10} = 700 \times 6 = 4200$$

Repeat with examples such as 60×0.7 and 300×0.08.

Refer again to **slide 3.2**. This time point to two of the numbers and ask pupils to give you their product. Ask pupils to explain how they arrive at their answers.

Ask pupils to do **N4.3 Exercise 3B** in the class book (p. 114).

Remind the class that a fraction can be changed into an equivalent fraction by multiplying (or dividing) both numerator and denominator by the same number.

Write on the board $30 \div 0.6$, reminding pupils that we can write this as $\frac{30}{0.6}$.

Explain that this time both numerator and denominator are multiplied by the same power of 10 to make the denominator (i.e. the divisor) a whole number.

$$30 \div 0.6 = \frac{30}{0.6} = \frac{30 \times 10}{0.6 \times 10} = \frac{300}{6} = 50$$

Repeat with examples such as $200 \div 0.5$, $4.8 \div 0.08$, $0.6 \div 0.03$, $0.04 \div 0.2$.

Refer once more to **slide 3.2**. This time point to two of the numbers and ask for their quotient. Ask pupils to explain how they arrived at their answers.

Ask pupils to do **N4.3 Exercise 3C** in the class book (p. 115).

Review Sum up the lesson by reminding pupils about the points on **slides 3.3** and **3.4**.

Invite pupils to the board to illustrate each point with an example.

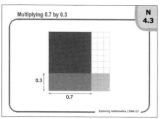

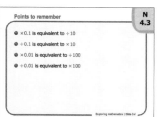

Homework Ask pupils to do **N4.3 Task 3** in the home book (p. 42).

4 Multiplying and dividing decimals 2

Learning points

For multiplication or division of a decimal by an integer:

○ estimate the answer;

○ do the equivalent whole-number calculation, then adjust the answer by dividing by the appropriate power of 10;

○ for multiplication, make sure that the number of decimal places in the answer is the same as in the product;

○ for division, add zeros to the number you are dividing if necessary;

○ use the estimate to check the size of the answer and that the decimal point is in the right place.

To solve word problems involving decimal measurements:

○ make sure that all quantities are in the same unit;

○ check that the answer makes sense in the context of the problem;

○ if appropriate, round answers to a suitable number of decimal places.

Starter

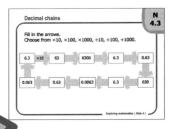

Say that this lesson is about written methods for multiplying and dividing decimals by whole numbers.

Project **slide 4.1** onto a whiteboard. Work with the class to fill in the arrows with operations to get from one number box to the next.

Give out **N4.3 Resource sheet 4.1**. Ask pupils to fill in the arrows and boxes on the sheet.

RS

Main activity

Demonstrate how to multiply and divide decimals with two places by a single-digit whole number using equivalent calculations.

For example, work out 6.42×7 by doing $642 \times 7 \div 100$. First estimate the answer as lying between $6 \times 7 = 42$ and $7 \times 7 = 49$. Compare the answer of 44.94 with the estimate, pointing out that the estimate helps to check that the decimal point in the answer is in the correct place.

Show two alternative methods, first a grid method then a short-multiplication method.

×	6	0.4	0.02
7	42	2.8	0.14

Answer: $42 + 2.8 + 0.14 = 44.94$

Stress that digits must be aligned when columns are used so that the decimal point is in the correct place in the answer. Stress that the initial estimate helps to check this.

Repeat with another example.

$$\begin{array}{r} 6.42 \\ \times 7 \\ \hline 44.94 \\ 21 \end{array}$$

Answer: 44.94

Select individual work from **N4.3 Exercise 4A** in the class book (p. 116).

Move on to division. For example, show how to do 47.2 ÷ 8 by working out the equivalent calculation 472 ÷ 8 divided by 10. First estimate the answer as lying between 40 ÷ 8 = 5 and 48 ÷ 8 = 6. Compare the answer of 5.9 with the estimate, pointing out again that the estimate helps to check that the decimal point in the answer is in the correct place.

Show the alternative short-division method. Again, stress that digits must be aligned to ensure that the decimal point is in the correct place in the answer, and the importance of the estimate in checking this.

$$5.\ 9$$
$$8\overline{)47.^72}$$
Answer: 5.9

Show an example where extra zeros need to be added in order to continue the division.

$$7.\ 6\ 6$$
$$5\overline{)38.^33^30}$$
Answer: 7.66

Extend to two-place decimals, this time showing how to continue the division to two decimal places, rounding the answer correct to one decimal place.

$$3.\ 5\ 7$$
$$9\overline{)32.^51^67}$$
Answer: 3.6
(correct to 1 d.p.)

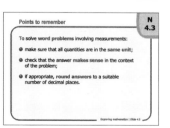

Select individual work from **N4.3 Exercise 4B** in the class book (p. 117).

Work through the word problems on **slides 4.2** and **4.3** with the class, to be done without calculators.

Stress the need to change quantities to the same units and to check that the answer makes sense in the context of the question.

Select individual work from **N4.3 Exercise 4C** in the class book (p. 118).

Review   Write on the board: 53.76 ÷ 8 = 6.82 and 5.37 × 4 = 21.48.

How can we check whether 5.37 × 4 = 21.48 is correct?

Remind pupils that they can use inverse operations and check whether 21.48 ÷ 4 returns them to the starting number of 5.37.

How can we check whether 53.76 ÷ 8 = 6.82 is correct?
[6.82 × 8 equals 54.56, not 53.76, so the answer 6.82 is wrong]

Finish by emphasising the points on **slides 4.4** and **4.5**.

Homework   Ask pupils to do **N4.3 Task 4** in the home book (p. 43).

5 Calculating percentages

Learning points

- Percentage means 'per 100', or 'in every 100'. 47% is equivalent to $\frac{47}{100}$ or 0.47.

- A quick way to find 20% of a quantity is to find 10% by dividing by 10, then multiply the result by 2 to find 20%. You can find 30%, 40%, 50%, … similarly.

- If there is no quick method for finding a percentage of a quantity, first find 1%, then multiply by the percentage.

- Always include any units in the answer.

Starter

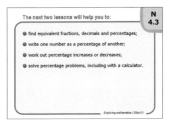

Use **slide 5.1** to discuss what pupils will learn in this and the next lesson. Say that this lesson is about calculating percentages.

Remind the class that 100% means '100 in every hundred', or one whole. 47% means '47 in every hundred', and is written as $\frac{47}{100}$, or as 0.47. Point out that the digits are the same in the percentage and decimal equivalents, and that fractions can be simplified where appropriate, e.g. 35% is equivalent to $\frac{35}{100}$, which simplifies to $\frac{7}{20}$.

What is 45% as a decimal? As a fraction? And 5%? And 175%?

Remind pupils how to change a decimal or a fraction to the equivalent percentage by multiplying it by 100. For example, 0.21 is equivalent to $0.21 \times 100\%$, or 21%, and $\frac{3}{20}$ is:

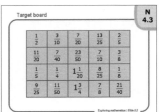

$$\frac{3}{\cancel{20}^1} \times \cancel{100}^5 = 15\%$$

Use the target board on **slide 5.2**. Point to different fractions. Ask pupils to write on their whiteboards the percentage equivalent to each fraction.

Main activity

What is 32 as a percentage of 40?

Establish the fraction $\frac{32}{40}$ and multiply by 100 to give the equivalent percentage of 80%. Do a couple more examples, e.g. 55 out of 200 and 3 out of 8.

Use the **Calculator tool** to discuss the calculator method to find, say, 13 as a percentage of 65:

$$\boxed{1}\,\boxed{3}\,\boxed{\div}\,\boxed{6}\,\boxed{5}\,\boxed{\times}\,\boxed{1}\,\boxed{0}\,\boxed{0}\,\boxed{=}$$

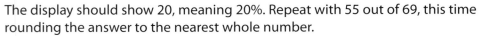

The display should show 20, meaning 20%. Repeat with 55 out of 69, this time rounding the answer to the nearest whole number.

Show **slide 5.3**. Get pupils to answer on their whiteboards as you point to one of the blue numbers and one of the pink numbers and ask:

What is (blue number) as a percentage of (pink number)?
How did you work it out?

Repeat several times. After a while, change the order of pink and blue, asking:

What is (pink number) as a percentage of (blue number)?

Remind the class of quick ways to calculate percentages.

- To find 50% of a number or quantity, halve it. To find 25%, find half of 50%. To find 75%, add 50% and 25%.

- To find 10%, divide the number or quantity by 10. To find 5%, find 10%, and then halve it. To find 15%, find 10%, then add 5%.

- To find 20%, find 10%, then multiply by 2 to get 20%. Find 30%, 40%, … similarly.

What do we do when there is no quick method?

Draw out that the method is to find 1% by dividing by 100, then to multiply the result by the relevant percentage. This can be done mentally, in a written calculation or by using a calculator, depending on the numbers involved.

Launch **Calculate percentages** and use it to work through different examples. **‹XL›**

Stress that units must be included in answers. Where calculators are used, discuss the interpretation of the display in the context of the problem.

Give each pair a copy of **N4.3 Resource sheet 5.1**. Ask them to cut out the cards and place them in the boxes to make four true statements. When they are sure that all statements are correct they can write the numbers in the boxes. **‹RS›**

Select individual work from the rest of **N4.3 Exercise 5** in the class book (p. 120).

Review Ask pupils to discuss the puzzle on **slide 5.4** in pairs.

Take feedback. Assume Andy had £100 in May. Then he had £90 in June. In July, his savings had increased by 11% of £90, i.e. by £9.90, giving him a total of £99.90. So Andy had the most savings in his account in July.

Finish by stressing the points on **slide 5.5**.

Homework Ask pupils to do **N4.3 Task 5** in the home book (p. 44).

6 Percentage increases and decreases

Learning points

- There are two ways of finding a selling price after a percentage discount:
  - calculate the discount, then subtract it from the original price;
  - subtract the percentage discount from 100%, then calculate this percentage of the original price.

- There are two ways to find a new amount after a percentage increase:
  - calculate the increase, then add it to the original amount;
  - add the percentage increase to 100%, then calculate this percentage of the original amount.

- If you are given the original and final amounts, and are asked to find the percentage increase or decrease, work out the increase or decrease as a percentage of the original amount.

Starter

You may wish to adapt this lesson so that it takes place in a room equipped with enough computers for one between each pair of pupils.

Say that this lesson is about estimating and calculating percentages, including finding percentage discounts and price increases.

Show the class how to estimate a percentage, e.g. estimate 53% of £270 as 50% of £270, or £135. Find the actual answer of £143.10 using a calculator. Repeat with 29% of 80 kg and 74% of 200 litres.

Give each pair a set of cards cut out from **N4.3 Resource sheet 6.1**. Ask pairs to use estimation to match each calculation to its answer. Pairs that finish quickly can check their answers with a calculator. In feedback, discuss and compare the strategies used to make the estimates.

Main activity

Ask pupils what they understand by *percentage increase* and *percentage decrease*. Ask where such things occur in everyday life (e.g. discounts in sales, increases from inflation, pay rises). Discuss the meanings of *cost price* and *sale price*.

> **A refrigerator is reduced by 12% in a sale. Its original price was £350. What is its sale price?**

Calculate 12% of £350 = £42. Deduct this from the original price:
£350 − £42 = £308. Then calculate 88% of £350 = £308.

Stress that deducting 12% is equivalent to finding 88%.

Repeat both methods to find the total restaurant bill of £65 after a service charge of 15% has been added.

Show pupils how to set up a spreadsheet table to calculate discounts (for an example, see the Excel file **Discount**). Explain how to enter suitable formulae for the discount and sale price, and how to copy these down the columns. Show that when the original price of a particular item is replaced, the discount and sale price are calculated automatically.

Show the class how the data in a spreadsheet table can be plotted on bar charts or bar-line graphs to compare original prices, or original prices and the sale prices. Point out that for a 10% discount the bar representing the sale price is 90% of the length of the bar representing the original price. Point out also that a discount of 10% off a more expensive item saves more money than a discount of 10% off a cheaper item.

If possible, get pupils to work in pairs at computers and to set up their own table for calculating a price discount or increase, e.g. for last-minute holiday bargains offered at a discount, or for increases in the rental charges of mobile telephones.

Alternatively, select from **N4.3 Exercise 6** in the class book (p. 122).

Review
Show pupils how to calculate a percentage change by working out the change as a percentage of the original amount. Work one or two examples on the board, e.g.

A TV is reduced from £350 to £280. What is the percentage discount?

The discount is £350 − £280 = £70.

£70 as a percentage of £350 is $\frac{70}{350} \times 100\% = 20\%$.

Some jeans are increased from £56 to £63. What is the percentage increase?

The increase is £63 − £56 = £7.

£7 as a percentage of £56 is $\frac{7}{56} \times 100\% = 12.5\%$.

Sum up the lesson by stressing the points on **slides 6.1** and **6.2**.

Round off the unit by referring again to the objectives. Suggest that pupils find time to try the self-assessment problems in **N4.3 How well are you doing?** in the class book (p. 124).

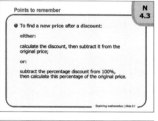

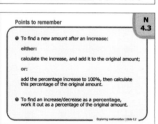

Homework
Ask pupils to do **N4.3 Task 6** in the home book (p. 45).

N4.3 Mental test

Read each question aloud twice.

Allow a suitable pause for pupils to write answers.

1 What is fifty per cent of ten?

2004 KS3

2 One book costs one pound ninety-five pence.
How much do six books cost?

2006 KS2

3 What number is nought point eight less than nine?

2007 KS3

4 Increase one pound fifty by fifty per cent.

2004 KS3

5 A book costs five pounds and ninety-nine pence.
What is the total cost of three of these books?

2007 KS3

6 What is twenty per cent of seven hundred?

2007 KS3

7 What is six point two multiplied by one thousand?

2005 KS3

8 How many nought point fives are there in ten?

2003 KS3

9 Divide nought point nine by one hundred.

2007 KS2

10 A tile is nought point two metres long. One hundred tiles are placed end to end in a row. How long is the row?

1998 KS2

11 Write the fraction three fifths as a percentage.

2007 KS3

12 What percentage of fifty pounds is thirty-five pounds?

2004 KS3

Key:
KS3 Key Stage 3 test   KS2 Key Stage 2 test
Question 1 is at level 4; questions 2 to 10 are at level 5;
questions 11 and 12 are at level 6.

Answers

1 5	2 £11.70
3 8.2	4 £2.25
5 £17.97	6 140
7 6200	8 20
9 0.009	10 20 metres
11 60%	12 70%

N4.3 Check up and resource sheets

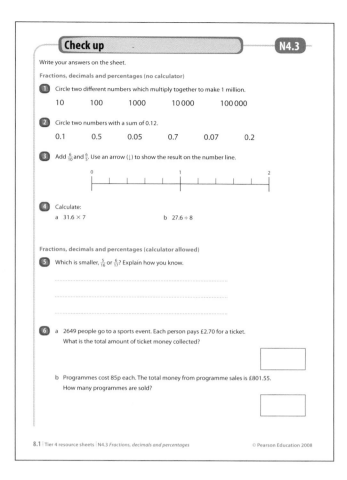

Check up · — N4.3

Write your answers on the sheet.

Fractions, decimals and percentages (no calculator)

1 Circle two different numbers which multiply together to make 1 million.

10   100   1000   10 000   100 000

2 Circle two numbers with a sum of 0.12.

0.1   0.5   0.05   0.7   0.07   0.2

3 Add $\frac{6}{10}$ and $\frac{6}{5}$. Use an arrow (↓) to show the result on the number line.

0   1   2

4 Calculate:

a 31.6×7 b $27.6 \div 8$

Fractions, decimals and percentages (calculator allowed)

5 Which is smaller, $\frac{5}{16}$ or $\frac{6}{17}$? Explain how you know.

....

....

....

6 a   2649 people go to a sports event. Each person pays £2.70 for a ticket.
What is the total amount of ticket money collected?

b   Programmes cost 85p each. The total money from programme sales is £801.55.
How many programmes are sold?

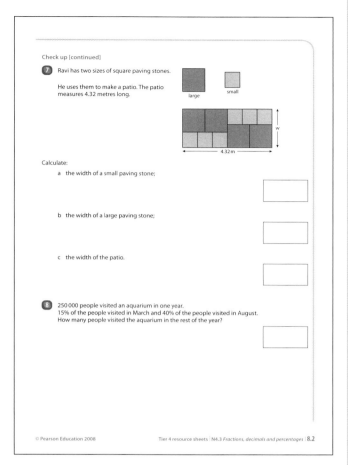

Check up [continued]

7 Ravi has two sizes of square paving stones.

He uses them to make a patio. The patio measures 4.32 metres long.

large   small

4.32 m

Calculate:

a   the width of a small paving stone;

b   the width of a large paving stone;

c   the width of the patio.

8 250 000 people visited an aquarium in one year.
15% of the people visited in March and 40% of the people visited in August.
How many people visited the aquarium in the rest of the year?

Resource sheet 1.1 · — N4.3

Write your answers on the sheet.

1 Copy and complete this table. Use your calculator.

Fraction	Decimal	Decimal correct to three decimal places
$\frac{12}{35}$		
$\frac{9}{23}$		
$\frac{3}{8}$		
$\frac{4}{11}$		
$\frac{5}{13}$		

2 Draw a string to connect each balloon to its correct place on the number line.

$\frac{12}{35}$ $\frac{9}{23}$ $\frac{3}{8}$ $\frac{4}{11}$ $\frac{5}{13}$

0.3   0.35   0.4

3 Write the fractions in the balloons. Write each fraction in its simplest form.

0.3   0.35   0.4

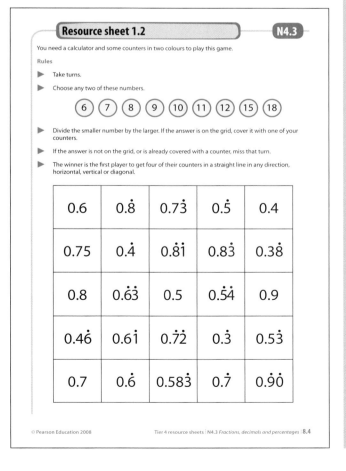

Resource sheet 1.2 · — N4.3

You need a calculator and some counters in two colours to play this game.

Rules

▶ Take turns.

▶ Choose any two of these numbers.

6   7   8   9   10   11   12   15   18

▶ Divide the smaller number by the larger. If the answer is on the grid, cover it with one of your counters.

▶ If the answer is not on the grid, or is already covered with a counter, miss that turn.

▶ The winner is the first player to get four of their counters in a straight line in any direction, horizontal, vertical or diagonal.

0.6	0.$\dot{8}$	0.7$\dot{3}$	0.$\dot{5}$	0.4
0.75	0.$\dot{4}$	0.8$\dot{1}$	0.8$\dot{3}$	0.38$\dot{}$
0.8	0.$\dot{6}\dot{3}$	0.5	0.5$\dot{4}$	0.9
0.46$\dot{}$	0.6$\dot{1}$	0.7$\dot{2}$	0.$\dot{3}$	0.53$\dot{}$
0.7	0.$\dot{6}$	0.58$\dot{3}$	0.$\dot{7}$	0.$\dot{9}\dot{0}$

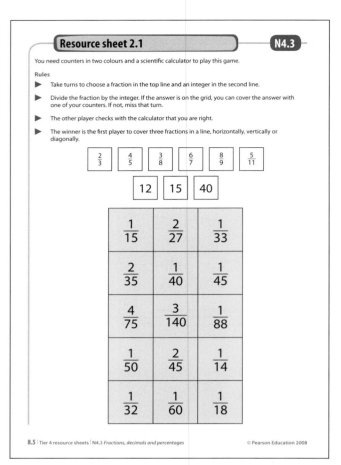

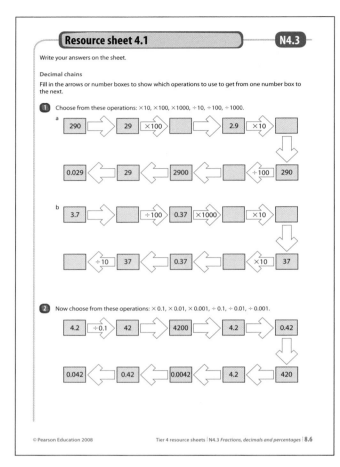

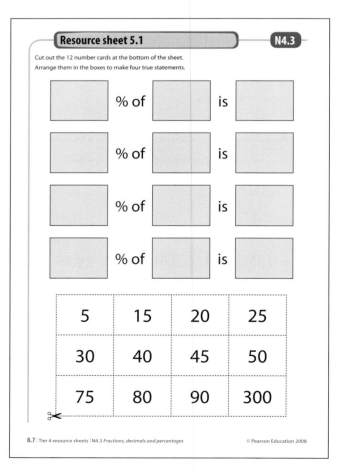

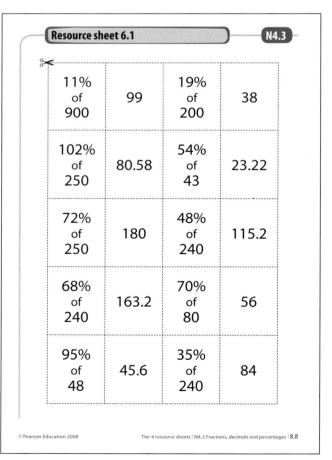

N4.3 Answers

Class book

Exercise 1A

1

Fraction	Decimal	Decimal correct to three decimal places
$\frac{12}{35}$	**0.342857...**	**0.343**
$\frac{9}{23}$	**0.391304...**	**0.391**
$\frac{3}{8}$	**0.375**	**0.375**
$\frac{4}{11}$	**0.363636...**	**0.364**
$\frac{5}{13}$	**0.384615...**	**0.385**

2

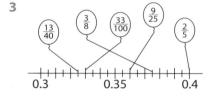

3

4 a $\frac{1}{5}$ b $\frac{2}{7}$ c $\frac{11}{20}$

    d $\frac{7}{11}$ e $\frac{11}{13}$ f $\frac{8}{17}$

5 a $\frac{4}{15}, \frac{3}{10}, \frac{1}{3},$ b $\frac{23}{40}, \frac{3}{5}, \frac{13}{20}, \frac{7}{10}$ c $\frac{11}{30}, \frac{5}{12}, \frac{7}{15}, \frac{3}{5}$

6 Sam eats more, $\frac{7}{8}$; John eats $\frac{6}{8}$

7 Rashida is wrong. $\frac{5}{6} = \frac{10}{12}$

Exercise 1B

1 This is a game

2

$\frac{1}{7}$	0.1428571
$\frac{2}{7}$	0.2857142
$\frac{3}{7}$	0.4285714
$\frac{4}{7}$	0.5714285
$\frac{5}{7}$	0.7142857
$\frac{6}{7}$	0.8571428

   a The digits after the decimal point cycle through 142857.

   b 1.1428571, 1.2857142, 2.2857142

   c With 12 digits, $\frac{1}{7}$ is 0.1428571428571

3 $\frac{11}{14}$

Exercise 2A

There are two games.

Exercise 2B

1 a $\frac{2}{15}$ b $\frac{18}{77}$ c $\frac{16}{21}$ d $\frac{7}{32}$

   e $\frac{4}{9}$ f $\frac{3}{11}$ g $\frac{9}{26}$ h $\frac{5}{9}$

2 a $149\frac{1}{2}$ b $29\frac{3}{4}$ c $12\frac{1}{2}$ d $345\frac{3}{5}$

   e $\frac{1}{240}$ f $\frac{3}{242}$ g $\frac{1}{144}$ h $\frac{1}{192}$

Exercise 3A

1 a 1400   b 0.37   c 0.5

   d 90   e 3000   f 0.007

   g 0.24   h 2400   i 0.28

   j 56   k 0.016   l 0.6

   m 0.72   n 0.65   o 680

Exercise 3B

1 a 0.12   b 0.3   c 0.008

   d 0.006   e 0.4   f 0.01

   g 0.009   h 0.036   i 0.02

2 a 1800   b 8   c 400

   d 15   e 630   f 1.6

Exercise 3C

1 a 200   b 5   c 40

   d 10   e 70   f 0.6

2 a 50   b 50   c 500

   d 7   e 400   f 500

   g 800   h 0.7   i 0.05

Exercise 4A

1 a 316.2   b 68.81   c 71.16

   d 432.9   e 2.3   f 29.2

Exercise 4B

1 a 29.2   b 1.54   c 0.59   d 7.29

2 a 7.0   b 2.6   c 2.6   d 1.0

Exercise 4C

1 9.726 litres

2 13.04 m²

3 3.485 m

4 £8.95

5 £10.05

6 0.15 kg or 150 g

7 £17.85

Exercise 5

1 There is only one correct way of grouping the numbers into four trios but for each trio a different arrangement is possible:
5% of 300 = 15 or 300% of 5 = 15
40% of 75 = 30 or 75% of 40 = 30
50% of 90 = 45 or 90% of 50 = 45
25% of 80 = 20 or 80% of 25 = 20

2 a 37%   b 70%   c 2%
     d 62.5%   e 104%   f 810%

3 a 0.85   b 0.62   c 0.09
     d 1.5   e 0.13   f 0.175

4 a $\frac{9}{10}$ b $\frac{21}{25}$ c $\frac{1}{20}$
     d $1\frac{3}{4}$ e $\frac{41}{100}$ f $\frac{14}{25}$

5 a 6%   b 36%   c 80%
     d 45%   e 225%   f 37.5%

6 a £100   b 400 kg   c 22 cm
     d 16.8 g   e 60 litres f £135
     g 375 ml   h 280 m

7 a 28%   b 90%
     c 62.5%   d 77.8% (1 d.p.)
     e 52%   f 72.2% (1 d.p.)

8 a 598   b £624   c 37.76 kg
     d 213.75 m e 126°   f 0.88 litres
     g £9.69   h 1 hour 21 minutes

Exercise 6

1 74% of £90 = £66.60
9% of £36 = £3.24
47% of 165 = £77.55
21% of £200 = £42.00
103% of £49 = £50.47

2 a Trainers £32.20   b Cricket bat £85.56
     c Sports bag £20.70 d Tennis socks £6.21
     e Golf clubs £391   f Tennis racket £78.20
     g Ice skates £66.70   h Football £43.47

3 a Sports car £26 059
     b Hatchback £12 875
     c Convertible £51 500
     d Saloon £19 312.50
     e Mini £8240
     f People carrier £38 007
     g Estate £10 506
     h Four-wheel drive £48 667.50

Extension problems

4 There is no difference. For example, if the holiday costs £800, then 115% of 80% of £800 is the same as 80% of 115% of £800.

5 The newspaper is wrong. For example, if Rohini was earning £100 000 and had a 15% pay rise she would earn £115 000. If she then had a 10% pay rise, she would earn £126 500. The overall increase is £26 500, which is 26.5%.

How well are you doing?

1 a 7   b 50   c 5 out of 100

2 a $\frac{1}{10}, \frac{1}{100}$ b 11%   c $\frac{2}{9}$

3 7.4 × 9.4

4 a $\frac{7}{16}$ b £60

5 $\frac{3}{5}$ $\frac{3}{4}$ $\frac{17}{20}$ $\frac{9}{10}$

6 6300

7 7.5%

Home book

TASK 1

1 a $\frac{13}{20}$ b $2\frac{4}{5}$
     c $\frac{1}{8}$ d $\frac{4}{25}$

2 For example, $\frac{3}{4}$

3 For example, 0.6

4 For example, $\frac{11}{40}$

5 a $\frac{7}{24}$ b $\frac{5}{12}$

6 a 0.18$\dot{5}$ b 0.5$\dot{4}$ c 2.$\dot{3}$ d 0.6$\dot{1}$

TASK 2

1 a $2\frac{5}{8}$ b $\frac{4}{25}$ c $\frac{14}{25}$ d $\frac{2}{3}$

2 $\frac{1}{2}$ m²

3 $\frac{7}{40}$

4 $6\frac{3}{4}$

5 $\frac{4}{21}$

6 $2\frac{4}{5}$

7 $\frac{3}{5}$

8 $\frac{1}{9}$

9 $\frac{1}{3}$

TASK 3

1

×	0.5	0.8
0.6	**0.3**	**0.48**
0.2	**0.1**	**0.16**

2

×	0.06	0.2
0.05	**0.003**	**0.01**
0.9	**0.054**	**0.18**

3

×	**0.03**	**0.7**
0.4	0.012	0.28
0.8	0.024	**0.56**

TASK 4

1 a 10.8 cm   b 9.8 cm
   c 2.59 cm   d 13.17 cm

2 a 1.665 cm   b 1.7 mm
   c 1.65 mm   d 1.695 cm

3 a 52 g   b 85.52 g

TASK 5

1 31.25%

2 60%

3 a $\frac{16}{25}$ b 16 girls

4 a $\frac{7}{20}$ b 715 pupils

5 a 20.2 litres   b 166.1 km
   c £11.20   d 100 g or 0.1 kg

6 The maximum that Robert can win is £1055.
The minimum that Robert can win is £1045.

TASK 6

1 The tennis racket is cheapest in shop C.
Shop A: £91.00
Shop B: £91.30
Shop C: £90.52

2 Store B will sell the cheapest video phone.
Store A: £381.50
Store B: £381.15
Store C: £383.25

3 a 37.5% decrease   b 5% increase
   c 38.9 % decrease   d 5% increase
   e 7.5% decrease

CD-ROM

Check up

1 10 and 100 000, or 100 and 10 000

2 0.05 and 0.07

3

4 a 221.2   b 3.45

5 $\frac{5}{16} = 0.3125$ and $\frac{6}{17} = 0.353$ (to 3 d.p.)
So $\frac{5}{16}$ is smaller.

6 a £7152.30   b 943 programmes

7 a 72 cm or 0.72 m   b 1.08 m
   c 1.8 m

8 112 500 people

Enquiry 1

Before they start, pupils should be able to:

- design a data collection sheet or questionnaire to use in a simple survey
- construct frequency tables for discrete data, grouped where appropriate in equal class intervals
- interpret pie charts
- understand and use the mean of discrete data
- use the range and one of the mode, median or mean to describe a set of data.

Objectives based on NC levels 5 and 6 (mainly level 5)

In this unit, pupils learn to:

- identify mathematical features of a context or problem
- conjecture and generalise
- select appropriate procedures and tools, including ICT
- make accurate diagrams and graphs on paper and on screen
- refine findings and approaches on the basis of discussion with others
- record methods, solutions and conclusions, relating them to the context
- evaluate alternative strategies and approaches

and to:

- discuss a problem that can be addressed by statistical methods and identify related questions to explore
- decide which data to collect to answer a question, the sample size and degree of accuracy needed, and identify possible sources
- plan, construct and use two-way tables for recording
- construct and interpret:
  - bar charts and frequency diagrams for grouped discrete data
  - pie charts for categorical data
  - simple scatter diagrams
- calculate statistics for sets of discrete data, recognising when it is appropriate to use the range, mean, median and mode and, for grouped data, the modal class
- construct and interpret stem-and-leaf diagrams, and compare two simple distributions, using the range and one of the mode, median or mean
- relate summary statistics and findings to the questions being explored.

Lessons

1 **Specifying the problem and planning**

2 **Processing data**

3 **Representing data**

4 **Interpreting data**

5 **Comparing groups**

6 **Presenting results**

About this unit

This unit includes work on: developing statistical problems; constructing and interpreting tables, graphs and charts; and discussing and interpreting data.

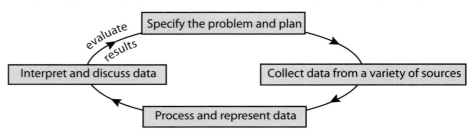

The data-handling cycle permeates the work in this unit; its sections are based on the stages of the cycle. Issues involved in collecting data are addressed throughout as factors that influence planning, processing and interpreting the data. Most of the teaching is focused on the interpretation of data.

Assessment

This unit includes:

- a self-assessment section (*S4.2 How well are you doing?* class book p. 144);
- a set of questions to replace or supplement questions in the exercises or homework tasks, or to use as an informal test (*S4.2 Check up*, CD-ROM).

Common errors and misconceptions

Look out for pupils who:

- choose an inappropriate type of chart or graph to represent the data;
- have difficulty in choosing and reading a scale for a frequency axis;
- label the axes of a chart incorrectly;
- plot dependent and independent variables on the wrong axes;
- when comparing two pie charts, fail to appreciate that the total represented in each pie chart may be different;
- confuse the mean, median and mode;
- write the range as an interval instead of a value.

Key terms and notation

data, information, questionnaire, survey, discrete

frequency table, tally chart, axis, axes, bar chart, horizontal axis, vertical axis, interval, pie chart, scale, sector, scatter graph, two-way table, stem-and-leaf diagram

interpret, represent

Practical resources

large sheets of paper and marker pens

coloured pens or pencils

compasses, protractor, pencil and ruler

calculators

Exploring maths

Tier 4 teacher's book
Answers for Unit S4.2 , pp. 160–165

Tier 4 CD-ROM
PowerPoint files
    S4.2 Slides for lessons 1 to 5
Excel files
    Reading data
Tools and prepared toolsheets
    S4.2 Toolsheets for lesson 2
    Calculator tool
    Protractor tool
Tier 4 programs
    Stem-and-leaf

Tier 4 class book
S4.2, pp. 126 – 145
S4.2 How well are you doing? p. 144

Tier 4 home book
S4.2, pp. 47 – 55

Tier 4 CD-ROM
S4.2 Check up
S4.2 Pupil resource sheets
    2.1 One per pupil
    5.1 One per group
    6.1 One per pupil (optional)

Useful websites

WorldClimate www.worldclimate.com

Stats4Schools www.stats4schools.gov.uk

The International CensusAtSchool Project www.censusatschool.ntu.ac.uk

National Literacy Trust www.literacytrust.org.uk

Florence Nightingale's Statistical Diagrams www.florence-nightingale.co.uk

1 Specifying the problem and planning

Learning points

When you plan how to solve a problem, consider:

- ◉ who might be interested in the answer;
- ◉ why they might be interested in it;
- ◉ what data you will need to collect:
- ◉ how you will do this.

Starter

This lesson will help you to:
S 4.2
- ◉ discuss a problem and find questions to explore;
- ◉ decide what information is needed to answer a question and how accurate it needs to be;
- ◉ think about where to find information;
- ◉ plan and use the best method to collect information.

Mystery chart
S 4.2

Use **slide 1.1** to discuss what pupils will learn in this lesson. Say that the lesson is about starting a statistical enquiry.

Show **slide 1.2**. Ask pairs to discuss the chart for a minute.

> **What could the graph be about?**

Ask a few pairs to share their ideas. Then tell the class that the graph shows the rainfall for a particular place. Label the axes.

> **What do you think the horizontal axis shows?**
> **How many bars are there?**
> [the 12 bars are likely to be the months of the year]

> **What do you think the vertical axis shows?** [rainfall]

> **What units is rainfall likely to be measured in?** [in mm]

> **What might a suitable title be?**

Explain that the vertical axis goes up in 10 mm steps. Depending on the class's ability, question them about features of the graph, or ask them to estimate the rainfall for different months, or move on to more detailed interpretation.

> **What do you notice about the pattern of rainfall over a year?**

> **Can anyone guess which city the data is for or where it might be?**
> [Edinburgh]

Pupils should notice that the city is somewhere in the northern hemisphere where it rains fairly consistently all year round, with more in the summer and autumn. The data source is www.worldclimate.com.

Main activity

What do we need to find out?
S 4.2

Do people read fewer books than they used to?

a Who might be interested in the answer to this question? Why?

b What data do you need to collect to find out if the statement is true?

How would you do this?

Introduce a problem on reading habits. Tell pupils that the problem is:

> **Do people read fewer books than they used to?**

> **What do we need to find out?**

Split the class into groups of four. Show **slide 1.3**. Tell some groups to consider question A and the rest to consider question B.

A Who might be interested in the answer to this question? Why?

B What data do you need to collect in order to find out if the statement is true? How would you do this?

Ask groups to record answers on large sheets of paper. Allow them 5 to 10 minutes to carry out the task and to record their work.

Use the groups' posters to share ideas. For example, those working on A might think that libraries, bookshops, publishers and schools would be interested in people's reading habits. Those working on B might consider using a questionnaire, and some ways of ensuring that they ask appropriate groups of people.

Ask groups to work on **S4.2 Exercise 1A** of the class book (p. 127).

Then ask pupils to work in pairs on **S4.2 Exercise 1B** in the class book (p. 128).

Review Show the Excel file **Reading data**. Tell pupils that it came from the Stats4Schools website (www.stats4schools.gov.uk). It shows some of the data for the first 20 entries from over 1000. Scroll across the data so that pupils can see what is on the sheet.

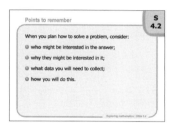

> Why do you think more than 1000 people were asked?
>
> Where do all the people in this sample live? [the north]
>
> Why do some people have several answers for one question?
>
> Why do you think the survey asked for people's marital status?
>
> What questions could you answer with this data?

Ask pupils to remember the points on **slide 1.4**.

Homework Ask pupils to do **S4.2 Task 1** in the home book (p. 47).

2 Processing data

Learning points

- In a pie chart the angle at the centre of the circle is proportional to the frequency for each category.

- The number of degrees per person or item can be calculated by:
  360° ÷ total number of items or people

Starter

Use **slide 2.1** to discuss objectives for this and the next lesson. Say that this lesson is about using pie charts.

Show **slide 2.2**. Ask pupils which speech bubble shows the correct average for the set of numbers shown.

> How could you work out the average as 6? As 5? As 4.6?

Ensure that pupils understand that there are three different types of average. The number that occurs most often (6 in this case) is the *mode*. The *median*, 5, is the middle number if we list them in order. The *mean*, 4.6, is the sum of all the numbers divided by the number of numbers in the set.

> Which of the methods do you think gives the best average for this set of numbers?

Main activity

Each pupil will need a copy of **S4.2 Resource sheet 2.1** and some coloured pens or pencils.

Ask four pupils to choose their favourite colour from red, green, yellow and blue. With pupils, record the frequencies in the first table on the resource sheet. Explain that the accompanying pie chart has four equal sectors, one for each person. Ask pupils to colour the pie chart to represent the results in the table. For example, if two people chose the colour blue, then two sectors of the pie chart should be coloured blue.

Repeat, using 8, 12 and 10 pupils. The frequency tables are left blank so that you can ask pupils a different question if you prefer. Record results in the frequency tables and ask pupils to produce the pie charts.

Choose one of the pie charts.

> What fraction of pupils chose the colour blue?

> Which is the group's favourite colour? How do we know?

> What percentage of pupils chose red?

As an extension, ask pupils to draw the corresponding bar chart for each pie chart.

Show **Toolsheet 2.1**, which reproduces the pie charts on Resource sheet 2.1. Use the **Protractor tool** when discussing the size of the angles for the pie chart sectors.

If there are four people in our survey, we need four equal sectors in our pie chart. How many degrees should we make each sector? [90°]

If we have 10 people, how many degrees will represent one person? [36°]

If there were 12 people in our survey, how big would each sector need to be? [30°]

How can we work out the degrees we need for each person?

Establish that the sectors need to be the same size and so have the same number of degrees. Demonstrate how to find this using the **Calculator tool**.

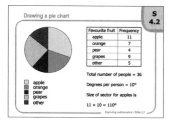

Use **slide 2.3**. Demonstrate how to draw a pie chart. Start with the frequency table. Ask the questions below and click to reveal each part of the calculation after the answer.

How many people are there in the survey? [36]

How many degrees represent one person? [10°]

How large should the sector for apples be? [11 × 10 = 110°]

A final click will reveal the pie chart and key.

Ask pupils to do **S4.2 Exercise 2** in the class book (p. 130). They will need a calculator, protractor, compasses, ruler and pencil.

Review   Who likes reading more, boys or girls?
How could you find out the answer to this question?

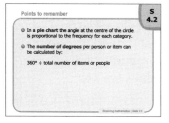

Show **slide 2.4**. Explain that this is real data from a survey by the National Literacy Trust.

Use the pie charts to explain who likes reading more, boys or girls.

How many boys didn't like reading at all? [we can't tell]

Do more girls than boys like reading very much? [we can't tell]

Pupils should notice that the proportion of boys who don't like reading is much higher than for girls, and that more than half the girls but less than half the boys like reading very much or quite a lot.

Emphasise that we can't discuss actual numbers, only proportions or percentages, so it is not possible to say that more girls than boys like reading. You could use a number example to make this clear to pupils.

Ask pupils to remember the points on **slide 2.5**.

Homework   Ask pupils to do **S4.2 Task 2** in the home book (p. 48).

3 Representing data

Learning points

- A stem-and-leaf diagram is used to group data so that the original data is kept.

- A two-way table can be read both across the page and down. It allows two types of information to be presented and compared in the same form.

Starter

Say that this lesson is about representing grouped data in bar charts, stem-and-leaf diagrams and two-way tables.

Show the grouped frequency diagram on **slide 3.1**. Explain that this shows the number of books borrowed per week from a school library.

> **In how many weeks were 100 to 119 books borrowed?** [5]

> **In how many weeks were 220 to 239 books borrowed?** [0]

> **In which group would you put a week when 103 books were borrowed?** [100−119]

> **Why do you think that the data is grouped?**
> **What do you notice about the groups?**
> **What do you notice about the bars?**

> **What is the modal class for the frequency diagram?** [there are three: 120−139, 140−159, 160−179]

> **Explain what the graph shows about the borrowing of library books.**

> **What was the highest number of library books borrowed in one week?** [you can't tell but it was between 240 and 259]

Ensure pupils understand the key points in drawing the grouped frequency diagram for discrete data, including equal class intervals, gaps between bars and the labelling of the axes. They should also notice that class intervals do not overlap.

Main activity

Launch **Stem-and-leaf** to show how to draw a stem-and-leaf diagram. The first screen shows the number of goals scored by squad members in a season. Discuss how you could represent the data. Pupils should notice that it needs grouping because there are few repeats of values. Explain that a stem-and-leaf diagram is like a grouped frequency diagram but all the individual values are kept.

Explain that the key shows that the 'stem' is the tens digit and the 'leaf' is the units digit.

> **What is the 'stem' for 15?** [1] **What is the 'leaf' part for 15?** [5]

> **What is the 'stem' for 1?** [0] **What is the 'leaf' part for 1?** [1]

Ask pupils to drag values from the list to their correct places in the diagram. They should notice that only the units digit appears on the right-hand side of the vertical line and that the stem appears once on the left. When all the numbers are in place, press 'Order numbers' to finish the diagram.

Which is the modal class? [0−9]

What was the highest number of goals scored? [32]
What was the lowest? [0]

The program contains other data sets if you need further examples.

Ask pupils to do **S4.2 Exercise 3A** in the class book (p. 132). Some of the height data in this exercise is taken from www.censusatschool.ntu.ac.uk.

Show **slide 3.2**, a blank two-way table. Explain that it can be read both across and downwards. Add the data for the class to the table.

How many girls in the class visit the library?
Where does this number go?

How many girls in the class don't visit the library?
Where does this number go?

What do the different totals show on the table?

How many pupils are there in the class altogether?

Ask pupils to do **S4.2 Exercise 3B** in the class book (p. 133).

Review

Use **slide 3.3**, which shows a back-to-back stem-and-leaf diagram for the heights of 20 boys and 20 girls. The data source is www.censusatschool.ntu.ac.uk.

Is the smallest pupil a boy or a girl? [a boy]

How many boys are 165 cm tall? [two]
How many girls are 165 cm tall? [none]

Are the boys or girls taller? Explain your answer.

Ask pupils to remember the points on **slide 3.4**.

Homework

Ask pupils to do **S4.2 Task 3** in the home book (p. 50).

4 Interpreting data

Learning points

- A scatter graph allows you to look for a connection between the two quantities. One quantity is put on the horizontal axis and the other on the vertical axis.

- Each point on the scatter graph represents a pair of values.

Starter

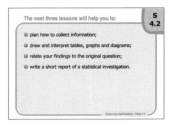

Use **slide 4.1** to discuss the objectives for the next three lessons. Say that this lesson focuses on scatter graphs.

Show the scales on **slide 4.2**. Check that pupils can read the scales correctly and mark places on them. Ask, for example:

> What do the small divisions on the first scale stand for? [4 units]
>
> On the first scale, where would 88 be?
>
> Where would 102 be?

Main activity

Ask pupils to work in pairs on question 1 of **S4.2 Exercise 4A** in the class book (p. 135). Allocate to each pair data set 1 or data set 2.

Ask pairs to share their ideas with the whole class. They should mention graphs they could draw and statistics they could calculate.

Now ask each pair to find another pair who have used the other data set, so that each group of four has a copy of both data sets.

Ask these groups to work on question 2 of **S4.2 Exercise 4A**.

After about two minutes, ask for feedback. The groups may suggest drawing a comparative bar chart with the rainfall and temperature bars for each month side by side. Alternatively they may suggest drawing a bar chart for rainfall and a line graph for temperature, which is a common approach used in geography.

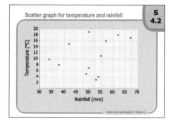

Show **slide 4.3**. Explain that this is a scatter graph. It allows us to look for a connection between the two quantities. This means that we could see if the rainfall decreases as the temperature increases in Paris.

What does each dot on the scatter graph represent? [a month]

Can you find the dot for January?

What do you notice about the scales?

Point out that the rainfall scale does not start at zero, but starts at a convenient number below the lowest value. Explain the zigzag notation for axes not starting at zero. Make sure that pupils understand how to read the scales on the graph and how to place the point for each month where the two values meet.

Ask pupils to do **S4.2 Exercise 4B** in the class book (p.136). They will need rulers, pencils and graph paper.

Then ask them to work in groups of four on **S4.2 Exercise 4C** (p. 138).

Review   Ask groups to present some of their answers and explanations for Exercise 4C. Pick one question from the exercise and ask:

Can you think of a question that this graph (or pair of pie charts) would help us to answer?

Why is this graph useful?

What other graphs, charts or statistics would be helpful in answering this question?

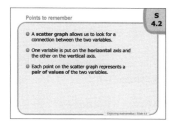

For example, pupils might suggest that the graph for question 1 could be used to help answer a question comparing the climates of India and The Netherlands. The graph gives us a good way of comparing the temperatures in two cities. Pupils might suggest comparing the mean and range of the temperatures and extending the study to look at other aspects of climate such as rainfall.

Sum up with the points on **slide 4.4**.

Homework   Ask pupils to do **S4.2 Task 4** in the home book (p. 52). They will need graph paper.

5 Comparing groups

Learning points

◉ Simple statistics and a range of charts, graphs and tables are useful for making comparisons between sets of data.

Starter

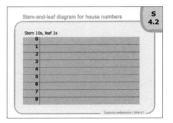

Say that this lesson is about comparing groups using a range of charts, graphs and tables.

Ask pupils to write their house numbers on their whiteboards.

Show **slide 5.1**. Pick pupils with suitable numbers to add their house numbers to the stem-and-leaf diagram. Pupils may need to move numbers as they add theirs to keep the numbers strictly in order.

Alternatively, ask all those pupils with numbers in a particular range, e.g. between 10 and 19, to come to the front with their whiteboards and arrange themselves in order before you transfer the set of numbers onto the board.

Main activity

Put pupils into groups of four. Give each group copies of the photographs from **S4.2 Resource sheet 5.1**.

> **What do you notice about the people in the photos?**
>
> **What could you count or measure in relation to the people?**
>
> **Are the groups of people different or the same on these measures?**

Encourage pupils to consider attributes such as weight, height and age.

Ask groups to use the photographs to do **S4.2 Exercise 5A** in the class book (p. 139).

Encourage groups to discuss answers and to justify their points of view to the rest of the group. Pupils might need help in estimating some mean weights: suggest approximate mean weights for adult males (72 kg) and females (62 kg).

Now ask pupils to do **S4.2 Exercise 5B** (p. 141).

Review
Choose some of the photos from **Resource sheet 5.1**. Ask groups to explain answers and reasoning for some of the questions.

Other groups could challenge answers if they disagree.

Extend the activity by sketching on the board possible distributions for the heights of the runners and swimmers; omit numbers from the scales. Ask pupils to identify the two groups and to explain their reasoning. Repeat for the weights of the tug-of-war teams and the runners.

Sum up the lesson using **slide 5.2**.

Homework
Ask pupils to do **S4.2 Task 5** in the home book (p. 54). Note that the data collected in this homework is needed for the next lesson in this unit.

6 Presenting results

Learning points

◉ Choose the best chart type to answer the question that you have been asked.

◉ A scatter graph is used to look for connections between quantities.

Starter Say that this lesson is about presenting the results of a statistical investigation.

Launch **Toolsheet 6.1**. Go through each category in turn and ask pupils to indicate how many books they read last month. Fill in the frequencies in order in the table.

> **What would this information look like as raw data?**
>
> **How does the table help us to understand the data?**

Open the minimised frequency diagram.

> **What does this show us about the data? Why is it useful?**
>
> **What is the difference between a frequency diagram and a stem-and-leaf diagram?**
>
> **When would you prefer to use a grouped frequency diagram?**

Change the display option to 'Pie chart' using the icon.

> **What does the pie chart show us?**
>
> **What does the pie chart not show us?**
>
> **How would you choose which type of diagram to use?**

Make sure that pupils are clear about the differences between the different types of chart. Stress that they should choose the chart type that helps them best answer the question they are working on at the time.

Main activity Use the homework from lesson 5 as a stimulus for discussion about questions we could answer using such data, issues related to data collection, sources of data and accuracy of the data collected.

> **What kinds of questions do you have about people's reading habits?**

Pupils might suggest questions relating to whether older people read more, which gender reads more, who likes what kinds of books or the different types of reading material people enjoy.

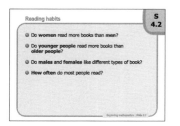

Some questions are on **slide 6.1**. Pick one and ask:

> **How could we collect information to answer the question?**
>
> **Are there other places we could look for this kind of data?**
>
> **How accurate do you think your results might be?**
>
> **What factors might affect the accuracy of your results?**

Pupils should suggest that some people may not tell the truth, or that there may be recording or transcription errors. They should also note that it is important to ask a suitable range of people for your question.

Pupils will need the data they collected for the homework in Task 5. An alternative data set is provided on **S4.2 Resource sheet 6.1**.

RS

Pupils should initially work in groups of six to collate data before breaking into pairs. Ask them to share the data they collected for homework from Task 5 and to provide a set of the data about themselves. This should allow each group access to at least 30 sets of data. Ask each group to choose one of the questions on **slide 6.1** to answer, or to make up their own question.

Ask pupils to work in pairs on **S4.2 Exercise 6** in the class book (p. 142).

Review

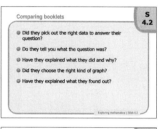

Each group of six pupils should have produced three booklets answering the same question. Ask them to use the questions on **slide 6.2** to compare the booklets and pick out the best.

Ask some of the groups to explain to the class what they did and what they found out. Focus feedback on the choice of graphical representation and how accurate and reliable they think their answers are. You could also discuss how they could find out the answer to their questions more accurately.

Ask pupils to remember the points on **slide 6.3**.

Round off the unit by referring again to the objectives. Suggest that pupils find time to try the self-assessment problems in **S4.2 How well are you doing?** in the class book (p. 144).

Homework

Ask pupils to do **S4.2 Task 6** in the home book (p. 54).

Check up
S4.2

Write your answers on the sheet.

1. A PE department asked all the pupils in school to opt for their favourite sport to do in PE lessons in the summer term. The results are recorded in the table below.

Year	Swimming	Tennis	Football	Badminton	Trampolining	Totals
7	23		22	36	20	116
8		17	11	20	21	114
9	34	21	45	6	12	
10	17	34	16	40	12	119
11	11	46		37	9	
Totals	130		103		74	579

a Fill in the missing values in the table.

b What is the favourite sport in Year 7? ....

c Which sport is most popular overall? ....

d In which year group is tennis most popular? ....

e In which year group is trampolining least popular? ....

2. Simon has started drawing a scatter graph for the height and foot length for 20 pupils. He has plotted the points for the first 10 people.

a Add the next 10 people in the table below to his scatter graph.

Height (cm)	148	150	160	147	152	145	154	140	140	152
Foot length (cm)	23.5	24	28	16.5	25	25	22	25	23	16

b Looking at the graph, do you think that tall people have big feet? Explain why.

....
....
....

Resource sheet 2.1
S4.2

Write your answers on the sheet.

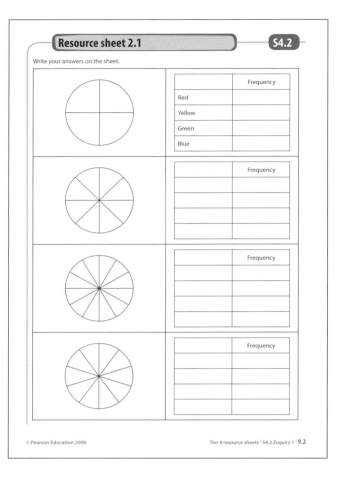

		Frequency
Red		
Yellow		
Green		
Blue		

	Frequency

	Frequency

	Frequency

Resource sheet 5.1
S4.2

Resource sheet 5.1 [continued]

Resource sheet 6.1   S4.2

Key

1 How many books did you read last month?

2 How much do you like reading: very much, quite a lot, a bit or not at all?

3 How often do you read for pleasure: every day or almost every day, once or twice a week, once or twice a month, never or almost never?

4 What types of books do you like?

5 What other sources of reading material do you read? For example, magazines, newspapers, catalogues etc.

6 Gender and age

Q	Person 1	Person 2	Person 3	Person 4	Person 5
1	2	None	12	15	4
2	A bit	Not at all	A lot	A lot	Quite a lot
3	Once or twice a week	Never …	Every day …	Every day …	Once or twice a week
4	Non-fiction	None	Thrillers	Romance	Fiction
5	Magazines, texts, email	Newspaper, catalogues, texts	Magazines, newspapers, texts	Magazines, texts	Comics
6	M, 17	M, 42	M, 36	F, 34	F, 22
	Person 6	**Person 7**	**Person 8**	**Person 9**	**Person 10**
1	None	7	9	1	6
2	Never …	A lot	A lot	A bit	Quite a lot
3	Never …	Every day …	Every day …	Once or twice a week	Every day …
4	Crime	Fiction	Thrillers	Classics	Thrillers
5	Catalogues	Magazines	Magazines, newspapers, texts, email	Newspaper	Comics, texts, email
6	M, 48	F, 62	F, 27	M, 58	M, 15
	Person 11	**Person 12**	**Person 13**	**Person 14**	**Person 15**
1	3	3	8	1	2
2	A bit	Not at all	Very much	Not at all	Quite a lot
3	Once or twice a week	Once or twice a week	Every day …	Once or twice a month	Once or twice a week
4	Non-fiction	Fiction	Fiction	Non-fiction	Fiction
5	Email	Comics	Texts, email, magazines	Comics	Texts
6	M, 13	M, 7	F, 14	F, 10	F, 13

Q	Person 16	Person 17	Person 18	Person 19	Person 20
1	None	None	1	2	9
2	Not at all	Not at all	A bit	A bit	Very much
3	Never …	Never …	Once or twice a week	Once or twice a week	Every day …
4	None	Romance	Non-fiction	Thrillers	Romance
5	Texts	Texts, email, magazine	Texts	Newspaper	Newspaper
6	M, 23	F, 17	M, 18	M, 41	F, 37
	Person 21	**Person 22**	**Person 23**	**Person 24**	**Person 25**
1	4	None	1	5	3
2	Very much	Quite a lot	Quite a lot	Very much	Quite a lot
3	Every day …	Once or twice a month	Once or twice a week	Every day …	Every day …
4	Historical	Crime	Classics	Thrillers	Fiction
5	Newspaper	Magazines	Newspaper	Newspapers and magazines	Magazines
6	M, 72	F, 56	M, 71	M, 58	F, 45
	Person 26	**Person 27**	**Person 28**	**Person 29**	**Person 30**
1	None	1	1	2	2
2	Not at all	Not at all	Quite a lot	Quite a lot	Quite a lot
3	Never …	Once or twice a month	Once or twice a week	Every day …	Every day …
4	True stories	Non-fiction	Romance	Fiction	Fiction
5	Texts, emails and magazines	Texts, emails and magazines	Texts, emails and magazines	Texts	Texts
6	F, 21	M, 14	F, 16	F, 12	M, 11

Class book

Exercise 1A

These answers are all examples.

1 a People with small children or the elderly who don't like the heat, travel agents, employers.

  b Collect some data on what are popular holiday destinations, how hot it is there and ask people if they think that is too hot. Use a questionnaire and the Internet to find out the temperatures.

2 a People who don't have school-age children, travel agents and employers.

  b Collect some data on the weather in different holiday resorts using the Internet or a travel book.

3 a Publishers, authors.

  b Find out what other dictionaries are available using a library, bookshop or the Internet. Use the Internet to find out how many copies they sold last year.

4 a Children, publishers.

  b Collect some data by asking children what magazines they already like, what things they like to read in a magazine, whether they would like a new kind of magazine.

Exercise 1B

These answers are all examples.

1 Where do people go on holiday in August? What temperatures do they like on holiday? Which is the hottest month in popular holiday destinations?

2 What kinds of holiday do people go on in February? Which holiday destinations are sunny in February? How far do people want to travel?

3 How many people own a dictionary? What do they use it for? How often do they buy a new dictionary?

4 What magazines do people my age buy? How much do they spend per month on magazines? What is the most popular magazine for people my age?

Exercise 2

1 a 18°

  b 72°

  c

Reading enjoyment	Number of pupils	Angle
Very much	4	72°
Quite a lot	6	108°
A bit	8	144°
Not at all	2	36°

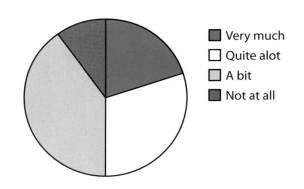

■ Very much
□ Quite alot
■ A bit
■ Not at all

2 a 10°

  b

How often pupils read out of school	Number of pupils	Angle
Every day or almost every day	14	140°
Once or twice a week	11	110°
Once or twice a month	5	50°
Never or nearly never	6	60°

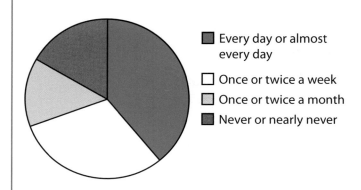

■ Every day or almost every day
□ Once or twice a week
■ Once or twice a month
■ Never or nearly never

3 a 6°

b

Type of book	Number of books	Angle
General fiction	15	90°
Light romance	4	24°
Mystery−detection	6	36°
Adult non-fiction	9	54°
Children's' fiction	12	72°
Children's non-fiction	14	84°

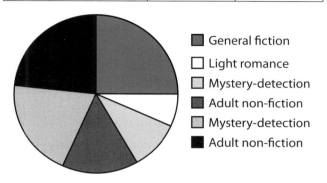

- General fiction
- Light romance
- Mystery-detection
- Adult non-fiction
- Mystery-detection
- Adult non-fiction

4 a 3.6°

b

Do you read enough?	Percentage of pupils	Angle
Yes	48%	172.8
No, but I want to	32%	115.2
No, and I don't want to	20%	72

Percentage of pupils

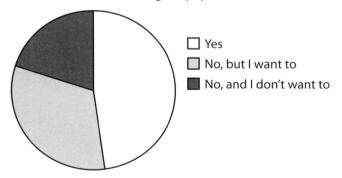

- Yes
- No, but I want to
- No, and I don't want to

Exercise 3A

1 a

Stem (kg)	Leaf (0.1 kg)
2	7 8 9 9
3	1 4 6 6 6 8 9
4	1 2 4 5 6 6 7 8
5	0

b 5.0 kg

c 2.3 kg

2 a

Stem (tens)	Leaf (units)
2	5 5 8 9 9
3	2 2 3 5
4	0 1 4 4 4 4 5

b The number of overdue library books is fairly evenly spread, although there are slightly more in the group 40−49.

3 a

Stem (tens of cm)	Leaf (units)
13	0 4
14	0 3 5 5 5
15	0 3 4 4 5 5 7 7
16	0 1 2 5 5 7
17	0 1 9
18	
19	0

b The pupils are very unlikely to all be from the same year as there is a 60 cm range in their heights.

Exercise 3B

1 a Males

b 73%

2 a Decreasing

b Cyclists and 'other road users'

c Pedestrians

d The total of the row totals should equal the total of the column totals.

3 a 321

b 59

c 2339

d 578

e 11−15 year olds. This age group are likely to be almost always out on their own without their parents. There may be more children in the 0−4 age group, for example, but these would be with an adult if they are out on the pavement or near a road and therefore have fewer accidents. Older children may be more likely to show off to their friends or to take more risks on the roads.

Exercise 4A

1–2 This is for discussion in pairs and groups.

Exercise 4B

1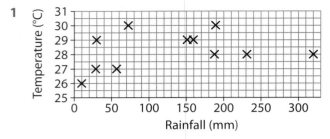

2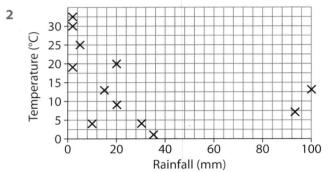

3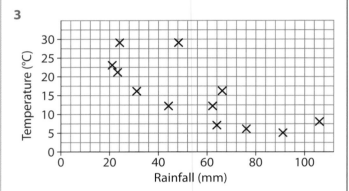

4 You could use the graphs to see if there was a connection between temperature and rainfall. For example, does it rain less in hotter places? Is the connection between rainfall and temperature different in different types of climate?

Exercise 4C

1 Dark bars are Nairobi, light bars are Amsterdam.

2 Left-hand pie chart is boys, right-hand is girls.

3 Left-hand pie chart is primary, right-hand is secondary.

4 Calcutta is the dark bars and New York the light.

Exercise 5A

1 a Babies

 b Elderly people

 c Perhaps 10 or 11 years

 d Perhaps 35 – 45 years

 e Babies, swimmers, mixed group, tug-of-war teams, runners, elderly (tug-of-war teams and runners could be swapped)

2 a Babies

 b Tug-of-war teams

 c Very approximately 50 kg

 d Very approximately 70 kg

 e Babies, swimmers, mixed age, runners, elderly, tug-of-war teams (could be some variations, pupils will need to argue their case)

3 a Mixed-age group

 b Some of the adult-only groups and the mixed-age group

 c The mean height will increase.

 d There may be little change in the mean heights, possibly the tug-of-war team members are taller.

Exercise 5B

1 a

Age	Frequency
1–10	7
11–20	5
21–30	7
31–40	3
41–50	1
51–60	4
61–70	3
71–80	3
81–90	7

 b

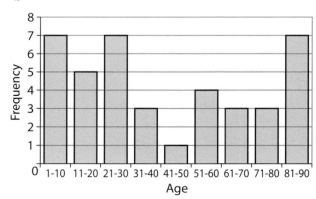

 c 1–10, 21–30, 81–90

 d The people are well spread out across the age range with least in the 41–50 age range.

2 a

Shoe size	Frequency
1–2	2
3–4	11
5–6	8
7–8	12
9–10	4
11–12	3

b

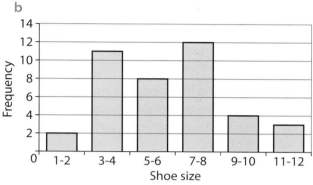

c 7–8

d The majority of the group have shoe sizes between 3 and 8.

Presenting results

Exercise 6

This is group and paired work. Each pair's booklet is evaluated by the group.

How well are you doing?

1 a There are lots of possible answers including libraries, publishers, schools and colleges.

b One possibility would be to ask people about the different sources of information they use. Alternatively you could look for data about how books sales or library usage has changed over time.

c For example:
What do you use the Internet for?
What do you use books for?
Do you think books are still useful? Why?

2

Type of book	Angle
Crime	54°
Non-fiction	234°
Fantasy	72°

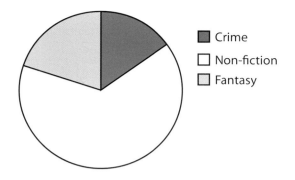

3 135°

4 a 3 minutes

b 8 matches

c 81 minutes

d Between 21 and 39 minutes because more than half the goals came in this period.

5 a 9 + 11 + 10 = 30 ÷ 3 = 10
10 is the middle number (median)

b 6, 8, 12, 14

Home book

TASK 1

1 a

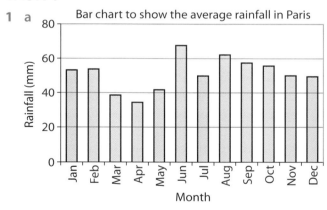

b

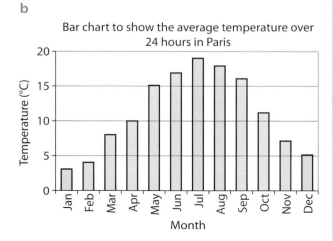

c

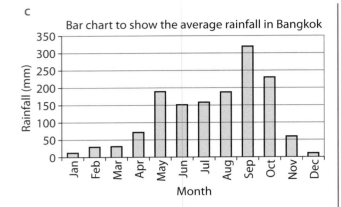
Bar chart to show the average rainfall in Bangkok

d

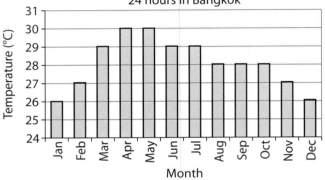
Bar chart to show the average temperature over 24 hours in Bangkok

2 There is less variation in the rainfall in Paris compared to the rainfall in Bangkok. The winter in Bangkok is much drier than in Paris but in the summer Bangkok has a lot more rain, particularly in September, than in Paris.

3 The average 24-hour temperature in Bangkok varies only 4 degrees over the year. In Paris the variation is 16 degrees.

4 Any suitable comment demonstrating an understanding of the impact these differences would make

TASK 2

1 a Indonesia 25.7°C (to 1 d.p.),
United Kingdom 11.4°C (to 1 d.p.),
Venezuela 21.2°C (to 1 d.p.)

b Indonesia 26°C,
United Kingdom 6°C, 13°C, 16°C and 18°C,
Venezuela 22°C

c Indonesia 1°C,
United Kingdom 13°C,
Venezuela 8°C

d In Indonesia because the temperature doesn't vary much.

e In Indonesia the range is very small showing that the temperature doesn't vary much at all. In the UK the variation in temperature is the greatest and Venezuela is in between.

2 a Indonesia 141 mm (to nearest mm),
United Kingdom 45 mm (to nearest mm),
Venezuela 73 mm (to nearest mm)

b A wide range of values in some countries means the mode is not representative.

c Indonesia 122.5 mm,
United Kingdom 44.5 mm,
Venezuela 79 mm

d In Indonesia the median is not very useful because there is a rainy season so the median doesn't tell you that in some months there is a lot of rain.

TASK 3

1 a 1012 km   b 1298 km

c Dublin and Athens   d Kiev and Warsaw

e Oslo and Warsaw, Rome and Athens

f 3964 km

2 a 79   b 8B   c 8B

TASK 4

1

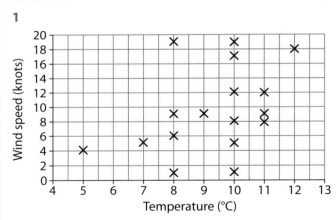

2

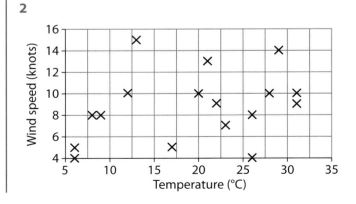

3 You could use these graphs to look for a connection between wind speed and temperature. For example, is it colder in windier places?

TASK 5

This involves collecting data for the next lesson.

TASK 6

1 Suitable graphs are likely to be bar charts for each of the three sets of data. Pie charts are not suitable. Pupils may try to draw stem-and-leaf diagrams but these won't help with the remainder of the task.

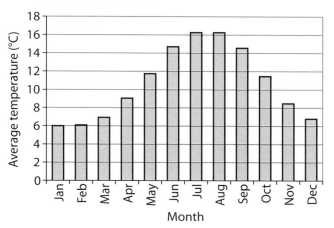

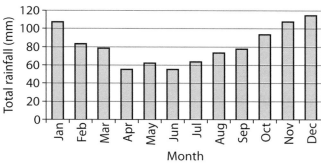

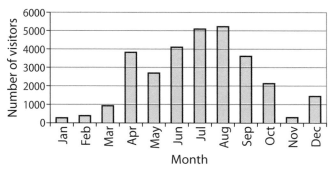

2 The temperature is highest in July and August and lowest in December through to March. The rainfall is highest from November through to January and lowest from April through to July. The visitor numbers are highest in July and August and lowest in November, January and February.

3 a The young family should go in September when it is still warm but not as busy.

   b If you want it very quiet and peaceful you should go in November, January or February because visitor numbers are at their lowest.

   c For a dry walking holiday you should go in April or June when there is least rain.

4 Pupils' choice with reasons

CD-ROM

Check up

1 a

Year	Swim	Tennis	Football	Badm	Tramp	Totals
7	23	**15**	22	36	20	116
8	**45**	17	11	20	21	114
9	34	21	45	6	12	**118**
10	17	34	16	40	12	119
11	11	46	**9**	37	9	**112**
Totals	130	133	103	139	74	579

   b Badminton

   c Badminton

   d Year 11

   e Year 11

2 a

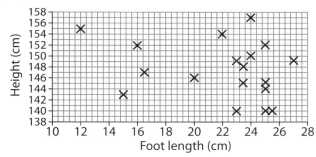

   b Not necessarily. Some of the taller people have short feet.

Functions and graphs

Previous learning

Before they start, pupils should be able to:

- express simple functions in words
- generate coordinate pairs that satisfy a simple linear rule
- recognise straight-line graphs parallel to the x-axis or y-axis.

Objectives based on NC levels 5 and 6 (mainly level 5)

In this unit, pupils learn to:

- identify the mathematical features of a context or problem
- try out and compare mathematical representations
- manipulate algebraic expressions and equations
- visualise and manipulate dynamic images and explore the effect of varying values
- select appropriate procedures and tools, including ICT
- draw accurate graphs on paper and on screen
- conjecture and generalise, identifying exceptional cases or counter-examples

and to:

- express simple functions in symbols and represent them in mappings or on a spreadsheet
- generate points in all four quadrants and plot graphs of linear functions (y given explicitly in terms of x), on paper and using ICT
- recognise that equations of the form $y = mx + c$ correspond to straight-line graphs
- discuss interpret graphs arising from real situations.

Lessons

1 **Plotting points**

2 **Functions and inverse functions**

3 **Functions, equations and graphs**

4 **Sketching graphs**

5 **Interpreting equations of graphs**

6 **Interpreting real-life graphs 1**

About this unit

Relationships can be represented as mappings, functions, equations or graphs. This unit helps pupils to make links between these different representations. Pupils have previously used 'function machines', finding outputs for given inputs using the four operations ($\times$, $\div$, $+$, $-$). In this unit, algebra is used to summarise the instructions.

The introductory lesson revises plotting points in all four quadrants. Pupils are taught to draw a graph accurately by plotting points, and to look at an equation and visualise then sketch its graph. They use features of well-known graphs, such as $y = x$, to help them. They also learn to sketch and interpret graphs of real situations.

Graph-plotting ICT tools offer rapid visual images of graphs that help pupils to know instinctively what a graph should look like. Pupils should not become dependent on the software but should record what they see to help them to generate their own mental images when they are working with paper and pencil.

Assessment	This unit includes:
	◉ a self-assessment section (*A4.3 How well are you doing?* class book p. 160);
	◉ a set of questions to replace or supplement questions in the exercises or homework tasks, or to use as an informal test (*A4.3 Check up*, CD-ROM).
Common errors and misconceptions	Look out for pupils who:
	◉ plot coordinates the wrong way round;
	◉ don't understand that graphs extend beyond the axes drawn unless the context provides limits;
	◉ don't know how to label axes on graphs correctly;
	◉ have forgotten the correct order for number operations;
	◉ don't know that letters represent numbers.
Key terms and notation	coordinates, rectangular coordinates, Cartesian coordinates, coordinate pair, x-coordinate, y-coordinate, (x, y), grid, origin, axis, axes, x-axis, y-axis, first/second/third/fourth quadrant, gradient, intersect, intersection
	equation, expression, mapping, function, function machine, input, output, inverse function, formula, formulae, graph, linear, straight-line graph, relationship, rule, variable, coefficient
	generate, plot, sketch, draw, interpret
	algebra, algebraic, symbol, operation
	parallel, perpendicular, reflection, rotation, the notation A′, congruent
Practical resources	basic calculators for pupils for lesson 4, for each pair of pupils, individual whiteboards graphics calculators, or computers graph paper, squared paper with the graph-plotting tools

Exploring maths

Tier 4 teacher's book
Answers for Unit A4.3 , pp. 183 – 185

Tier 4 CD-ROM
PowerPoint files
   A4.3 Slides for lessons 1 to 6
Tools and prepared toolsheets
   A4.3 Toolsheets for lessons 1, 4, 5
   Polygon tool
   Coordinates and functions tools
   Points and lines tools
Tier 4 programs
   Transformations
   Function machine – match my
   function

Tier 4 class book
A4.3, pp. 146 – 161
A4.3 How well are you doing? p. 160

Tier 4 home book
A4.3, pp. 56 – 61

Tier 4 CD-ROM
A4.3 Check up

Useful websites

Graphs – card sort
www.emaths.co.uk/worksheets/Algebra/JuneGraphSort.pdf
Double operation function machine
www.crick.northants.sch.uk/Flash%20Studio/cfsmaths/Fmach/fmach.swf
Alien functions
www.mathsonline.co.uk/nonmembers/resource/algebra/index.html
Challenging maths problems
www.nrich.maths.org.uk/public/leg.php
Algebra topics
swgfl.skoool.co.uk/keystage3.aspx?id=65#24_30
Straight-line graphs
www.autograph-maths.com/inaction/td/straight-line.htm

1 Plotting points

Starter

Say that this lesson rehearses plotting points using coordinates in all four quadrants.

Tell the class that they will learn how to use given information to work out how to draw shapes on a grid. Some pupils may not have plotted points beyond the first quadrant, in which case you will need to do some additional teaching.

Show **Toolsheet 1.1**, a grid with axes $-10 \leqslant x \leqslant 10$ and $-10 \leqslant y \leqslant 10$.

Explain that (x, y) is an *ordered pair* of numbers. Remind pupils how to plot points given by the coordinates (x, y), using examples in all four quadrants.

Explain that points plotted on rectangular axes are called 'Cartesian coordinates' and tell pupils a little of the history of Descartes. Descartes is also known for his theory about the origins of the Moon. A large crater named after him was the landing site of Apollo 16 in 1972.

Invite pupils to the board to plot points using coordinates that you give them. Include coordinates in all four quadrants. Use the term 'negative' rather than 'minus' to describe negative numbers. If you are using the ICT tool set, click on 'Show coordinates' to check the points plotted.

Display **Toolsheet 1.2**, which shows ten points A−J on the grid using all four quadrants. Get pupils to write the coordinate pairs on their whiteboards. Check that they are writing the coordinates in brackets and in the correct order. When all pupils are confident in plotting points, continue to the main activity.

Main activity

Show **Toolsheet 1.3**. Explain that points A and B are two vertices of a square. Ask pupils to discuss the problem in pairs.

> Find three squares that have points A and B as vertices.

> One square of the grid has an area of one square centimetre.
> What is the area of each of the three squares you have identified?

To show the squares, select the **Draw polygon tool**. Adjust the properties of the polygon if wanted. Click at each of the vertices of the three squares to draw. One square has its third and fourth vertices at $(-3, 2)$, $(1, -2)$ and has an area of 16 cm^2. Two squares have their third and fourth vertices at $(-7, 2)$, $(-3, 6)$ and $(5, -2)$, $(1, -6)$; each of these squares has an area of 32 cm^2.

Launch **Transformations**. Select a colour and drag a triangle to the first quadrant. Ask pupils to give you the coordinates of the three vertices. Enter their suggestions in the coordinate box, then click on 'Go'. Crosses to mark the points will appear.

SIM

Rotate the shape in an axis by clicking three times on the icon on the right-hand side of the screen. If you wish, click on 'Shadow on' before you do so. As before, ask pupils to identify the coordinates of the vertices of the images.

Click on 'Start again' and continue as necessary. For example, you could create your own irregular shape. To do this, click on 'Create new shape'. Click on coordinates in one of the quadrants to create a closed shape. Click on 'Done' when it is completed to shade the shape, then change the colour if you wish. Proceed as before, asking pupils to identify coordinate points.

Select individual work from **A4.3 Exercise 1** in the class book (p. 147). Pupils will need squared paper.

Review

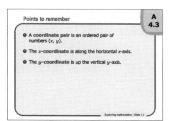

Launch **Transformations** again. Divide the class into two teams and give each team a colour. Explain that the class is going to play the game 'Four in a row'. Each team takes turns.

SIM

Ask named pupils around the class to give coordinates with the aim of getting four points in a vertical, horizontal or diagonal straight line. Enter the nominated coordinates yourself, and click on 'Go'. When the cross appears, click on the team's colour to colour the cross appropriately.

You could make the game harder by insisting that the first point must be in the third quadrant.

Finish the lesson by stressing the points on **slide 1.1**.

Homework

Ask pupils to do **A4.3 Task 1** in the home book (p. 56). They will need squared paper.

2 Functions and inverse functions

Learning points

- You can show a relationship between two variables x and y in a mapping diagram like this:

$x \rightarrow y$
$1 \rightarrow 6$
$2 \rightarrow 10$
$3 \rightarrow 14$
$4 \rightarrow 18$
$x \rightarrow 4x + 2$

- You can also write it as a function like this:

$x \rightarrow$ | multiply by 4 | $\rightarrow$ | add 2 | $\rightarrow y$

- The inverse function is

$x \leftarrow$ | divide by 4 | $\leftarrow$ | subtract 2 | $\leftarrow y$

Starter

Use **slide 2.1** to discuss the objectives for the next two lessons. Say that this lesson is about functions and inverse functions.

Remind pupils how to draw a function machine like this: $x \rightarrow$ | add 3 | $\rightarrow y$.

Give numerical values for the input x and ask pupils for the output y. Then give numerical values for the output y and ask pupils for the input x.

Repeat for different functions using the four operations ($+$, $-$, $\times$, $\div$).

Progress to functions that combine operations such as:

$x \rightarrow$ | multiply by 3 | $\rightarrow$ | add 5 | $\rightarrow y$

Main activity

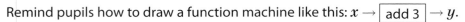

Show **slide 2.2**. Ask pupils to work in pairs to find the functions [multiply by 6; add 9; multiply by 2 then subtract 1]. Assign some output numbers for each function and ask for the input numbers. Ask pupils how they work out the input when given the output. As an alternative, this could be set up as a spreadsheet.

Show the class how to write the inverse functions like this:

$x \rightarrow$ | multiply by 6 | $\rightarrow y$
$x \leftarrow$ | divide by 6 | $\leftarrow y$

$x \rightarrow$ | add 9 | $\rightarrow y$
$x \leftarrow$ | subtract 9 | $\leftarrow y$

$x \rightarrow$ | multiply by 2 | $\rightarrow$ | subtract 1 | $\rightarrow y$
$x \leftarrow$ | divide by 2 | $\leftarrow$ | add 1 | $\leftarrow y$

Show **slide 2.3**. Ask pupils to work in pairs to match the functions and their inverses. Then invite pupils to come to the board and link the function with its inverse.

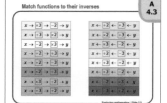

Select individual work from **A4.3 Exercise 2** in the class book (p. 150).

Review

SIM

Launch **Function machines – match my function**, showing a single-function machine. Click 'Go' twice and ask pupils to write on their whiteboards the correct function. Repeat for other functions.

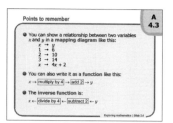

Now select 'Settings', and switch to two functions for 'Match my function'.

WEB

Alternatively, use one of the other resources listed in the useful websites section. For example, **Alien functions** simulates a calculator with nine extra buttons. The task is to work out what function each of these buttons carries out.

Sum up with the points on **slide 2.4**.

Homework

Ask pupils to do **A4.3 Task 2** in the home book (p. 57). As an alternative, refer pupils with computers at home to the program **Alien functions**.

3 Functions, equations and graphs

Learning points

- ◎ You can show a relationship between two variables x and y in a mapping diagram, as a function, as an equation or as a graph.
- ◎ A linear equation has terms in x but not x^2 or any higher power.
- ◎ You can draw a graph of a linear function by plotting three pairs of values (x, y).
- ◎ A linear graph is always a straight-line graph.
- ◎ Inspect relationships carefully to see whether they are linear or more complex functions.

Starter

Say that this lesson is about representing information as a function, as an equation and as a graph.

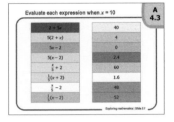

Begin by revising the order of operations. Show **slide 3.1**, a matching exercise. Ask pupils to evaluate each expression when x is 10, matching the correct value in the right-hand column. Point out the change in precedence when brackets are used.

Main activity

Draw this mapping diagram on the board.

$$x \quad \rightarrow \quad y$$
$$0 \quad \rightarrow \quad 1$$
$$1 \quad \rightarrow \quad 3$$
$$2 \quad \rightarrow \quad 5$$
$$3 \quad \rightarrow \quad 7$$

Ask pupils to work out the function which is

$$x \rightarrow \boxed{\text{multiply by 2}} \rightarrow \boxed{\text{add 1}} \rightarrow y.$$

Remind them that working out the differences between the numbers in the y-column can help them to work out the function. In this case the difference is always 2. Link this with the work they have done on sequences in Unit A4.1.

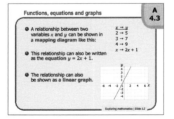

Show **slide 3.2**. Explain that the function is a way of generalising a set of instructions, and that there are several different ways of representing this information. The function can be written as an equation $y = 2x + 1$. This is a *linear equation* because there are no terms in x that are squared or of any higher power.

The information can be represented in a graph by finding three values of x and y and plotting them on rectangular axes. (Two points define the line and the third point acts as a check.) Explain that any three values can be chosen for x and then the corresponding values for y can be calculated. Show pupils how to work out these values and how to draw the graph.

As an alternative, use the **Coordinates and functions tools** to create axes for $0 < x < 10$ and $0 < y < 10$, and to plot the points. Draw the graph using the **Line through 2 points tool**.

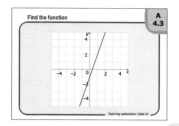

Explain that when they draw the graph they should extend the line beyond the points plotted: the line extends infinitely and is limited only by the size of the axes drawn. Give out squared paper and ask pupils to draw the graph accurately using a pencil and ruler. Make sure that they label the axes and name the graph.

Show **slide 3.3**. Draw a mapping diagram on the board. Ask pupils to inspect the graph and give you three pairs of values for x and y that lie on the line.

> Work out the function. What is it as an equation?

Ask pupils to do **A4.3 Exercise 3** in the class book (p. 153). They will need squared paper.

Review

Review the different ways of representing information as mappings, functions, equations and graphs. Draw this mapping diagram on the board.

$$
\begin{array}{ccc}
x & \rightarrow & y \\
0 & \rightarrow & 0 \\
1 & \rightarrow & 1 \\
2 & \rightarrow & 4 \\
3 & \rightarrow & 9
\end{array}
$$

> What is the function?

> Is the function linear?

> What do you notice about the differences between the y-values?

> What is the equation for this function?

> Would the graph of this function be a straight line? How do you know?

Sum up with the points on **slide 3.4**.

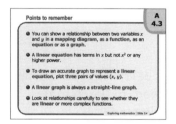

Homework

Ask pupils to do **A4.3 Task 3** in the home book (p. 58). They will need squared paper.

4 Sketching graphs

Learning points

- Graphs of the form $y = ax$, where a is a constant, are straight-line graphs that pass through the origin.
  - The steepness of the line is called its gradient.
  - The number in front of x is called the coefficient of x.
    The larger the coefficient of x, the greater the gradient.
- A sketch of a graph is a neat drawing that shows some of its features.

Starter

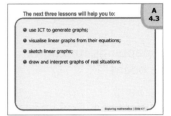

The main part of this lesson needs to take place in a room with enough computers equipped with graph-plotting software or the graph-plotting tool, for one computer between each pair of pupils. Alternatively, pairs could use graphics calculators.

Use **slide 4.1** to discuss the objectives for lessons 4, 5 and 6. Say that this lesson is about using ICT to generate graphs and sketching their main features.

Show **Toolsheet 4.1**. This shows lines parallel to the x- and y-axes such as $x = 7$, $y = 4$. The equations are not shown on the screen.

> **What are the equations of the lines?**
>
> **What is the equation of the x-axis? The y-axis? How do you know?**

If necessary, get pupils to inspect the graphs and find pairs of coordinates on the lines that they can put in mapping diagrams to help them to find the function.

Main activity

Explain that in the last lesson pupils did *accurate drawings* of linear graphs using pencil and ruler on graph paper. Today they are going to learn to *sketch* some linear graphs from their equations. A sketch is a neat drawing not to scale.

Say that they are going to use their computers or graphics calculators to generate some graphs to help them build up pictures in their imagination. Some pupils may have done this previously, in which case they should attempt to sketch the graphs first and then check them with the computer.

Arrange pupils in pairs at the computers, or give out graphics calculators, one per pair. Ask them to draw the graph of $y = x$ and check that they all are able to do this. Make sure that the axes are 'square' or 'equal aspect' for this work.

Ask pupils to describe this graph. Draw out that the graph passes through the origin and is at 45° to both axes.

Ask pairs to do **A4.3 Exercise 4** questions 1 and 2 in the class book (p. 154).

Ask the class to explain what they have noticed about the graphs in question 1. Make a list of the things they note such as:

- all the graphs are straight-line or linear graphs;
- they are all parallel to the line $y = x$;
- the graph of $y = x + 3$ cuts (intersects) the y-axis at the point (0, 3).

Ask pupils to sketch the graph $y = x + 11$ on a blank set of axes. Ask a pupil to sketch the graph on the board. Get them to explain how they know what to draw. Do the same for $y = x - 7$. Do some more until all pupils are confident in sketching the graphs. You may want pupils to sketch several graphs on the same axes.

> Ask pairs to do **A4.3 Exercise 4** questions 3 and 4 in the class book (p. 154).

Ask the class to explain what they have noticed about the graphs in question 3. Make a list of the things they note such as:

- the larger the number in front of x, the steeper the graph.

Explain that the number in front of the x is called the *coefficient* of x. Explain that the steepness of the line is called the *gradient*. Rewrite the sentence above as:

- the larger the coefficient of x, the greater the gradient.

Ask pupils to hand-sketch the graph $y = 7x$ on a blank set of axes. Get them to explain how they know what to draw. Invite a pupil to sketch the graph on the board.

Do the same for $y = 0.25x$ and $y = -5x$. Do more examples until all pupils are confident in sketching the graphs.

> Ask pairs to do **A4.3 Exercise 4** questions 5 to 7 in the class book (p. 154–155). They will need squared paper for question 7.

Review

Invite individuals to hand-sketch these graphs on the board.

$$y = 3x + 4 \qquad y = 3x - 12 \qquad y = 2x + 9 \qquad y = 4x - 5 \qquad y = -3x + 6$$

Ask pupils to explain for each graph how they know what to draw.

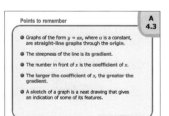

Alternatively, use the **Axes tool** to create axes $-20 \leqslant x \leqslant 20$, $-20 \leqslant y \leqslant 20$. Invite pupils to draw the graphs using the **Line tool**.

Sum up the lesson by stressing the points on **slide 4.2**.

Homework

Ask pupils to do **A4.3 Task 4** in the home book (p. 59). They will need squared paper.

5 Interpreting equations of graphs

Learning points

- Every linear function can be represented as a straight-line graph with an equation of the form $y = ax + b$.
- The gradient of the graph is a. The intercept on the y-axis is $(0, b)$.

Starter Say that this lesson is about visualising graphs from their equations, and working out the equations of linear graphs.

Use the **Axes tool** to create axes $-20 \leqslant x \leqslant 20$, $-20 \leqslant y \leqslant 20$. Invite pupils to draw these graphs on the board using the **Line** or **Pen tool**, and to explain how they know what to draw.

$$y = 2x \qquad y = x - 6 \qquad y = 3x + 7 \qquad y = 6x - 1 \qquad y = -x + 4$$

Main activity Use pupils' knowledge to draw out facts about linear equations. Write $y = 5x - 7$ on the board and ask pupils to sketch the graph on their whiteboards. Clear the board and set up the same axes. Use the **Function graph tool** to check. Select $y = ax + b$ and input the coefficients.

What is the coefficient of y? What is the coefficient of x?

Explain that this equation is in the form $y = ax + b$, where a and b are constants. The coefficient of y must always be 1.

What is the gradient of the graph?

What is the intercept on the y-axis?

Give me the gradient and intercept of the graph of each of these equations:

$$y = 7x \qquad y = 5x - 10 \qquad y = 4x + 15 \qquad y = 3x - 11 \qquad y = -6x + 3$$

If necessary, generate the graphs using the **Function graph tool**. Check the values of the gradients and intercepts.

Draw axes on the board and a line intercepting the y-axis at a positive integer. Number the axes.

Draw in a right-angled triangle with a difference of 1 along the x-axis as shown.

Explain that the gradient is the increase in the y-coordinate for an increase of 1 in the x-coordinate. For the diagram shown, this is a gradient of 2.

Draw a steeper line and show that the gradient is a larger number (e.g. 4).

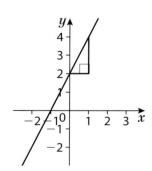

Explain that every linear function can be shown as a straight-line graph with an equation of the form $y = mx + c$. Here m is the gradient of the line, and c is the intercept of the line on the y-axis, where $x = 0$.

Show on the board how to find the equations of the two lines using their gradients m and intercepts c.

Ask pupils to do **A4.3 Exercise 5** in the class book (p. 156).

Review

Ask pupils to explain what is meant by the gradient of a graph.

Show **Toolsheet 5.1**. Use the triangle to work out the gradient of the graph by calculating height ÷ base. Explain that you could use different points on the graph but you have chosen these because the height and base are whole-number units in length.

Ask pupils to give the coordinates of the intercept on the y-axis.

Use these facts to work out the equation of the graph.

Repeat for further linear graphs.

Finish by reminding pupils of the points on **slide 5.1**.

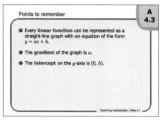

Homework

Ask pupils to do **A4.3 Task 5** in the home book (p. 59).

6 Interpreting real-life graphs 1

Learning points

- ◉ A distance-time graph or travel graph describes stages in a journey.
- ◉ A conversion graph shows how to change one unit to another.
- ◉ When you draw or interpret graphs of real situations, take care with the scales on the axes.

Starter Say that this lesson will help pupils to draw and interpret graphs of real situations.

Remind pupils of the formula to calculate the average speed of a journey:

average speed = distance ÷ time

Ask pupils to use their whiteboards to find average speeds given distance and time, journey times given speed and distance travelled, and distance given speed and journey time.

Main activity Show **slide 6.1**. Ask pupils to inspect the graph. Tell them that Sam leaves home in her car at 8:30 am. The graph represents her journey. Inspect the axes and ask pupils to describe the scales.

> At what time did Sam make her first stop?
>
> How long was Sam's first stop?
>
> When did Sam arrive at the point that was 100 miles from home?
>
> How many miles had Sam travelled from her first stop?
> How long did Sam stay at this point?
>
> At what time did Sam arrive back home?
>
> Which was the fastest part of Sam's journey? How do you know?
>
> Which was the slowest part of Sam's journey? How do you know?

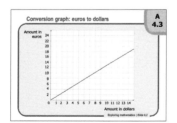

Show **slide 6.2**. Explain that this is a conversion graph for euros/dollars. Inspect the axes and ask pupils to describe the scales.

Ask pupils to use the graph to convert amounts that you give them. Get them to convert from dollars to euros and from euros to dollars.

> Estimate the gradient of the graph.
>
> What is the equation of the graph?

Explain that in this case the graph passes through the origin because euros are directly proportional to dollars.

Select individual work from **A4.3 Exercise 6** in the class book (p. 157).

Review

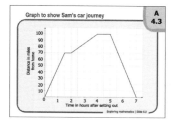

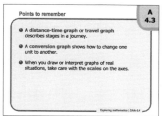

Show **slide 6.3**. For each part of the journey ask pupils to work out the gradient of the graph.

Draw out that the gradient represents the average speed of the car. Explain that distance is proportional to time and write $d \propto t$ and $d = st$, where d is the distance, s the average speed (a constant) and t the time.

Ask pupils to remember the points on **slide 6.4**.

Round off the unit by referring again to the objectives. Suggest that pupils find time to try the self-assessment problems in **A4.3 How well are you doing?** in the class book (p. 160).

Homework

Ask pupils to do **A4.3 Task 6** in the home book (p. 60).

A4.3 Check up

Check up
A4.3

Write your answers in your book.
You will need squared paper, pencil and ruler for these questions.

1. Three vertices of a parallelogram are given by P (6, 3), Q (1, 3) and R (4, 6).
   What are the coordinates of the fourth vertex?
   There are two solutions. Find both of them.

2. Find the outputs y for the given inputs x for this function:

   $$x \rightarrow \boxed{\text{multiply by 6}} \rightarrow \boxed{\text{subtract 5}} \rightarrow y$$

   a $x = 2$ b $x = 5$ c $x = 0$ d $x = -2$

3. Work out the functions for these mappings.

   a $x \rightarrow y$ b $x \rightarrow y$
      $1 \rightarrow 12$ $1 \rightarrow 4$
      $2 \rightarrow 22$ $2 \rightarrow 13$
      $3 \rightarrow 32$ $3 \rightarrow 22$
      $x \rightarrow$ $x \rightarrow$

4. Write the inverse function for $x \rightarrow \boxed{\text{multiply by 9}} \rightarrow \boxed{\text{subtract 7}} \rightarrow y$.

5. Use squared paper to draw an accurate graph for the linear equation $y = 5x - 1$.

6. Sketch the graph of $y = 0.5x + 4$.

7. Imagine the graph of the linear equation $y = 8x + 2.5$.
   a What is the gradient of the graph?
   b What is the intercept on the y-axis?

8. Let c be the temperature measured in degrees Celsius.
   Let f be the temperature measured in degrees Fahrenheit.
   The graph of $f = 1.8c + 32$ converts degrees Fahrenheit to degrees Celsius.
   a Draw the graph.
   b Use the graph to estimate what 20 °C is in degrees Fahrenheit.

       Tier 4 resource sheets | A4.3 *Functions and graphs* | **10.1**

A4.3 Answers

Class book

Exercise 1

1 A (6, 2), B (2, 5), C (−2, 3), D (−4, 1), E (−8, 3),
   F (−8, −1), G (−4, −4), H (−2, −2), I (2, −1),
   J (5, −4)

2 a (2, 3) and (−5, 3) **or** (2, −7) and (−5, −7)
   b (−1, 0) and (−5, 4) **or** (3, 0) and (−1, −4)
      or (−5, 8) and (−9, 4)
   c (−2, −1) and (−6, 5)
   d (−1, −3)

3 (−3, −1)

4 (2, 5), (3, 7), (4, 7), (6, 5)

5 a (−2, 3), (−7, 5), (−6, 2)
   b (2, −3), (7, −5), (6, −2)
   c (−3, −2), (−5, −7), (−2, −6)
   d (3, 2), (5, 7), (2, 6)

6 K (−8, 1) and N (6, 1) **or** K (−8, −9) and N (6, −9)

Extension problem

7 a (−4, 0) and (3, −3)
   b 29 square units

Exercise 2

1 a 16   b 46
   c 24   d 65
   e 34   f 99
   g 59   h 53

2 a 14   b 28
   c 56   d 49
   e 84   f 105
   g 350   h 700

3 a 16   b 40
   c 34   d 82
   e 37   f 103
   g 112   h 127

4 a 4 → 19   b 4 → 22
      5 → 23   5 → 28
      6 → 27   6 → 34
      $x \to 4x + 3$ $x \to 6x - 2$

5 a $x \leftarrow$ | subtract 15 | $\leftarrow y$

   b $x \leftarrow$ | add 8 | $\leftarrow y$

   c $x \leftarrow$ | divide by 7 | $\leftarrow$ | add 3 | $\leftarrow y$

   d $x \leftarrow$ | subtract 19 | $\leftarrow$ | divide by 12 | $\leftarrow y$

   e $x \leftarrow$ | multiply by 4 | $\leftarrow$ | add 8 | $\leftarrow y$

   f $x \leftarrow$ | subtract 7 | $\leftarrow$ | divide by 4 | $\leftarrow$
      | multiply by 3 | $\leftarrow y$

6 a and U, b and W, c and P, d and Q, e and V, f and
   S, g and R, h and T

Extension problem

7 a 70   b 75
   c 110   d 90
   e 140   f 480
   g 290   h 165

Exercise 3

1 a 49   b 85
   c 31   d 5
   e 3.4   f 10.6
   g 7.4   h 0.2

2

x	−3	−2	−1	0	1	2	3	4
y	−21	−13	−5	3	11	19	27	35

x	−1.5	−1	−0.5	0	0.5	1	1.5	2
y	−7	−5	−3	−1	1	3	5	7

x	3.1	3.2	3.3	3.4	3.5	3.6	3.7	3.8
y	17.7	18.4	19.1	19.8	20.5	21.2	21.9	22.6

x	−6	−5	−4	−3	−2	−1	0	1
y	−3	−2.5	−2	−1.5	−1	0.5	0	0.5

x	−3	−2	−1	0	1	2	3	4
y	−20	−11	−2	7	16	25	34	43

3 Pupils' graphs

Extension problem

4 Any three pairs of coordinates on the line
   $y = 4x - 3$

Exercise 4

1. Pupils' graphs generated by computer or graphics calculator

2. Pupils' comments such as:
   - all the graphs are straight-line or linear graphs;
   - they are all parallel to the line $y = x$;
   - the graph of $y = x + 3$ cuts (intersects) the y-axis at the point (0, 3).

3. Pupils' graphs generated by computer or graphics calculator

4. Pupils' comments such as:
   - all the graphs are linear graphs;
   - all the graphs pass through the origin;
   - the larger the coefficient of x, the steeper the graph.

5. Pupils' graphs generated by computer or graphics calculator

6. Pupils' comments such as:
   - all the graphs are linear graphs;
   - they are all parallel to the line $y = -x$;
   - the graph of $y = -x + 3$ cuts (intersects) the y-axis at the point (0, 3).

7. Pupils' sketches of graphs checked by computer or graphics calculator

Exercise 5

1. a 1, (0, 0)   b 2, (0, 1)
   c 4, (0, 8)   d 2, (0, −3)
   e 6, (0, 2)   f 0.5, (0, 4)
   g 1, (0, −7)   h 8, (0, −10)
   i −1, (0, 1)   j −3, (0, −6)

2. a 3, (0, 0)   b 3, (0, 2)
   c −2, (0, 1)   d −4, (0, −1)

Extension problems

3. a $y = 3x + 6$ b $y = x + 9$
   c $y = 10x - 2$ d $y = 0.5x + 5$
   e $y = -4x + 7$ f $y = -x$

4. a 2   b 5
   c 1   d $\frac{1}{3}$
   e −3   f 3
   g 1   h 4

Exercise 6

1. a 10:00 am
   b 4 miles
   c 1 hour
   d 6 miles
   e 6 miles per hour
   f 12:15 pm
   g 1:15 pm
   h 10 miles per hour

2. a Approximately 8 kilometres to 5 miles
   b Approximately 3 miles to 5 kilometres
   c About 400 kilometres
   d About 69 miles per hour
   e About 48 kilometres per hour
   f About 400 metres

3. a About £2.50
   b About 200 bunches
   c 2240 bunches
   d £313.75

4. a £6   b £3
   c 30p   d 3p
   e £15   f £30
   g £2.25   h £1.20

How well are you doing?

1. a 91.44 m   b 109.36 yards

2. a 146   b 18   c yes

3. a $y = -x + 4$ b pupils' graphs

4. a Gradient 5   b Intercept (0, 7)

5. a

n	$\rightarrow$	$n + 2$
4	$\rightarrow$	**6**
18	$\rightarrow$	20

   b

n	$\rightarrow$	$2n$
4	$\rightarrow$	**8**
10	$\rightarrow$	20

   c

n	$\rightarrow$	$\frac{n}{5}$		n	$\rightarrow$	$n + 20$
25	$\rightarrow$	5		25	$\rightarrow$	5

6. Pupils' graphs

Home book

TASK 1

1 A $(4, 1)$, B $(6, 4)$, C $(-2, 1)$, D $(-3, 4)$, E $(-6, 3)$, F $(-7, -4)$, G $(-5, -2)$, H $(-3, -5)$, I $(2, -1)$, J $(5, -2)$

2 a $(2, 6), (-3, 1)$
   b $(7, 6), (2, 11)$ **or** $(-8, 1), (-3, -4)$

TASK 2

1 a 19   b 43
   c 59   d 83
   e 75   f 67
   g 7   h 4.6

2 a $4 \rightarrow 21$ b $4 \rightarrow 26$
      $5 \rightarrow 26$ $5 \rightarrow 33$
      $6 \rightarrow 31$ $6 \rightarrow 40$
      $x \rightarrow 5x + 1$ $x \rightarrow 7x - 2$

3 a $x \leftarrow$ | divide by 15 | $\leftarrow$ | add 9 | $\leftarrow y$

   b $x \leftarrow$ | multiply by 4 | $\leftarrow$ | subtract 8 | $\leftarrow y$

   c $x \leftarrow$ | add 6 | $\leftarrow$ | divide by 17 | $\leftarrow y$

TASK 3

1

x	-3	-2	-1	0	1	2	3	4
y	-5	-3	-1	1	3	5	7	9

x	-1.5	-1	-0.5	0	0.5	1	1.5	2
y	-15	-11	-7	-3	1	5	9	13

x	0.1	0.2	0.3	0.4	0.5	0.6	0.7	0.8
y	1.6	2.2	2.8	3.4	4.0	4.6	5.2	5.8

2 Pupils' graphs

TASK 4

1 Pupils' sketches

2 The coefficient of x is -4 and this is the gradient. The graph crosses the y-axis at $(0, 5)$.

3 A linear graph is a straight-line graph.

TASK 5

1 a $1, (0, 0)$ b $7, (0, 5)$
   c $3, (0, 13)$ d $8, (0, -7)$
   e $-1, (0, 3)$ f $0.5, (0, 6)$
   g $-1, (0, -9)$ h $\frac{1}{2}, (0, -\frac{1}{6})$

2 a $y = 2x + 5$ b $y = 14$
   c $y = 9x - 8$ d $y = 0.5x - 0.5$
   e $y = -4x + 3$ f $y = -x - 5$

TASK 6

1 a 11:30 am
   b 2.5 miles
   c Half an hour
   d 1:30 pm
   e 4.5 miles
   f 5:30 pm
   g E to F
   h 3 miles per hour

CD-ROM

Check up

1 $(9, 6)$ or $(-1, 6)$

2 a 7
   b 25
   c -5
   d -17

3 a $x \rightarrow 10x + 2$
   b $x \rightarrow 9x - 5$

4 $x \leftarrow$ | divide by 9 | $\leftarrow$ | add 7 | $\leftarrow y$

5 Pupils' graph

6 Pupils' sketch

7 a 8
   b $(0, 2.5)$

8 a Pupils' graph
   b Approximately 68°F

Proportional reasoning

Previous learning

Before they start, pupils should be able to:

- understand percentage as the 'number of parts per 100' and calculate simple fractions and percentages of quantities and measurements
- divide a quantity in a given ratio.

Objectives based on NC levels 5 and 6 (mainly level 5)

In this unit, pupils learn to:

- identify mathematical features of a context or problem
- make connections with related contexts
- use accurate notation
- calculate accurately, selecting mental methods or a calculator as appropriate
- estimate, approximate and check working, giving accurate solutions appropriate to the context or problem
- refine own findings and approaches on the basis of discussion with others

and to:

- apply understanding of the relationship between ratio and proportion
- simplify ratios, including ratios expressed in different units, recognising links with fraction notation
- divide a quantity into two or more parts in a given ratio
- calculate fractions of quantities, using a calculator where appropriate
- interpret percentage as the operator 'so many hundredths of' and calculate percentages
- use equivalent fractions, decimals and percentages to compare proportions
- use the unitary method to solve problems involving ratio and direct proportion
- enter numbers and interpret the display of a calculator in different contexts.

Lessons

1 **Dividing a quantity in a given ratio**

2 **Solving ratio problems**

3 **Scale drawings**

4 **The unitary method**

5 **Fraction, decimal and percentage operators**

6 **Solving problems**

About this unit

Proportional reasoning is a key feature of the Key Stage 3 curriculum. Ideas of ratio or proportion occur in fractions and percentages, in calculations of rate and speed, and in scale drawings, enlargements and similarity. They also occur in other subjects, for example, in map work in geography or in density, pressure and power in science.

Lessons 5 and 6 are adapted from two lessons in the Secondary Strategy's *Year 8 intervention lessons and resources*.

Assessment

This unit includes:

- an optional mental test that could replace part of a lesson (p. 196);
- a self-assessment section (*N4.4 How well are you doing?* class book p. 182);
- a set of questions to replace or supplement questions in the exercises or homework tasks, or to use as an informal test (*N4.4 Check up*, CD-ROM).

Common errors and misconceptions

Look out for pupils who:

- don't understand that $2:8$ is the same ratio as $1:4$;
- make errors when scaling quantities up or down;
- think that increasing a map scale increases the map distance (whereas it decreases the map distance);
- misinterpret fraction, decimal and percentage equivalents, e.g. think that because 10% is $\frac{1}{10}$ or 0.1, 5% as a fraction is $\frac{1}{5}$ or 0.5.

Key terms and notation

problem, solution, method, pattern, relationship, represent, solve, explain, justify

calculate, calculation, calculator, multiply, divide, product, quotient

proportion, direct proportion, ratio, unitary ratio, scale, scale factor, and the notation $a:b$

fraction, numerator, denominator, proper fraction, improper fraction, mixed number, cancel, simplify, convert, equivalent, equivalence

decimal, whole number, decimal place, units, tenths, hundredths, thousandths

per cent (%), percentage, rate, discount, increase, decrease

Practical resources

counting stick
calculators for pupils
individual whiteboards
large sheet of paper for each pair

ruler and piece of string for each pupil
Internet access to the website www.multimap.com or similar (optional)

Exploring maths

Tier 4 teacher's book
N4.4 Mental test, p. 196
Answers for Unit N4.4, pp. 201–205

Tier 4 CD-ROM
PowerPoint files
   N4.4 Slides for lessons 1 to 6
Prepared toolsheets
   N4.4 Toolsheets for lessons 2, 3 and 4

Tier 4 class book
N4.4, pp. 162–183
N4.4 How well are you doing? p. 182

Tier 4 home book
N4.4, pp. 62–69

Tier 4 CD-ROM
N4.4 Check up
N4.4 Pupil resource sheets
   1.1 One set per pair
   5.1 One set per pair
   6.1 One set per pair
   6.2 One set per group of four

Useful websites

Ratio pairs 2
www.nrich.maths.org/public/leg.php?group_id=2&code=27#results

Pumpkin pie problem
http://nrich.maths.org/public/viewer.php?obj_id=1026

Orange drink
http://nrich.maths.org/public/viewer.php?obj_id=2420

Percentages
nlvm.usu.edu/en/nav/vlibrary.html

A wide variety of maps with different map ratios
www.multimap.com

1 Dividing a quantity in a given ratio

Learning points

- A proportion is a fraction or percentage.
  If 1 in every 4 beads is red, the proportion of red beads is $\frac{1}{4}$ or 25%.

- A ratio compares two or more quantities with each other. We usually use whole numbers in a ratio and write them without units. Ratios are simplified similarly to fractions.

- To divide a quantity into two parts in the ratio $a:b$, find the fractions $\dfrac{a}{a+b}$ and $\dfrac{b}{a+b}$ of the quantity.

Starter

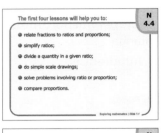

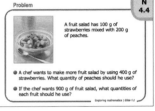

Use **slide 1.1** to discuss objectives for the first four lessons. Say that this lesson is about dividing a quantity in a given ratio.

Show **slide 1.2** and pose the two questions on the fruit salad mix. Continue with similar questions, making sure that pupils explain their methods.

Main activity

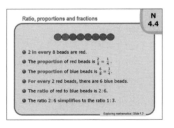

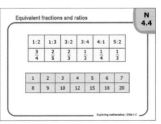

Remind the class of the meaning of *ratio* and *proportion* by showing the eight beads on **slide 1.3**. Reveal and discuss each statement about the beads.

Remind pupils that ratios such as 1:2, 2:4, 3:6, 4:8, … are *equivalent ratios*. Ratios can be scaled up or down by cancelling them, just like fractions.

Show pupils how to simplify a ratio with mixed units, e.g. 1 m : 30 cm. Point out that quantities must be converted into the same unit before they can be cancelled, and that ratios are normally written without units. Give a few examples of ratios for pupils to simplify, such as: 75p to £1, 350 g to 1 kg, 600 mm to 50 cm to 1 m.

Show **slide 1.4**. Ask pupils to match pairs of numbers from the lower grid to equivalent ratios or fractions in the upper grid (e.g. 3 and 6 are in the ratio 1:2, or 3 is $\frac{1}{2}$ of 6).

Click on the slide so that the lower table disappears. Point to one of the ratios or fractions and ask pupils to give equivalent ratios or fractions using their own numbers.

Extend to ratios in three parts by showing **slide 1.5**.

186 | N4.4 *Proportional reasoning*

Ask pupils to do **N4.4 Exercise 1A** in the class book (p. 163). Each pair will need a set of cards made from **N4.4 Resource sheet 1.1** for question 4.

Remind pupils how to divide a quantity into two parts in a given ratio.

> How can we divide £35 into two parts in the ratio 2 : 5?

Explain that we need $2 + 5 = 7$ equal shares. For one share we calculate £35 ÷ 7 = £5, for two shares we calculate £5 × 2 = £10 and for five shares we calculate £5 × 5 = £25.

This is the same as finding $\frac{2}{7}$ of 35 and $\frac{5}{7}$ of 35.

Extend to dividing a given quantity into three parts in a given ratio.

> How can we divide 80 kg of carrots into three parts in the ratio 1 : 4 : 5?

This time we need $1 + 4 + 5 = 10$ equal shares. For one share we calculate 80 kg ÷ 10 = 8 kg. For four shares we calculate 8 kg × 4 = 32 kg, and for five shares we calculate 8 kg × 5 = 40 kg.

This is the same as finding $\frac{1}{10}$ of 80 kg, $\frac{4}{10}$ of 80 kg and $\frac{5}{10}$ of 80 kg.

Repeat by dividing £72 in the ratio 3 : 2 : 7.

Ask pupils to do **N4.4 Exercise 1B** in the class book (p. 165).

Review Extend the problem posed in the starter by asking the questions on **slide 1.6**.

Make sure that pupils explain fully how they worked out their answers.

Sum up by showing **slide 1.7**.

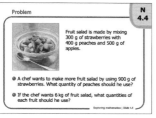

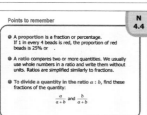

Homework Ask pupils to do **N4.4 Task 1** in the home book (p. 62).

2 Solving ratio problems

Learning points

- A unitary ratio is written in the form $1 : m$.
  To convert a ratio of $2 : 15$ to a unitary ratio, divide by 2 to get $1 : 7.5$.

- Unitary ratios are useful for comparing ratios.

- A scale factor tells you how many times bigger one number is than another.

Starter   Say that this lesson is about comparing ratios and solving ratio problems.

Use a counting stick.

Point to a division on the stick and ask questions such as:

> What proportion of the stick lies to the left of this point? To the right?

> What is the ratio of the length to the left of this point to the length to the right?

Count along the stick in threes from 3 to 30, pointing as you go. Then count along the stick in fives from 5 to 50. Now combine the two by counting along the stick:

> three to five; six to ten; nine to fifteen; twelve to twenty; fifteen to twenty-five; …

Stress that each pair of numbers is in the same ratio, since they all simplify to $3 : 5$.

Main activity   Show pupils how to compare two ratios. Write on the board the two ratios $1 : 4$ and $2 : 9$. Say that the ratio of currants to sultanas in two fruit cakes is $1 : 4$ in one cake and $2 : 9$ in the other cake.

> Which cake has the greater proportion of sultanas?
> How could you compare these ratios?

Lead the class towards reducing the second ratio to $1 : 4.5$ and the conclusion that the second cake has a higher proportion of sultanas. Explain that this is a *unitary ratio*, since one of the numbers is 1. Unitary ratios are useful for making comparisons.

> Ask pupils to do **N4.4 Exercise 2A** in the class book (p. 167).

Remind the class that ratio is a way of comparing two quantities. Write on the board that to make a soft drink you need 10 ml of cordial for every 90 ml of water.

> What is the ratio of cordial to water?

> What fraction of the soft drink is cordial? What fraction is water?

> How much cordial will I need to make two soft drinks?
> How much water will I need?

> How much water will I need if I use 50 ml of cordial?

Discuss answers. Use **Toolsheet 2.1** to show how to use a number line and multiplication to scale up the quantities.

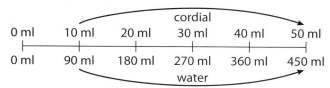

cordial

| 0 ml | 10 ml | 20 ml | 30 ml | 40 ml | 50 ml |

| 0 ml | 90 ml | 180 ml | 270 ml | 360 ml | 450 ml |

water

How much water do I need for 30 ml of cordial? [270 ml]

How much soft drink will I get with 70 ml of cordial? [70 ml + 630 ml = 700 ml]

How much cordial do I need with 45 ml of water? [5 ml]

Refer to the number line where necessary.

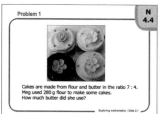

Problem 1
N 4.4

Cakes are made from flour and butter in the ratio 7 : 4. Meg used 280 g flour to make some cakes. How much butter did she use?

Problem 2
N 4.4

Purple paint is made by mixing 600 ml of blue with every 400 ml of red paint.

How much purple paint can be made by mixing red paint with 6 litres of blue paint?

Show pupils how to solve a problem where we are told a ratio and the size of one part, and have to calculate the size of the other part or the size of the whole.

Show the cake problem on **slide 2.1**.

Explain that 280 g flour is $\frac{7}{11}$, so $\frac{1}{11}$ is $280 \div 7 = 40$ g.

The butter is $\frac{4}{11}$, or $40 \times 4 = 160$ g.

Another way to think about this problem is to say that the ratio 7 : 4 must be equivalent to the ratio 280 : **?**, where **?** is the number of grams of butter. We scale 7 up by multiplying by 40 to get 280, so we do the same to 4 to get $4 \times 40 = 160$ g of butter. Explain that we call 40 the *scale factor*.

Repeat with the paint problem on **slide 2.2**, discussing both approaches.

Ask pupils to do **N4.4 Exercise 2B** in the class book (p. 168).

Review

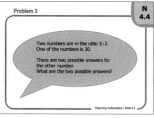

Problem 3
N 4.4

Two numbers are in the ratio 5 : 2. One of the numbers is 30.

There are two possible answers for the other number. What are the two possible answers?

Discuss the number problem on **slide 2.3** [solution: 12 or 75].

Finish by reminding the class of the points on **slide 2.4**.

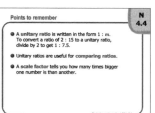

Points to remember
N 4.4

● A unitary ratio is written in the form 1 : m. To convert a ratio of 2 : 15 to a unitary ratio, divide by 2 to get 1 : 7.5.

● Unitary ratios are useful for comparing ratios.

● A scale factor tells you how many times bigger one number is than another.

Homework   Ask pupils to do **N4.4 Task 2** in the home book (p. 63).

3 Scale drawings

Learning points

- A scale drawing is a smaller drawing of an actual object.
- The scale gives the relative size of the drawn length to the actual length.
- The scale must always be stated next to the drawing.
- A map ratio is the ratio of the distance on the map to the actual distance on the ground.
- Map ratios are always given in the form $1:n$ and have no units.
  For example, a scale of 1 cm to 50 m is a map ratio of 1 : 5000, since 50 m is 5000 cm.
- A distance 'as the crow flies' is the shortest distance between two points, measured as a straight line.

Starter Explain that this lesson is about scale drawings and maps.

Remind the class that 5 miles is about the same as 8 kilometres.

A car has travelled 15 miles. How many kilometres is that?

Model the solutions using **Toolsheet 3.1**. Demonstrate that 5 is scaled up by a factor of 3 to make 15, so 8 must be scaled up by a factor of 3 to make 24.

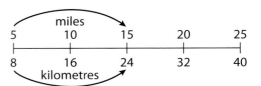

A car has travelled 48 kilometres. How many miles is that?

Show that 8 is scaled up by a factor of 6 to make 48, so 5 must be scaled up by a factor of 6 to make 30.

Repeat with similar questions.

Main activity Show **slide 3.1**. Say that the squares of the grid are centimetre squares, and that the red rectangle is a scale drawing of a room. The scale is 1 cm to 2 m. Stress that the scale is always written at the side of the drawing.

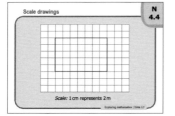

What are the actual dimensions of the room?

What would be the dimensions of the room if the scale were 1 cm to 5 m?

Draw on the board a rectangle to represent a swimming pool of length 24 metres and width 16 metres. Say that the scale of a drawing of the pool is 1 cm to 4 m.

What is the size of the rectangle in the scale drawing?

What is the size of the rectangle if the scale is 1 cm to 2 m?

Point out that if you double the scale to 1 cm to 8 m, the original drawing is halved in size.

Explain the importance of choosing a sensible scale for scale drawings.

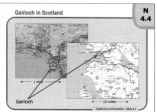

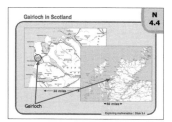

Use **slides 3.2 to 3.4** to draw out what pupils already know and remember about map scales, e.g. from geography lessons. If possible, omit these slides and show the class a series of maps of different scales focusing on the locality of the school, perhaps using the maps on the website **www.multimap.com**. Make sure that 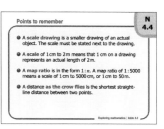 **WEB** pupils understand that a larger scale decreases, not increases, the map distance. Discuss the level of detail as the scale of the map increases, and what maps with different scales are useful for.

Discuss the ways in which the scale of a map may be presented:

- by showing a line or scale marked with a distance, as on the map on **slide 3.3**;

- by stating a scale, e.g. 1 cm represents 10 km;

- by stating a map ratio, which is the ratio of the distance on the map to the actual distance on the ground. Map ratios are always given as unitary ratios in the form $1 : n$ and have no units.

Work through a couple of examples on the board. For example, to write a scale of 1 cm to 10 km as a map ratio, both distances must be expressed in the same units. Since 10 km is $10 \times 1000 \times 100$ cm $= 1\,000\,000$ cm, the map ratio is $1 : 1\,000\,000$.

Give each pupil a piece of string. Refer the class to the map in question 2 of **N4.4 Exercise 3B** in the class book (p. 172). Show them how to use a ruler to find a direct distance 'as the crow flies' between two places on a map. Show also how to use string to estimate an actual distance along a footpath or road.

Review

Give some examples of map scales and ask pupils to explain how to change them to map ratios, e.g. 1 cm to 200 m, 1 cm to 8 km, 1 cm to 50 km.

Summarise the lesson using the points on **slide 3.5**.

Homework

Ask pupils to do **N4.4 Task 3** in the home book (p. 65). Remind them that they will need a piece of string.

Learning points

◉ Two sets of numbers are in direct proportion when the ratio of corresponding numbers is the same. For example, (5, 8) and (20, 32) are in direct proportion since 5 : 20 = 8 : 32.

◉ When you solve direct proportion problems:

– a four-cell diagram helps you to see relationships between numbers and decide what calculation to do;

– the unitary method involves reducing the value of one of the variables to 1;

– corresponding quantities must be in the same units.

TO

Starter   Say that this lesson is about direct proportion, and that you will give an example of a direct proportion problem. Say that in a box of sweets there are 5 toffees for every 2 chocolates.

There are 15 toffees in the box. How many chocolates are there?

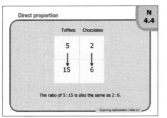

Use **Toolsheet 4.1** to model the solution. Demonstrate that 5 is multiplied by 3 to make 15 (i.e. scaled up by a factor of 3), so 2 must be multiplied by 3 to make 6.

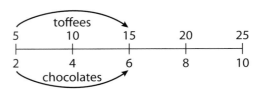

How many sweets are there altogether in the box?

What fraction of the sweets are toffees? What fraction are chocolates?

Use **slides 4.1** and **4.2** to discuss the relationships between the numbers involved.

Remind pupils that when they solve direct proportion problems using a four-cell diagram, they can work either left to right or top to bottom, and scale numbers up or down. The best way will depend on the relationships between the numbers.

Main activity   Use **slides 4.3** and **4.4** to show two simple direct proportion problems that can be solved without using calculators.

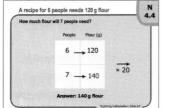

1   A recipe for 6 people needs 120 g flour. How much flour will 7 people need?

2   A recipe for 8 people needs 500 g flour. How much flour will 6 people need?

Summarise the approaches to these problems by saying that:

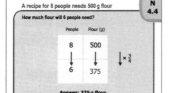

◉ most people solve direct proportion problems that they meet in everyday life using informal approaches;

◉ a four-cell diagram helps you to organise the information in a structured way to make the relationships between the numbers more obvious, and to identify the calculation needed to scale numbers up or down;

◉ as with other word problems, corresponding quantities in direct proportion problems need to be in the same units.

So to get going with a straightforward problem involving direct proportion, either use a number line or create a four-cell diagram, labelling the columns with the two variables.

Use **slides 4.5** and **4.6** to show a harder problem:

> A recipe for 6 people needs 140 g flour.
> How much flour will 14 people need?

This time it isn't easy to spot a relationship between the numbers, so an intermediate step is used to find the amount needed for one person. Work through the steps on **slide 4.6**, showing how to arrive at the answer by using a calculator. Say that this method is known as the *unitary method*, because the value of one of the variables is reduced to 1.

Work through a second example on the board to show how to record the steps.

> The mass of 120 ml of olive oil is 90 g.
> What is the mass of 58 ml of olive oil?

	Oil (ml)	Mass (g)
	120	90
÷ 120	1	0.75
× 58	58	43.5

Ask pupils to do **N4.4 Exercise 4** in the class book (p. 176).

Review Show the three problems on **slides 4.7, 4.8** and **4.9**.

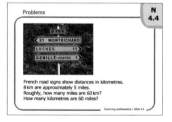

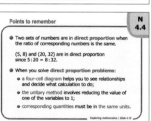

Ask pupils to discuss in pairs how they would do each question, and whether or not they would use a calculator. Take feedback.

Round off by stressing the points on **slide 4.10**.

Homework Ask pupils to do **N4.4 Task 4** in the home book (p. 66).

5 Fraction, decimal and percentage operators

Learning points

- An operation can be described in different ways. For example, for 16 →10, the relationship could be described as '× 5 then ÷ 8', '× $\frac{5}{8}$', '× 0.625', '× 62.5%', '÷ 1.6'.

- When you solve problems involving fractions, decimals and percentages, decide which is the most efficient way to calculate.

Starter

Use **slide 5.1** to discuss the objectives for this and the next lesson.

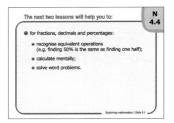

Practise halving and doubling decimals. Ask a few questions for pupils to answer on whiteboards. Discuss the strategies used each time:

> What is half of 0.3? What number would you double to get 0.12?

Play Bingo using **slide 5.2**. Ask pupils to draw four boxes on their whiteboards. They should choose four different numbers from the slide and write them in their boxes. Read out the clues below in any order. If pupils have the answer in one of their boxes they can cross it out. The first player to cross out all four numbers calls out 'Bingo!'.

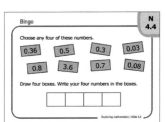

- Double nought point one eight. [0.36]
- Half of nought point six. [0.3]
- Twice nought point two five. [0.5]
- Divide one point six by two. [0.8]
- Multiply nought point three five by two. [0.7]
- Double double nought point nought two. [0.08]
- Multiply nought point nought one five by two. [0.03]
- Double one point eight. [3.6]

Main activity

Draw a function machine on the board. Say that it only multiplies and divides. Write × 8 in the function box. Ask pupils to give you the output for different input numbers.

$$? \rightarrow \boxed{\times 8} \rightarrow ?$$

> What is the output when the input is 12? Or $1\frac{1}{4}$? Or 0.8?
>
> What is the input when the output is 12? Or $3\frac{1}{2}$? Or 0.4?

Repeat using different functions and whole-number, fraction and decimal inputs.

Now give 320 as the input.

> What is the output when the function is ÷ 10?
> Or × 0.1? Or × 10%? Or × $\frac{1}{10}$?
> What do you notice?

Repeat with 12 as the input number and use × $2\frac{1}{4}$, × 225% and × 2.25 as functions.

Write on the board: 0.5 → 2.

Ask pupils to identify the function. Remind them that only multiplication and division are allowed. Take feedback, drawing out alternatives.

Give each pair a set of cards made from **N4.4 Resource sheet 5.1** and a large sheet of paper. Ask pupils to group cards with the same relationship on the large sheet of paper and to label each group. Bring the class together to discuss results. **RS**

Write on the board: 20 → 15, 4 → 3, 10 → 7.5. Ask:

> Why have I grouped these cards together? Give me another example of a pair of numbers that belongs to this set.

> What patterns do you notice? How could you describe them?

Discuss equivalent functions, e.g. 'divide by 4 then multiply by 3' or 'multiply by 3 then divide by 4' or 'multiply by $\frac{3}{4}$' or 'multiply by 0.75' or 'multiply by 75%'.

Repeat with another set of cards with the same relationship.

Select individual work from **N4.4 Exercise 5** in the class book (p. 179).

Review

Take feedback on the exercise, discussing the approximations and the efficiency of the calculation strategies that pupils used, e.g. whether calculating 30% of 42 as 0.3×42 is more efficient than finding 10% and multiplying by 3.

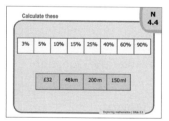

Show **slide 5.3**. Choose a percentage. Ask pupils to apply that percentage increase or decrease to the different quantities, calculating mentally and writing answers on whiteboards. Compare methods, highlighting the use of equivalent operations.

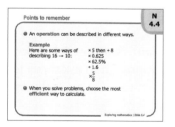

Repeat, this time using calculators. Again, compare methods. Draw out that when using a calculator it is more efficient to find 35% of a quantity by multiplying by 0.35 than, say, multiplying by 35 and dividing by 100.

Sum up using the points on **slide 5.4**.

Homework

Ask pupils to do **N4.4 Task 5** in the home book (p. 67).

6 Solving problems

Learning points

- When you solve word problems, read the question to yourself and decide what information to use.
- Choose a calculation method that is easy to use with the numbers in the problem.
- Always write down the calculations that you will do.
- Decide how you will check your work.

Starter Say that this lesson is intended to sharpen strategies for solving problems by calculating mentally with fractions, decimals and percentages.

Draw a line on the board. Label the ends with $\times 0$ and $\times 3$. Ask pupils to choose fraction, decimal or percentage operators to write on the line. Encourage them to use equivalent mixed number, proper and improper fraction, decimal and percentage operations.

> Where should you place $\times 0.8$, $\times 1\frac{1}{3}$, $\times 1\%$, $\times 2.125$, …?
>
> How do you decide where this operator should go?
>
> Which operators does $\times 1.37$ come between?
>
> How can you write this as a fraction operator? As a decimal operator? As a percentage operator?

Main activity Write 0.8×35 on the board. Explain that you can ask the same question in different ways, such as 80% of 35 or $\frac{4}{5} \times 35$. Ask pupils to answer the question and to describe their mental methods.

Repeat with different questions. Include questions that can reveal misconceptions, such as $\times 30\%$ being seen as the equivalent of $\times \frac{1}{3}$.

> How else could you write 225% of 52? $1\frac{1}{3}$ of 210?

RS ▶ Give each pair of pupils a set of cards made from **N4.4 Resource sheet 6.1**. Ask the pairs to group the cards into sets of equivalent calculations. Then ask them to find the answer for each set of calculations. Encourage them to work mentally as far as possible.

Discuss different strategies for calculating proportions of 72 with the class.

> Which calculations did you find difficult? Why?
>
> Were you surprised to find that any of the particular calculations were equivalent?

RS ▶ Pairs should double up to groups of four. Each group should nominate a recorder and a chair. Give each group a set of cards from **N4.4 Resource sheet 6.2**.

Ask groups to do **N4.4 Exercise 6** in the class book (p. 181). They should discuss the information on the cards and work out how much of each ingredient is used for a batch of cakes.

Review Discuss pupils' results and the strategies used.

Which ingredients did you work out first?

Did it matter in which order you worked on the different ingredients?

Were any calculations difficult to do mentally?

What information did you use to check that your results were right?

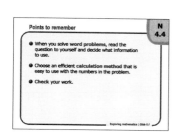

Sum up the lesson using the points on **slide 6.1**.

Round off the unit by referring again to the objectives. Suggest that pupils find time to try the self-assessment problems in **N4.4 How well are you doing?** in the class book (p. 182).

Homework Ask pupils to do **N4.4 Task 6** in the home book (p. 68).

N4.4 Mental test

Read each question aloud twice.

Allow a suitable pause for pupils to write answers.

1 Three pencils cost sixty pence.
How much would four pencils cost?

2006 KS3

2 Two rulers cost eighty pence.
How much do three rulers cost?

2005 KS3

3 A quarter of a number is one point two five.
What is the number?

1998 KS3

4 In a group of forty-five children, there are twice as many boys as girls.
How many girls are there?

2006 KS2

5 Six cakes cost one pound eighty.
How much do ten cakes cost?

2002 KS2

6 What is three fifths of forty pounds?

2003 KS3

7 A bag of four oranges costs thirty-seven pence.
How much do twelve oranges cost?

2000 KS2

8 Write the ratio twelve to four as simply as possible.

2007 KS3

9 The ratio of men to women in a chess club is three to two.
There are fifty people in the club. How many are women?

2007 KS3

10 The ratio of boys to girls in a class is three to five.
There are twelve boys. How many girls are there?

2006 KS3

11 Jenny and Mark share some money in the ratio two to three.
Jenny's share is one hundred and ten pounds.
How much is Mark's share?

2003 KS3

12 The instructions for a fruit drink say to mix one part lemon juice with four
parts water. I want to make one litre of this fruit drink.
How much lemon juice should I use?
Give your answer in millilitres.

2004 KS3

Key:
KS3 Key Stage 3 test   KS2 Key Stage 2 test
Questions 1 and 2 are at level 4; questions 3 to 7 are at level 5;
questions 8 to 12 are at level 6.

Answers

1	80p	**2**	£1.20
3	5	**4**	15 girls
5	£3	**5**	£24
7	£1.11	**8**	3 : 1
9	20 women	**10**	20 girls
11	£165	**12**	200 millilitres

N4.4 Check up and resource sheets

Write your answers in your book.

Proportional reasoning (no calculator)

1. Write the ratio 18 : 27 in its simplest form.

2. Mixing 3 parts of blue paint and 2 parts of red paint makes purple paint.
For 25 litres of purple paint, how many litres of blue paint do you need?

3. Rectangle ABCD has a perimeter of 36 cm.
Sides AB and DC are twice as long as sides AD and BC.
Calculate the length of side AD.

A   B

D   Not actual size   C

4. The recipe on the right is for strawberry ice-cream for 8 people.

   a Jessica makes enough ice-cream for 12 people. How much cream does she use?

   b David makes ice-cream using 750 g of strawberries. How much sugar does he use?

   > **Strawberry ice-cream**
   >
   > 0.5 litre cream
   > 1 kg strawberries
   > 200 g sugar

5. a Stilton cheese costs £7.50 for 1 kg. Fran buys 200 grams of Stilton cheese. How much does she pay?

   b Cheshire cheese costs £8.40 for 1 kg. Jamie pays £2.10 for some Cheshire cheese. How many grams of Cheshire cheese does he buy?

Proportional reasoning (calculator allowed)

6. A packet contains 1.5 kilograms of cat food. Linda feeds her cat 60 grams of the cat food each day. How many days does the packet of cat food last?

7. Assume that one British pound (£1) is worth 1.9 US dollars ($).
In London, a magazine costs £3.50.
In New York, the same magazine costs $5.75.
In which city is the magazine cheaper, London or New York?
Explain how you know.

8. Shortbread is made using flour, butter and sugar.
The flour, butter and sugar are mixed in the ratio 4 : 3 : 2 by weight.
Khalid makes some shortbread using 600 g of flour.

   a How many grams of butter does he use?

   b How many grams of sugar does he use?

---

1 : 4	2 : 8
1 : 3	4 : 12
1 : 2	5 : 10
2 : 1	6 : 3
3 : 2	6 : 4
2 : 3	6 : 9
3 : 1 : 2	6 : 2 : 4
2 : 1 : 3	6 : 3 : 9

---

8 → 12	21 → 7	16 → 10
10 → 25	6 → 9	10 → 7.5
8 → 32	7 → $2\frac{1}{3}$	14 → 35
$\frac{1}{4}$ → 1	4 → 3	2 → 3
150 → 50	20 → 15	4 → 10
80 → 50	0.5 → 2	4 → 2.5

0.03×72	30% of 72	125 of 72	72×100
$\frac{1}{10}$ of 72	3% of 72	$\frac{3}{10}$ of 72	$\frac{5}{4}$ of 72
$72 \div \frac{1}{100}$	0.01×72	$\frac{1}{100}$ of 72	$33\frac{1}{3}$% of 72
125% of 72	$72 \div 10$	1% of 72	0.3×72
$\frac{1}{3}$ of 72	$72 \div 0.01$	0.1 of 72	$72 \div 100$

In total the cakes weigh 7200 grams.	An egg weighs about 50 grams.	Butter weighs 1.7 times as much as the eggs.
The chocolate weighs $\frac{1}{9}$ of the cake.	Raisins weigh 60% of the chocolate.	The flour weighs 175% of the chocolate.
Sugar weighs 225% of the nuts.	Flour weighs $\frac{7}{36}$ of the total.	The nuts weigh 0.7 of the chocolate.
Eggs weigh 125% of the chocolate.	The recipe contains 20 eggs.	The raisins weigh $\frac{6}{7}$ of the nuts.

N4.4 Answers

Class book

Exercise 1A

1 a A and D   b D

2 a 2:5   b 8:5
  c 5:1   d 5:3
  e 2:3:4   f 5:2:10

3 a 3:1   b 3:17
  c 10:1   d 3:2
  e 10:7   f 3:2:6

4 This is a game. The eight matching pairs are:
  1 : 4 and 2 : 8
  1 : 3 and 4 : 12
  1 : 2 and 5 : 10
  2 : 1 and 6 : 3
  3 : 2 and 6 : 4
  2 : 3 and 6 : 9
  3 : 1 : 2 and 6 : 2 : 4
  2 : 1 : 3 and 6 : 3 : 9

Exercise 1B

1 Anna's share was £800.

2 Side AD is 6 cm.

3 AB is 48 cm.

4 a 400 millilitres of tomato juice
  b 600 millilitres of carrot juice

5 5 : 12 : 3

6 a Strawberry juice: 100 ml
  b Raspberry juice: 300 ml
  c Water: 600 ml

7 a 105 men
  b 175 women
  c 70 children

Extension problems

9 C 2 : 4

10 20 soft centres
   8 hard centres
   The combined box has 16 hard centres and 32 soft centres, a ratio of 1 : 2 hard to soft centres.

Exercise 2A

1 a 1:4   b 1:6   c 1:2.75
  d 1:0.5   e 1:0.625   f 1:3.5
  g 1:0.28   h 1:4   i 1:2

2 C

3 1 litre of A has a ratio of 1 : 3.5 of orange to pineapple juice.
  1 litre of B has a ratio of 1 : 4 of orange to pineapple juice.
  So B has more pineapple juice.

4 A has a ratio of 1 : 1.5 currants to raisins.
  B has a ratio of 1 : 1.25 currants and raisins.
  So cake mix A has the greater proportion of raisins.

Exercise 2B

1 Paige's share is £160.

2 There are 63 members of the tennis club.

3 7.5 litres of yellow paint

4 12.5 cm tall

5 a 500 g of flour
  b 80 g of sugar

6 a 135 kg iron
  b 81 kg copper

7 a Lily's share is £200.
  b Alexandra's share is £350.

8 10.5 kg cement

Extension problems

9 a The maximum amount of purple paint that Peter can make is 750 ml (300 ml of red and 450 ml of blue).
  b The red paint in the new tin is two fifths of tin A and three tenths of tin B. The blue paint in the new tin is three fifths of tin A and seven tenths of tin B. The ratio of red to blue paint in the new tin is $\frac{2}{5} + \frac{3}{10} : \frac{3}{5} + \frac{7}{10}$, which simplifies to 7 : 13.

Exercise 3A

1 a 9 m
   b 21 m
   c 13.5 m
   d 15.6 m
   e 26.1 m

2 a 1 cm to 1.5 m
   b 7.5 m
   c 22.5 square metres

3 a 3.5 m
   b 2.5 m
   c 4.3 m (to 1 d.p.)
   d Length 14 cm; width 10 cm
   e 0.25 m

4 a 24 m
   b 15 cm
   c 4.5 cm

	Actual length	Length on scale drawing
5 a	3 m	**15 cm**
b	1.5 m	**7.5 cm**
c	50 cm	**2.5 cm**
d	**6 m**	30 cm
e	**2.5 m**	12.5 cm
f	**0.25 m**	1.25 cm

Exercise 3B

1 a 50 m   b 3 km
   c 200 m   d 100 km

2 a 100 m
   b High Street 560 m; St Peter Street 350 m
   c Approximately 830 m
   d Approximately 1.8 km

3 a 1 : 100 000   b 1 : 25 000
   c 1 : 20 000   d 1 : 200 000

4 a 250 m or 0.25 km
   b Approximately 3.25 km
   c i   Old Glasson to Norbreck Farm
          2 km
      ii The Hotel to Hillam
          2.5 km
      iii Crook Cottage to Hill House Farm
          3.75 km
   d Approximately 8.75 km

5 a 27 km   b 20 cm

6 a 1 : 12   b 1 : 36
   c 1 : 63 360   d 1 : 4
   e 1 : 15 840   f 1 : 110

Exercise 4

1 a 60p   b £2.47
   c £8.50   d £3.85
   e 100 oranges   f 6 marrows

2 a 20 cm; 12 inches
   b 17.5 pints; 20 litres
   c 121 pounds; 25 kilograms
   d 12.5 miles; 68 kilometres

3 a 15 miles   b 40 miles
   c 45 minutes   d 1 hour 30 minutes

4 a 400 g flour
      160 g currants
      200 g sugar
      240 g margarine
      $1\frac{1}{3}$ teaspoon spice
      40 ml milk
      120 ml beaten egg
   b 3 : 4
   c 18 buns
   d 180 g currants
      225 g sugar
      270 g margarine
      $1\frac{1}{2}$ teaspoon spice
      45 ml milk
      135 ml beaten egg

	litres	pints
5	1	**1.75**
	24	**42**
	13	**22.75**
	0.57 (to 2 d.p.)	1
	32	56
	68	119

6 a £2   b £4.40
   c 600 g   d £2.40
   e £5.28   f 500 g
   g Black olives are more expensive because, for
      example, 100 g black olives cost £2.40 and
      100 g of green olives cost £2.

7 a 12 euros   b 62.5 pence   c £35

Extension problem

8 **a** 1 pint of milk for 47p

b 5 kg of potatoes for £1.80

c 400 ml of orange juice for 58p

d 15 postcards for £7.80

Exercise 5

1

	Mark	Fraction	Decimal	%
Lena	21	$\frac{21}{40}$	0.525	52.5%
Stacey	37	$\frac{37}{40}$	0.925	92.5%
Pritam	25	$\frac{5}{8}$	0.625	62.5%
Michelle	34	$\frac{17}{20}$	0.85	85%
Cole	24	$\frac{3}{5}$	0.6	60%

2 **a** $\frac{23}{100} \times 700$; $\quad$ $0.23 \times 700 = 161$

b $\frac{41}{50} \times 600$; $\quad$ $0.82 \times 600 = 492$

c $\frac{17}{25} \times 900$; $\quad$ $0.68 \times 900 = 612$

3 **a** $\frac{9}{10} \times 420$; $\quad$ 90% of $420 = 378$

b $\frac{7}{20} \times 180$; $\quad$ 35% of $180 = 63$

c $1\frac{1}{4} \times 560$; $\quad$ 125% of $560 = 700$

4 **a** 62.5% of 1400; $\quad$ $0.625 \times 1400 = 875$

b 60% of 95; $\quad$ $0.6 \times 95 = 57$

c 45% of 510; $\quad$ $0.45 \times 510 = 229.5$

5 61% of $410 = 250.1$

35% of $930 = 325.5$

42% of $520 = 218.4$

94% of $165 = 155.1$

16% of $420 = 67.2$

86% of $515 = 442.9$

6 For example:

a Function 1: $\times 1.5$, $\times \frac{3}{2}$, $\times 150\%$, $\times 3 \div 2$, $\div \frac{2}{3}$

b Function 2: $\div 1.5$, $\div \frac{3}{2}$, $\times 66\frac{2}{3}\%$, $\times 2 \div 3$, $\times \frac{2}{3}$

c Function 3: $\times 75$, $\times \frac{3}{4}$, $\times 75\%$, $\times 3 \div 4$, $\div \frac{4}{3}$

d Function 4: $\div 1.25$, $\div \frac{5}{4}$, $\times 80\%$, $\times 4 \div 5$, $\times \frac{4}{5}$

7 **a** 7104 $\quad$ **b** 68.04 $\quad$ **c** 742.5

d 11.75 $\quad$ **e** 19.25 $\quad$ **f** 65.8

Exercise 6

Ingredients for the cakes:

Eggs $\quad$ 1 kg

Flour $\quad$ 1.4 kg

Butter $\quad$ 1.7 kg

Sugar $\quad$ 1.26 kg

Chocolate $\quad$ 800 g

Nuts $\quad$ 560 g

Raisins $\quad$ 480 g

How well are you doing?

1 5 : 6

2 **a** £2.10 $\quad$ **b** 250 g

3 320 km

4 8 oranges

5 36°

6 **a** 7 : 5 $\quad$ **b** 7 : 6

7 39 children

Home book

TASK 1

1 Any ratios equivalent to 36 : 48, e.g.
3 : 4, 6 : 8, 9 : 12, 12 : 16, 15 : 20, etc.

2 A £72 : £48

B £75 : £45

C £48 : £12 : £60

D £66 : £54

E £68 : £52

F £30 : £50 : £40

G £56 : £64

H £20 : £40 : £60

TASK 2

1 Jyoti has 105 and Gopal has 35 paperbacks.

2 Harry let in 24 goals.

3 The first box has the greater proportion of green peppers.

4 Rovers is more successful. Rovers scored 3.6 goals for every goal against. City scored 3.5 goals for every goal against.

5 The bakery sold 52 white loaves.

6 315 adults are watching the film.

7 **a** Amy's share is £16. **b** Rachel's share is £48.

8 78 daisies, buttercups and dandelions
(48 daisies, 24 buttercups and 6 dandelions)

TASK 3

1 a 1 km
   b Approximately 9 km
   c From Whitby to Sleights: 4.5 km
     From Lythe to Robin Hood's Bay: 12 km
   d Approximately 9 km

2 a 1 : 50 000   b 1 : 20 000 000
   c 1 : 500 000   d 1 : 1250

3 13.5 km

TASK 4

1 a 800 g haddock
     300 ml milk
     2.5 kg potatoes
     250 g cheese
     $2\frac{1}{2}$ tablespoon flour
   b 2 : 5
   c 7 people
   d 560 g haddock
     210 ml milk
     1.75 kg potatoes
     $1\frac{3}{4}$ tablespoon flour

2 a $53.20   b £150

3 a 264 miles   b 22 miles
   c 2 hours 30 minutes

TASK 5

1

70%	30%	20%	2%	80%	45%	15%	12%
$\frac{7}{10}$	$\frac{3}{10}$	$\frac{1}{5}$	$\frac{1}{50}$	$\frac{4}{5}$	$\frac{9}{20}$	$\frac{3}{20}$	$\frac{3}{25}$
0.7	0.3	0.2	0.02	0.8	0.45	0.15	0.12

2 a 25.2 m   b £55.10   c 1.755 km
   d £49.30   e 3.36 litres   f 189.84 kg
   g 6.4 cm   h £6.96   i £25.55

TASK 6

1 a 42.5%   b 32%
   c 16%   d 50%

2 a Classical: £13.20
   b Pop: £10.03
   c Rock: £12.16
   d Spiritual and gospel: £10.12
   e Hip-hop: £9.01
   f Music from China: £10.62
   g Rap: £6.97
   h Jazz: £12.54
   i Country and western: £10.08
   j Blues: £7.98

CD-ROM

Check up

1 2 : 3

2 15 litres of blue paint

3 AD = 6 cm

4 a 0.75 litre of cream
   b 150 g of sugar

5 a £1.50   b 250 g

6 25 days

7 The magazine is cheaper in New York, since £3.50 is equivalent to 6.65 dollars.

8 a 450 g butter   b 300 g of sugar

Transformations

Previous learning

Before they start, pupils should be able to:

- identify and visualise transformations and symmetries of 2D shapes: reflection and line symmetry, rotation and rotation symmetry, and translation
- recognise and visualise symmetries and simple transformations of 2D shapes
- solve simple problems involving ratio and proportion.

Objectives based on NC levels 5 and 6 (mainly level 5)

In this unit, pupils learn to:

- conjecture and generalise
- visualise and manipulate dynamic images and explore the effect of varying values
- make accurate mathematical diagrams on paper and on screen
- use accurate notation
- select appropriate procedures and tools, including ICT
- refine own findings and approaches on the basis of discussion with others

and to:

- find the midpoint of the line segment AB; given the coordinates of points A and B
- identify all the symmetries of 2D shapes
- transform 2D shapes by rotation, reflection and translation, on paper and using ICT, and try out mathematical representations of simple combinations of these transformations
- enlarge 2D shapes, given a centre of enlargement and a positive integer scale factor, and explore enlargement using ICT.

Lessons

1 **Repeated transformations**
2 **Combining transformations**
3 **Using ICT to explore transformations**
4 **Scale factor**
5 **Centre of enlargement**
6 **Enlargement, ratio and proportion**
7 **Finding the midpoint**

About this unit

Pupils need to be able to visualise transformations.
They should understand that, for reflection, rotation and translation, resulting images are congruent to the original objects. This means that, in the image and object, corresponding angles are equal and corresponding sides are equal.

For enlargement, pupils need to make the links to ratio and proportion and, later, to similar shapes. They should realise that although angles remain unaltered, the length of each side increases in the same ratio.

Assessment

This unit includes:

- a self-assessment section (*G4.3 How well are you doing?* class book p. 201);
- a set of questions to replace or supplement questions in the exercises or homework tasks, or to use as an informal test (*G4.3 Check up*, CD-ROM).

Common errors and misconceptions	Look out for pupils who mistakenly think that:

Common errors and misconceptions

Look out for pupils who mistakenly think that:
- the shape of the object changes when it is reflected, rotated or translated;
- all reflections are made in horizontal or vertical mirror lines;

and for pupils who:
- misread coordinates;
- reflect straight across diagonal lines;
- fail to link enlargements to given centres of enlargement;
- apply the scale factor to some but not all of the dimensions of a shape.

Key terms and notation

problem, solution, method, pattern, relationship, represent, solve, explain, justify

rotate, rotation, reflect, reflection, translate, translation, congruent, combination, 2D shape, symmetry, tessellate, tessellation

enlargement, ratio, proportion, scale factor, centre of enlargement

midpoint, end point, coordinates, line segment

Practical resources

squared paper, isometric paper
ruler and sharp pencil for each pupil
calculators for pupils
individual whiteboards
computers, one per pair of pupils
(lesson 2)

dynamic geometry software
(optional)
glue, scissors and a large sheet of
paper for each pair (lesson 3)
A4 and A3 paper

Exploring maths

Tier 4 teacher's book
Answers for Unit G4.3 , pp. 224–229

Tier 4 CD-ROM
PowerPoint files
   G4.3 slides for lessons 1 to 7
The Geometer's Sketchpad files
(optional; lessons 5 and 7)
   G4.3 Enlargement
   G4.3 Midpoint
Tools and prepared toolsheets
   Rotate tool
   Reflect tool
Tier 4 programs
   Transformations
   Transformation golf
   Tessellations
   Angle sums
   Enlargement
   Midpoints

Tier 4 class book
G4.3, pp. 184–202
G4.3 How well are you doing? p. 201

Tier 4 home book
G4.3, pp. 70–79

Tier 4 CD-ROM
G4.3 Check up
G4.3 Pupil resource sheets
   1.1 One per pupil
   2.1 One per group

Useful websites

Reflecting shapes, Rotate tiles, Post the shapes, Nine hole golf
www.mathsonline.co.uk/nonmembers/gamesroom

Bathroom tiles
www.bbc.co.uk/education/mathsfile/gameswheel.html

M. C. Escher
www.mcescher.com

Tessellations
www.tessellations.org/diy-basic1.htm

1 Repeated transformations

Learning points

◉ After reflection, rotation or translation, the object and image are congruent.

◉ Repeated rotations about the same centre of rotation can be replaced by a single rotation.

◉ Repeated translations can be replaced by a single translation.

Starter

Use **slide 1.1** to discuss the objectives for the first three lessons. Explain that this lesson is about repeated transformations.

Launch **Transformations**. Click on 'Create new shape', and click on three points in the first quadrant to create a scalene triangle. Click on 'Done' and colour it red. Click on 'Shadow on'.

Remind pupils that the shape in its original position is the *object* and in its new transformed position is the *image*.

> Where will the image be after a reflection in the x-axis?

Ask pupils to identify the coordinates of the image. Click on the triangle and then on the relevant reflection icon on the right of the screen.

Draw out through discussion that:

◉ the object and image are *congruent* (so corresponding sides and corresponding angles are the same);

◉ corresponding pairs of points on the image and object are the same perpendicular distance from the mirror line;

◉ the *mirror line* is a *line of symmetry* for the object and the image.

Click on 'Start again'. Draw another shape and this time reflect it in the y-axis. Repeat the discussion.

Click on 'Start again'. Draw another shape in the first quadrant, e.g. a rhombus. Explain that you want to rotate it 90° clockwise about the origin and that this is the *centre of rotation*.

> Where will the image be after the rotation?

Draw out through discussion that:

◉ the object and image are congruent;

◉ corresponding points on the image and object rotate through the same angle about the centre of rotation.

If you prefer, you could do the starter activities using the **Reflect tool** and the **Rotate tool**.

Main activity

Show **slide 1.2**.

> Describe the translation that takes shape A to shape B.

Click on the screen to show a movement of 6 units right and 9 units down. Explain that every point in the object is translated in the same way to its corresponding point in the image. Demonstrate this, annotating the image on the screen.

What translation would take shape A to shape C? Shape B to shape A?

Ask pairs to discuss and list the important facts about translation. Draw out that:

- the object and image are congruent;
- corresponding points on the image and object move through the same horizontal distance and the same vertical distance.

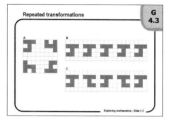

Show **slide 1.3**. Discuss the repeated transformations.

For the repeated rotation, make the links with rotation symmetry. Ask:

> Which transformation has been repeated? How do you know?
>
> What is the order of rotation symmetry of the final image?
>
> Where is the centre of rotation? How do you know?
>
> What could the angle of rotation have been each time?
> [90° clockwise or 270° anticlockwise]

For the repeated translation, ask:

> Which transformation has been repeated? How do you know?
>
> Describe the translation from one object to the image next to it on the right.
>
> Describe the translation from the first object to the last image, from left to right.

For the repeated reflection, ask:

> Which transformation has been repeated? How do you know?
>
> What sort of symmetry can be seen in this pattern?
>
> Where would you put the lines of reflection or mirror lines to create this pattern?

Select from **G4.3 Exercise 1** in the class book (p. 185). Pupils will need squared paper and **G4.3 Resource sheet 1.1**.

RS

Review

SIM

Launch **Transformations** again. Choose a shape and position it in the first quadrant. Put the 'Shadow' on. Reflect the shape in the vertical axis and then the horizontal axis.

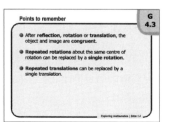

Choose the same shape again, make it a different colour, and position it in the original position on top of the object's shadow. This time rotate the shape by 180° about the origin. Discuss the results.

Repeat with different shapes placed initially in different quadrants.

Sum up with the points on **slide 1.4**.

Homework

Ask pupils to do **G4.3 Task 1** in the home book (p. 70). They will need squared paper.

2 Combining transformations

Learning points

- Reflection, rotation and translation can be combined to transform an object.
- Transformations can be combined in any order.
- Different combinations of transformations may have different effects.

SIM

Starter

This lesson preferably needs to take place in a computer room, with access to the program **Transformation golf** *from each computer.*

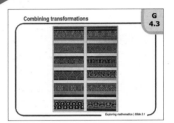

Remind the class that this lesson continues from the last one and is about combining *different* transformations.

Use the photographs on **slides 2.1** and **2.2** to discuss transformations. For example, choose a couple of the frieze patterns and ask:

> What transformations have been used to create this pattern?
>
> What are the similarities and differences between the ways these patterns have been created?

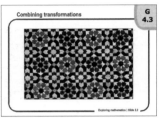

Discuss the tessellating lizards on **slide 2.3**. Establish that the different colours are not important, but the lizard shapes are congruent. Encourage pupils to explore the positions of lizards of each colour, and then to describe the transformations used.

SIM

RS

Main activity

Organise the class to work in pairs at computers. Ask them to launch the program **Transformation golf**. Explain that 'par' for a hole is the target number of shots. The aim is to use combinations of reflections, rotations and translations to get the ball in the hole. Ask the pairs to complete the course in as few shots as possible.

Give out **G4.3 Resource sheet 2.1**. This has a copy of each hole and can be used to record the different combinations of transformations needed.

When all pairs have played the whole game once, ask them to record their scores.

Now ask each pair to concentrate on one hole and explore combinations of transformations that create the same result with the fewest shots.

Ask pupils to do **G4.3 Exercise 2** in the class book (p. 187).

Review   Use the results recorded by pupils on **Resource sheet 2.1**.

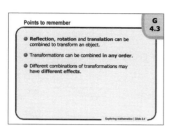

What other transformations are equivalent to a reflection horizontally followed by a reflection vertically?
[either a rotation through 180° about the point where the mirror lines cross, or two rotations through 90° about the same point, in either direction]

Is a rotation of 90° clockwise followed by a translation of one unit right equivalent to a translation one unit right followed by a rotation through 90° clockwise about the same centre of rotation? [no]

What combination would create the same effect as the first one?
[translation 1 unit up followed by a rotation through 90° clockwise]

Remind pupils of the points on **slide 2.4**.

Homework   Ask pupils to do **G4.3 Task 2** in the home book (p. 72).

3 Using ICT to explore transformations

Learning points

- Tessellations can be generated by reflections, rotations or translations.
- Some regular polygons will tessellate, e.g. equilateral triangles, squares, regular hexagons.
- Some regular polygons will not tessellate, e.g. regular pentagons.
- Some regular polygons will tessellate when combined with other regular polygons, e.g. octagons and squares.

Starter Explain that this lesson focuses on using transformations to create tessellations.

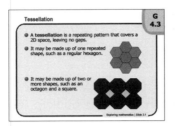

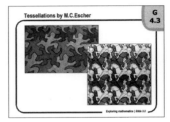

Show **slides 3.1, 3.2** and **3.3** to remind pupils that tessellations are repeating patterns made from basic shapes that fit together with no gaps. Some are simple, made up of the same shape repeated, whereas others are more complex.

Main activity Launch **Tessellations**. Click the square and 'Create copy'. Drag the square and repeat so that several squares have been placed together in a tessellation.

> **Can we do the same with the parallelograms?** [yes]

Click 'Reset'. Click the square and drag its vertices to form a parallelogram. Repeat the 'Create copy' procedure to show the tessellation of parallelograms.

> **Will congruent regular hexagons tessellate?**
> [yes; interior angles are 120° so three hexagons will fit together.]

Click 'Reset'. Use the arrows by the 'Shape 1' box to create a regular hexagon. Use the procedures described above to show that regular hexagons tessellate.

Ask pupils in pairs to compose a clear description of the tessellation. Their description should identify the shape being tessellated and the transformation used to produce the tessellation.

Ask a pair to share their description. Ask other pupils to help to refine it. Ask if any pair has a description using a different transformation. Aim to find two or three different descriptions. Establish that in this case the basic shape is a regular hexagon and the possible repeated transformations are: translation; reflection in a side; rotation through 120° about a vertex.

> **Will congruent regular octagons tessellate?** [no]

Click 'Reset'. Use the arrows by the 'Shape 1' box to create an eight-sided shape. Repeat the 'Create copy' procedure.

> **What do you notice?** [there are gaps]

> **What do you notice about the shape of the gaps?**
> [they are congruent squares]

Click 'Two shape tessellation on'. Resize the square that appears to fit one grid square by dragging each corner. Now click and drag the square to fill in the gaps in the tessellation. Repeat the 'Create copy' procedure to fill in the other gaps.

> **Can you explain why two octagons and a square will fit together around a point?**

Give pairs a minute or two to discuss this. Establish through discussion that the interior angle of a regular octagon is 135°, and of a square is 90°, so the sum of the angles of two regular octagons and one square at a point is 360°, i.e. no gaps.

> **What other tessellations could we make?**

Ask pupils to do **G4.3 Exercise 3** in the class book (p. 189). They will need squared paper. You may also want to provide glue, scissors and a large sheet of paper for each pair to create their own tessellation of an irregular shape.

Review

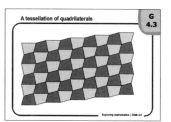

Refer to tessellations of regular triangles, squares and hexagons. Ask pupils to consider the interior angles of each tessellating shape and to explain why these shapes tessellate. Ask:

> **Will every regular polygon tessellate? Why? Why not?**

> **Will every quadrilateral tessellate? Why? Why not?**

Remind pupils that the four interior angles of any quadrilateral sum to 360° and will therefore fit around a point.

Launch **Angle sums**. Choose a quadrilateral. Drag its vertices to any position. Click near the midpoint of a side to rotate the quadrilateral about the midpoint. Build up a tessellation of the plane.

Show the tessellation of quadrilaterals on **slide 3.4**.

Summarise the lesson with the reminders on **slide 3.5**.

SIM

Homework   Ask pupils to do **G4.3 Task 3** in the home book (p. 73).

4 Scale factor

Learning points

- To describe an enlargement, give the centre of enlargement and the scale factor.

- All lengths in the object are multiplied by the scale factor to find corresponding lengths in the image.

- When lines are drawn linking corresponding points on the object and the image, they meet at the centre of enlargement.

- The object and image are similar shapes. Corresponding angles are the same.

Starter

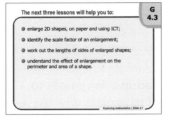

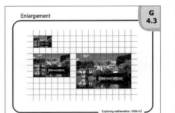

Show **slide 4.1** to explain the focus of this and the next two lessons. Say that this lesson looks at scale factors.

Ask the class to imagine a small rectangular photograph. Then say:

> Now imagine a photograph that is twice as big.
> How many times will the length of the original photo fit along the length of the bigger photo?
> How many times will the height of the original photo fit along the height of the bigger photo?

Repeat for a photo three times as big.

Show **slide 4.2**. Explain that the bigger photos are *enlargements* of the original photos. The length and height of the original photo have been multiplied by 2, the *scale factor*, to produce the first enlargement. In the second enlargement, the length and height of the original photo have been multiplied by scale factor 3.

Remind the class that the object and the image are *similar* shapes: they are the same shape, with the same angles, but a different size. Use the photographs to show that corresponding sides are in the same ratio.

Main activity

Show **slide 4.3**.

> What is the scale factor for these shapes? How did you work it out?

Establish that the scale factor can be calculated by dividing the length of one side on the image by the length of the corresponding side in the object.

Repeat for **slides 4.4** and **4.5**.

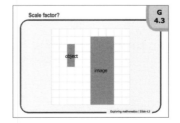 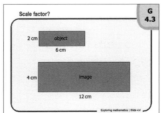 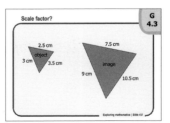

Display the rule for pupils:

For enlarged shapes:

scale factor = image length ÷ corresponding object length

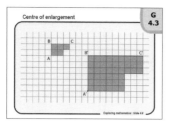

Show **slide 4.6**. Say that you want to make an enlargement of the shape, scale factor 3, with the image of point A at point A'. Ask pupils to discuss in pairs how to do this.

Click on **slide 4.6** to show the enlargement. Point out how corresponding lengths are linked to the scale factor.

Ask pupils to do **G4.3 Exercise 4** in the class book (p. 192).

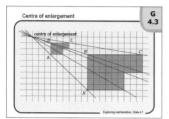

Show **slide 4.7**. Click on the slide to show the lines through A and A', then B and B'. Ask:

> Do you think the line joining C and C' will meet the other two lines? Where?

Click on the slide to draw the line through C and C'. Click again to demonstrate that all the lines joining corresponding points always meet at the same point, which is called the *centre of enlargement*.

Ask pupils to go back through their answers to question 2 of Exercise 4, draw lines joining corresponding points and mark each point where these lines cross as the centre of enlargement.

Review Ask pairs to discuss a solution to the problem on **slide 4.8**. Invite one or more pairs to demonstrate the solution.

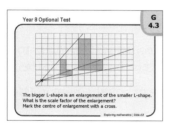

Sum up with the points on **slide 4.9**.

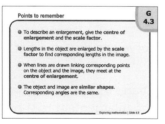

Homework Ask pupils to do **G4.3 Task 4** in the home book (p. 74). They will need squared paper.

5 Centre of enlargement

Learning points

- For an enlargement of scale factor 2:
  - the length of each side of the object is multiplied by 2;
  - the distance from the centre of enlargement to each point on the object is multiplied by 2.
- When you describe an enlargement, give the centre of enlargement and the scale factor.

Starter

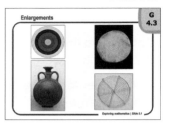

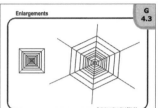

Explain to the class that they are going to continue exploring enlargements.

Show **slide 5.1**. Establish through discussion that all circles are enlargements of each other. Explain that concentric shapes are not necessarily circles but that they all have the same centre.

Show **slide 5.2**. Click to produce the first set of shapes. Agree that they are all squares.

> **What can you tell me about all squares?**
> [all squares are similar and are enlargements of each other]
>
> **Where is the centre of enlargement for this set of squares?**

Click on the slide to demonstrate that the lines joining corresponding vertices meet at the centre of enlargement.

Click again, and repeat with the second set of shapes (regular hexagons).

Main activity

Launch **Enlargement** or use **G4.3 Enlargement** for *The Geometer's Sketchpad* to create a starting point similar to the one shown. The object is the smaller shape.

Display the object and image. Ask pupils where the centre of enlargement is. Use the 'Hide/show' button to reveal it.

> **What is the scale factor for this enlargement?**
> **How did you work it out?**

Drag the centre of enlargement around. Ask pupils to observe and discuss what happens to the object and the image.

Reveal the lines joining corresponding points in the object and image. Show that they meet at the centre of enlargement. Move the centre of enlargement to show these lines always pass through the centre of enlargement.

Now reveal the coordinates. Move the centre of enlargement. Ask pupils to observe what happens to the pair of measurements.

Explain that if an object is enlarged by scale factor 2 then corresponding points of the image are twice as far from the centre of enlargement as those on the object.

Repeat with scale factor 3 and, if time allows, scale factor 4.

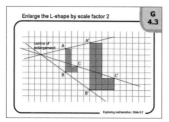

Show **slide 5.3** and give out squared paper. Ask pupils to draw the L-shape carefully and to mark the centre of enlargement. Explain that the shape is to be enlarged by a scale factor of 2. Reveal the labels and rays on the slide. Ask pupils to add these to their diagrams using their rulers.

> **How far is point A from the centre of enlargement?** [e.g. right 4, up 1]

> **How far will the corresponding point A′ be from the centre of enlargement?** [e.g. right 8, up 2]

Ask pupils to mark and label A′. Repeat with B′ and C′. Show these on **slide 5.3**.

Work anticlockwise around the shape from A, indicating the sides and saying:

> **If this object length is 4 units, how long is the corresponding image length?** [8 units]

Ask pupils to draw this in. Repeat for the other lengths. Click the slide to show the enlarged shape and its shading. Stress again that the lines joining corresponding points of the object and image meet at the centre of enlargement.

> Ask pupils to do **G4.3 Exercise 5** in the class book (p. 194). They will need squared paper.

Review   On the board draw two similar rectangles, as below. Say that one is an enlargement of the other. Ask how to work out how long the side marked x is. Discuss responses.

Repeat with two other rectangles, one 5 cm by 2 cm and the other 8 cm by x wide [$8 \div 5 \times 2 = 3.2$ cm].

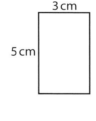
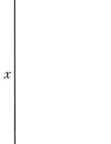

Finally consider the ratios of corresponding sides.

For the rectangles shown, the missing side could be calculated by the unitary method of solving ratios.

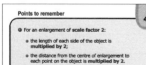

3	6	Given
1	2	Divide by 3 to find the simplest ratio.
5	10	Multiply by 5 to calculate the missing side

Discuss how the ratio in its simplest form (1 : 2) links with the scale factor 2.

Sum up with the points on **slide 5.4**.

Homework   Ask pupils to do **G4.3 Task 5** in the home book (p. 76). They will need squared paper.

6 Enlargement, ratio and proportion

Learning points

- Similar shapes are enlargements of each other.
- All angles remain unaltered by an enlargement.
- Lengths in the object are multiplied by the scale factor to find corresponding lengths in the image.
- You can use the unitary method to calculate missing lengths.

Starter   Say that the focus for this lesson is problem solving using enlargements.

Write $3 \times 4 = 6 \times \square$ on the board. Ask what number goes in the box and how to work it out. Discuss the methods used. Repeat for $7 \times 6 = 3 \times \square$ and $\square \times 5 = 6 \times 8$.

Main activity   Draw a pair of similar rectangles on the board. Tell the class that the larger rectangle is an enlargement of the smaller rectangle. Ask pupils to find the missing length.

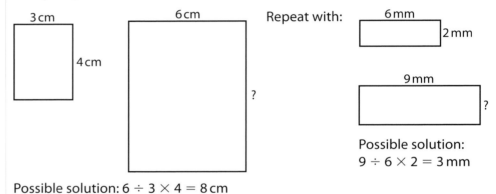

Possible solution: $6 \div 3 \times 4 = 8$ cm

Possible solution:
$9 \div 6 \times 2 = 3$ mm

Discuss different approaches to the problems. Establish that corresponding sides of the object and image are always in the same ratio. In the first problem the ratio 6 : 3 is the same as the ratio ? : 4. This relationship can also be written as:

$$\frac{6}{3} = \frac{\square}{4}$$

Ask pupils to do **G4.3 Exercise 6** in the class book (p. 197).

Lead an investigation into the sizes of metric paper. Fold a sheet of A3 paper in half to produce a rectangle that is the same size as A4 paper. Then fold a sheet of A4 paper in half to produce a rectangle that is the same size as A5. Stick the sheets of A3, A4 and A5 on the board. Ask pupils what they notice.

How would you make a sheet of A2 paper? [two sheets of A3 together]

Demonstrate this by placing it on the board to continue the sequence: A2, A3, A4, A5.

How would you make a sheet of A6 paper?

Demonstrate this and add it to the sequence on the board.

Explain that all these are enlargements of each other. Rearrange the papers to show them like this.

Draw a line from the bottom left corner through the opposite corner to demonstrate that the metric papers are all enlargements of each other.

Take a sheet of A4 paper. Write its dimensions on it: 297 mm by 210 mm.

Hold a sheet of A3 paper and show that the length of the shorter side is 297 mm.

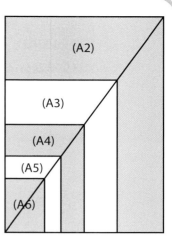

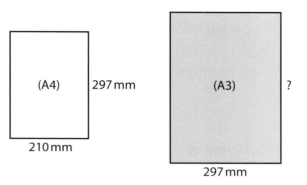

What is the length of the longer side of the A3 paper?
[297 ÷ 210 × 297 = 420 mm (to the nearest millimetre)]

Ask pupils to work in small groups to find the dimensions of A2 and A5 paper.

Review

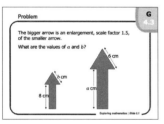

Show **slide 6.1**. Ask pupils to work in pairs on the problem. Establish that the angles remain constant under enlargement and that only the lengths are altered by the scale factor [$a = 12$, $b = 4$].

Sum up with the points on **slide 6.2**.

Homework Ask pupils to do **G4.3 Task 6** in the home book (p. 77).

7 Finding the midpoint

Learning points

Given a line segment AB:

- the x-coordinate of the midpoint is the mean of the x-coordinates of A and B;
- the y-coordinate of the midpoint is the mean of the y-coordinates of A and B.

Starter

Tell pupils that in this lesson they will learn how to find the midpoint of a line segment AB, given the coordinates of points A and B.

Write on the board these pairs of numbers:

3 and 5   6 and 10   24 and 26   −4 and 8   −5 and −10   23 and −27

Ask pupils to add the numbers in each pair and divide the total by 2, recording responses on their whiteboards.

Main activity

SIM

Launch **Midpoints**. Start with the screen not showing the coordinates of the points. Mark the midpoint.

Select either of the end points, A or B, and ask the class to write down the coordinates of this point on their whiteboards. Repeat for the other end point and for the midpoint, then reveal the coordinates on screen.

Move A and B around. With the class, explore the relationship between the three pairs of coordinates. Draw a table and record the results.

A	B	M
(1, 2)	(7, 4)	(4, 3)

What do you notice about the coordinates of A, B and the midpoint?

What happens if A is in the second quadrant and B is in the first quadrant?

What happens if A and B are both in the third quadrant?

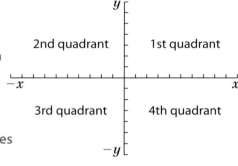

Pick other combinations for A and B in different quadrants.

How do you work out the coordinates of the midpoint, given the coordinates of the end points?

Draw out through discussion that the x-coordinate of the midpoint is the mean of the x-coordinates of the end points, and that the y-coordinate of the midpoint is the mean of the y-coordinates of the end points. Demonstrate how to calculate the midpoint, e.g.

The midpoint of A (5, 12) and B (−3, 2) is the point $\left(\dfrac{5-3}{2}, \dfrac{12+2}{2}\right)$, or (1, 7).

Ask pupils to do **G4.3 Exercise 7** in the class book (p. 199).

As an alternative to the above, you could use dynamic geometry software (see **G4.3 Midpoint**). Draw a line segment AB with its midpoint labelled M. List the coordinates of each of the three points. Create a button that can be used to hide the coordinates.

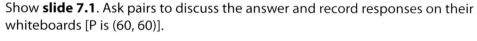

Review

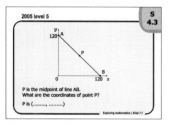

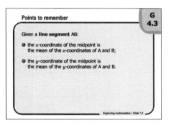

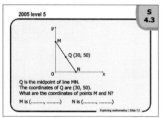

Show **slide 7.1**. Ask pairs to discuss the answer and record responses on their whiteboards [P is (60, 60)].

Repeat with **slide 7.2** [M is (0, 100); N is (60, 0)].

Take feedback on how the pairs approached the problem.

Finish by reminding pupils of the points on **slide 7.3**.

Round off the unit by referring again to the objectives. Suggest that pupils find time to try the self-assessment problems in **G4.3 How well are you doing?** in the class book (p. 201).

Homework

Ask pupils to do **G4.3 Task 7** in the home book (p. 78).

Check up   G4.3

Write or draw your answers on this sheet.

1 a Rotate the object through 90° clockwise about the centre of rotation.

   b Now rotate the image you have just drawn through 90° clockwise about the centre of rotation.

   c What single transformation would have the same effect on the object as two rotations of the object through 90° clockwise about the centre of rotation?

2 Show how four of the T-shaped tiles can fit together to make a 4 by 4 square.

3 Enlarge this shape by a scale factor of 2 from the given centre of enlargement.

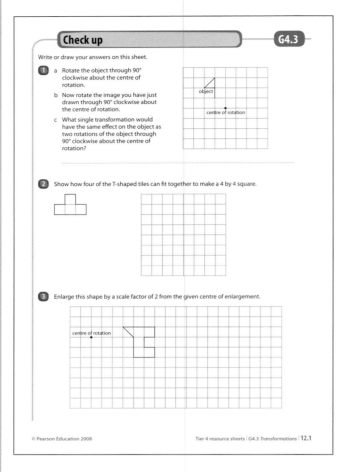

Check up [continued]

4 Here is a coordinate grid.

Plot these points on the grid: A (1, 2), B (5, 3), C (6, 6) and D (2, 5).
Join them in order to form the quadrilateral ABCD.

   a What are the coordinates of the midpoint of AC? (........, ...)

   b What are the coordinates of the midpoint of BD? (........, ...)

   c Draw the lines AC and BD.
      What are the coordinates of the point where the lines intersect? (........, ...)

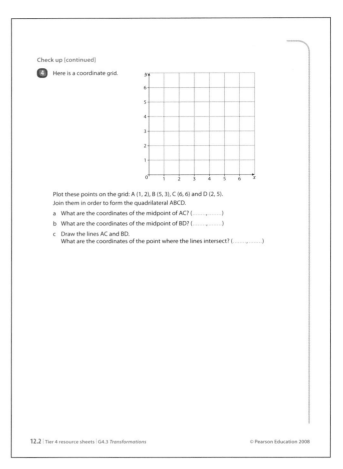

Resource sheet 1.1   G4.3

Write or draw your answers on the sheet.

1 Draw the image of the shaded shape after a rotation of:
   a 90° clockwise about (0, 0), and label the image A;
   b 180° about (0, 0), and label the image B;
   c 90° anticlockwise about (0, 0), and label the image C.

2 Draw the image of each shape after reflection in the given mirror line.

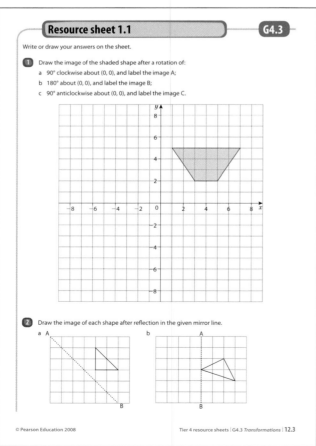

Resource sheet 1.1 [continued]

3 Draw the image of shape X after a translation of:
   a 5 units to the left and 6 units up. Label this image A.
   b 5 units to the right and 4 units up. Label this image B.
   c 4 units to the right and 3 units down. Label this image C.
   d 1 unit to the right and 7 units down. Label this image D.
   e 4 units to the left and 4 units down. Label this image E.

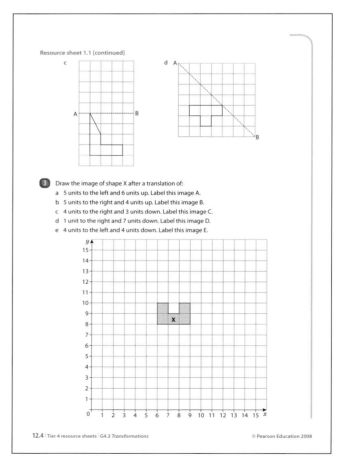

G4.3

Write or draw your answers on the sheet.

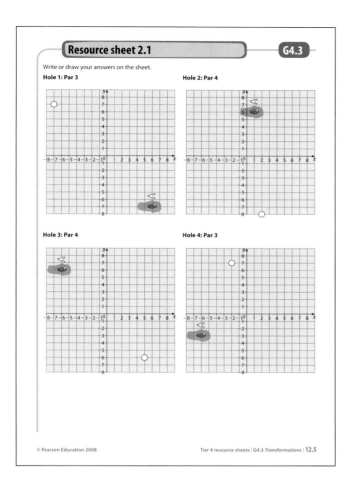

Hole 1: Par 3

Hole 2: Par 4

Hole 3: Par 4

Hole 4: Par 3

Resource sheet 2.1 [continued]

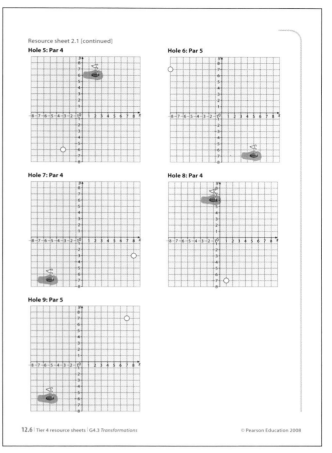

Hole 5: Par 4

Hole 6: Par 5

Hole 7: Par 4

Hole 8: Par 4

Hole 9: Par 5

Class book

Exercise 1

1

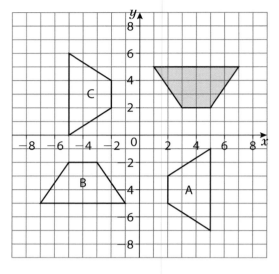

2 a

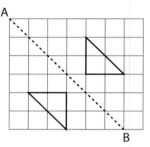

b

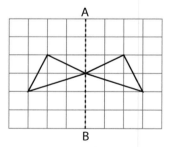

c

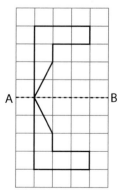

d

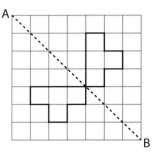

3

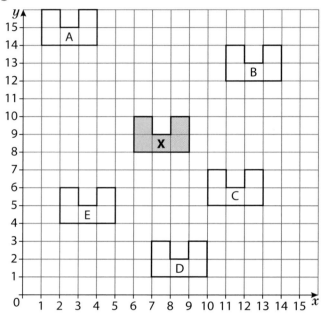

4

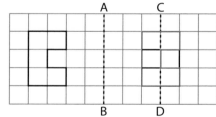

5 a A rotation of 27° clockwise

  b A rotation of 260° clockwise

  c A rotation of 90° clockwise

  d A rotation of 18° anticlockwise

6 A rotation of 90° anticlockwise, or a rotation of 270° clockwise

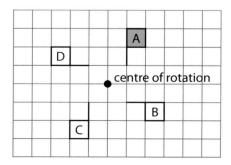

7 For example:

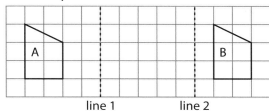

line 1   line 2

Exercise 2

1 a Pupil's plotted points: A (2, 1), A' (−2, 2)
  b Translation 1 unit up followed by a reflection in the y-axis

2 a Pupil's plotted points: B (4, 3), B' (4, −4)
  b Translation 1 unit up

3 a Pupil's plotted points: C (−3, 2), C' (2, −3)
  b Rotation through 90° clockwise about (0, 0)

4 a Rotation of 180° about (3, 0)
  b Rotation of 180° about (0, 0)
  c Translation 6 units right
  d Rotation through 90° clockwise about (0, 0)
  e Reflection in y-axis followed by reflection in the x-axis (or the other way round)

Extension problem

5 a Reflection in y-axis followed by reflection in $x = -3$
  b Rotation through 90°clockwise about (−2, −2) followed by a translation 4 units up

Exercise 3

1 Pupil's tessellation

2 Pupil's tessellation

3 a Pupil's tessellation of a rectangle
  b The interior angles of a rectangle are 90° so four of them will fit together at a point.

4 a Pupil's tessellation of a rhombus
  b Adjacent angles of a rhombus total 180°, so four of rhombuses will fit together at a point.

5 Pupil's tessellation

Exercise 4

1 a

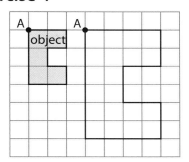

b

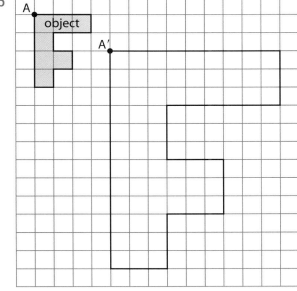

c

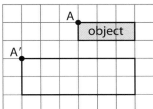

d

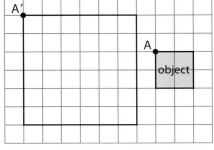

e

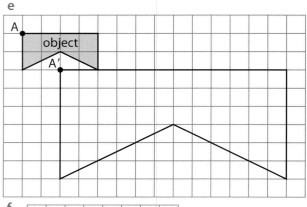

f

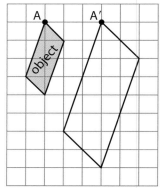

c

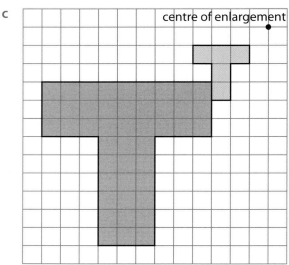

d

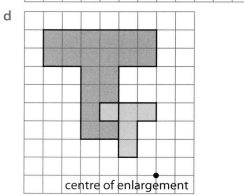

2 a 4   b 3   c 1.5   d 0.5

3 a 2   b 3   c 4   d 2
    e 2   f 4   g 6   h 8
    i 1.5   j 1.25

Extension problem

4 a $\frac{1}{4}$ b $\frac{1}{2}$ c $\frac{1}{2}$ d $\frac{1}{3}$

Exercise 5

1 a

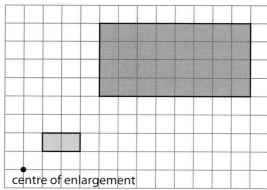

2

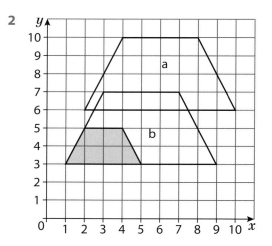

3 a Enlargement by scale factor 2, centre of enlargement (0, −4)

    b Enlargement by scale factor 2, centre of enlargement (7, 3)

Extension problems

4 Pupil's enlargement by scale factor 5 of a 1 by 2 rectangle

	Perimeter	Area
Original shape	6 units	2 square units
Enlargement	30 units	50 square units

a Multiply by 5, the scale factor
b Multiply by $25 = 5^2$, the square of the scale factor

5 Pupil's enlargement by scale factor 3 of inverted T-shape

	Perimeter	Area
Original shape	12 units	5 square units
Enlargement	36 units	45 square units

a Multiply by 3, the scale factor
b Multiply by $9 = 3^2$, the square of the scale factor

6 The perimeter of the object multiplied by the scale factor gives the perimeter of the image. The area of the object multiplied by the square of the scale factor gives the area of the image.

Exercise 6

1 a 12 cm   b 3 mm   c 2 cm

2 a 16 m   b 3.4 mm

3 $x = 9.6$, $y = 15$, so the missing lengths are 9.6 cm and 15 cm.

Extension problem

4 $c \times d = 16 \times 9 = 144$. So $c = 1$, $d = 144$ or $c = 2$, $d = 72$ or $c = 3$, $d = 48$; there could also be decimal answers.

Exercise 7

1 a (8, 5)   b (2, 4)   c (5, 1)
   d (5, 8)   e (5, 4)   f (5, 5)

2 a (7, 0)   b (9, 2)   c (3, −2)
   d (0, 0)   e (−6, −2.5)   f (−0.5, −0.5)

3 a WXYZ is a rhombus.
   b (1, −1)   c (1, −1)

4 (5, 3)

5 $x = 5$, $y = −1$

Extension problems

6 a E (5, 1), F (7, 3), G (5, 5), H (3, 3)
   b I (6, 2), J (6, 4), K (4, 4), L (4, 2)
   c 16 square units
   d 4 square units

e Scale factor 2
f Centre of enlargement (5, 3)

7 ABCD will be a parallelogram or special cases of a parallelogram as will the quadrilateral formed by joining the midpoints of AB, BC, CD, DA together.

How well are you doing?

1
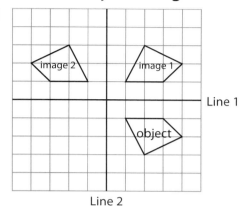

A rotation through 180° about the point where the two lines intersect.

2
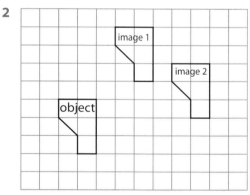

A translation of 6 units to the right and 2 units up.

3 a Scale factor 3
   b
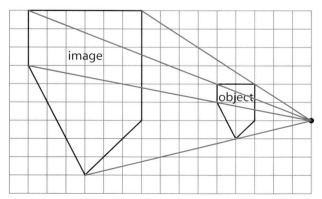

4

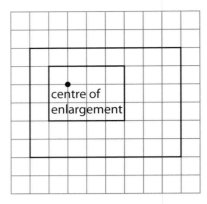

5 P (60, 60)

6 M (0, 100)   N (60, 0)

Home book

TASK 1

1 Pupil's wallpaper pattern
  a Translation 6 units down
  b Rotation of 180° about intersection of line A and line 1
  c Translation 12 units right, 6 units down

2 Pupil's wallpaper pattern using ICT

TASK 2

1 Rotation of 180° about (0, 0)

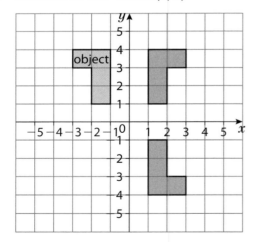

2

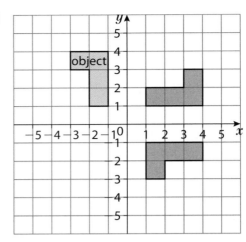

3 (4, 3)

TASK 3

1 **a** Pupil's tessellation
  b Pupil's tessellation

2 **a** Pupil's tessellation of isosceles triangles
  b The angle sum of a triangle is 180°, so six triangles can be put together at a point with no gaps or overlaps.

3 108 is not a factor of 360, so it is not possible to put regular pentagons together at a point with no gaps or overlaps.

4 **a** Pupil's tessellation of squares and equilateral triangles
  b $360° = 3 \times 60° + 2 \times 90°$, so three equilateral triangles and two squares will fit together around a point with no gaps or overlaps.

TASK 4

1 **a** 2   **b** 3   **c** 2   **d** 1.5

2

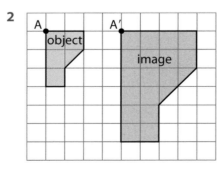

3 **a** Scale factor = 4
  b Centre of enlargement (1, 0)

TASK 5

1

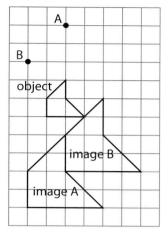

2 Enlargement of scale factor 3, centre of enlargement $(-7, 3)$

TASK 6

1 a   15 cm   b   6 m   c   56 cm

2 Yes; corresponding sides are in the same ratio, $\frac{10}{16} = \frac{5}{8}$ = scale factor 1.6

3 a   Scale factor 3   b   (0, 2)
     c   3 times bigger   d 3^2 = 9 times bigger

TASK 7

1 a   (2, 4)   b   (2, −3)   c   (2, 2)
     d   (0, 3.5)   e   (−2, −1)   f   (0, 0)

2 a   (4, 1)   b   (−6, −2)

3 (1, 2)

4 $x = 5, y = 1$

CD-ROM

Check up

1 a, b

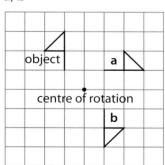

     c   A rotation of 180° about the centre of rotation

2

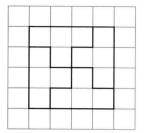

3

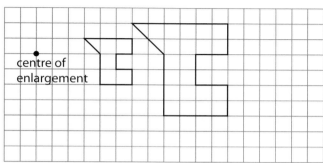

4

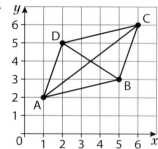

     a   (3.5, 4)   b   (3.5, 4)   c   (3.5, 4)

Equations and formulae

Previous learning

Before they start, pupils should be able to:

- construct and solve simple linear equations with whole-number coefficients (unknown on one side only) using a method such as inverse operations
- substitute positive integers into simple formulae.

Objectives based on NC levels 5 and 6 (mainly level 5)

In this unit, pupils learn to:

- identify the mathematical features of a problem or context
- try out and compare mathematical representations
- use accurate notation
- manipulate algebraic expressions and equations
- use logical arguments to establish the truth of a statement
- explore the effect of varying values
- refine own findings and approaches on the basis of discussion with others
- evaluate the efficiency of alternative strategies and approaches

and to:

- construct and solve linear equations with integer coefficients (unknown on either or both sides, without and with brackets), e.g. by using inverse operations or by transforming both sides in the same way
- use, derive and substitute integers into simple expressions and formulae from mathematics and other subjects.

Lessons

1 **Functions, equations and graphs**

2 **Solving linear equations**

3 **More linear equations**

4 **Forming equations and formulae**

5 **Equations with brackets**

6 **Equations with x on both sides**

About this unit

Many pupils see mathematics as unrelated facts that have to be memorised. This unit shows that this is not the case.

Lesson 1 brings out links between functions, equations and graphs. The unit moves on to show how inverse functions can be used to solve linear equations, which is then linked to the method of 'doing the same to both sides of the equation'.

Pupils see how to interpret a practical situation and use algebra to turn it into a mathematical problem.

Lessons 5 and 6 cover the solution of linear equations containing brackets, and those with the variable on both sides of the equation.

Assessment

This unit includes:

- a self-assessment section (*A4.4 How well are you doing?* class book p. 218);
- a set of questions to replace or supplement questions in the exercises or homework tasks, or to use as an informal test (*A4.4 Check up*, CD-ROM).

Common errors and misconceptions	Look out for pupils who:

Look out for pupils who:

- do not understand that $3x$ means $3 \times x$;
- do not understand that $\frac{x}{3}$ means $x \div 3$;
- do not recognise that $y = 2x + 3$ is identical to $2x + 3 = y$;
- do not understand that $y = 2x + 3$ has an infinite number of solutions while $11 = 2x + 3$ has only one solution;
- use informal methods to solve equations.

Key terms and notation

solve, solution, infinite, unique

function, inverse function, operation, inverse operation, equation, linear equation, formula, formulae

axis, axes, coordinates, ordered pair, linear graph

Practical resources

graphics calculators or graph-plotting tools

individual whiteboards

Exploring maths

Tier 4 teacher's book
Answers for Unit A4.4, pp. 245–249

Tier 4 CD-ROM
PowerPoint files
    A4.4 Slides for lessons 1 to 6
Tools and prepared toolsheets
    Coordinates and functions tools
Tier 4 programs
    Function machines – explore
    Equations – challenge

Tier 4 class book
A4.4, pp. 203–218
A4.4 How well are you doing? p. 218

Tier 4 home book
A4.4, pp. 80–85

Tier 4 CD-ROM
A4.4 Check up

Useful websites

Equation match
www.bbc.co.uk/education/mathsfile/gameswheel.html

Equation buster
www.emaths.co.uk/InterSoW/background.htm

Solving linear equations
www.adamzone.co.uk/linear.html

Algebra topics
swgfl.skoool.co.uk/keystage3.aspx?id=65#24_30

Linear equations
www.mathcentre.ac.uk/resources/leaflets/mathcentre/business/solv_linear_equations.pdf

1 Functions, equations and graphs

Learning points

- A function machine applies a rule or function to an input x and gives the related output y.

  Example: When the input $x = 4$ is put through the function $x \rightarrow \boxed{\text{multiply by 6}} \rightarrow \boxed{\text{add 5}} \rightarrow y$, the output y is 29.

  This function can be written as the equation $y = 6x + 5$.

- You can draw a graph of this linear equation. All the points on the graph are solutions of the equation.

Starter

Use **slide 1.1** to discuss what pupils will learn in the next three lessons. Say that this lesson looks at the links between functions, equations and graphs.

SIM

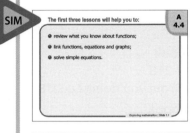

Use **slide 1.2** to revise knowledge of functions by asking pupils to work out the function and complete the mapping diagram. Alternatively launch **Function machines – explore**.

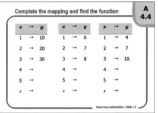

Main activity

Write a function such as $x \rightarrow \boxed{\text{add 5}} \rightarrow y$ on the board. Explain that when any input x is put through the function machine 'add 5' it results in a unique output y. Establish that all pupils know how to calculate outputs given inputs and vice versa.

Ask pupils to write on their whiteboards the outputs for inputs such as 7, -3, 2.5, 0.7 and 0.

Now ask them to write the inputs for outputs such as 19, 0, 5.5, 3 and -8.

Explain that the function $x \rightarrow \boxed{\text{add 5}} \rightarrow y$ can be written as the linear equation $y = x + 5$.

Show that it can also be represented as a straight-line graph.

TO

Use the **Function graph tool** to draw the graph of $y = x + 5$. Select $y = ax + b$ and input the coefficients. Establish that the horizontal axis represents x and the vertical axis represents y.

Ask pupils to give you pairs of coordinates (x, y) that lie on the straight line. Include one or two decimal values.

Establish that there is an infinite number of points on the line. These ordered pairs (x, y) are all 'solutions' of the equation.

Remind pupils that there are points on the line beyond the actual graph they can see by asking, for example:

What would be the value of y when $x = 100$?

Ask pupils to explain how they would draw the graph accurately on paper. Agree that they would need to work out three values of x and y to plot. Remind them that they should draw a straight-line graph using a pencil and ruler, continuing the graph to the edge of the grid.

Ask pupils to give you the equations for functions using all four operations such as:

$x \rightarrow \boxed{\text{subtract 5}} \rightarrow y \qquad y = x - 5$

$x \rightarrow \boxed{\text{multiply by 3}} \rightarrow y \qquad y = 3x$

$x \rightarrow \boxed{\text{divide by 2}} \rightarrow y \qquad y = \dfrac{x}{2}$

Go on to combined operations such as $x \rightarrow \boxed{\text{multiply by 3}} \rightarrow \boxed{\text{add 5}} \rightarrow y$.

For each equation, use the **Function graph tool** on a suitable axes to draw the graphs. Ask pupils to give you some of the solutions by identifying coordinates of points on the graphs.

Ask pupils to do **A4.4 Exercise 1** in the class book (p. 204). They will need graph paper.

Review

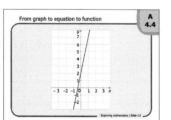

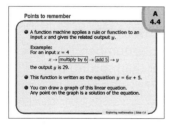

Show **slide 1.3**. Ask pupils to look carefully at the graph and work out its equation ($y = 5x + 2$).

Ask them to write this as a function on their whiteboards.

Ask pupils around the class to give you some of the solutions (x, y) to the equation.

Sum up with the points on **slide 1.4**.

Homework Ask pupils to do **A4.4 Task 1** in the home book (p. 80).

2 Solving linear equations

Learning points

- The equation $x + 16 = 31$ has a unique solution.
- To solve the equation you can use the inverse function.

$$x + 16 = 31 \qquad x \rightarrow \boxed{+16} \rightarrow 31$$

subtract 16 $\qquad x = 15 \qquad\qquad 15 \leftarrow \boxed{-16} \leftarrow 31$

- What you do to one side of the equation you must do to the other to keep the equation in balance.

Starter

Say that this lesson is about solving equations. Start by asking pupils to write on their whiteboards the inverse operations of the operations you say. For example:

What is the inverse of 'add 7'?

What is the inverse of 'multiply by 10'?

When you have covered all four operations orally, draw functions with single operations on the board. Ask pupils to write the inverse functions on their whiteboards. For example:

function: $x \rightarrow \boxed{\text{multiply by 3}} \rightarrow y$ inverse function: $x \leftarrow \boxed{\text{divide by 3}} \leftarrow y$

Main activity

Explain that you are going to show how to solve simple linear equations using inverse functions. Some pupils may have done this work previously. In this case, use questioning to establish what they know and give them the exercises as revision.

Write the equation $y = x + 3$ on the board. Use the **Function graph tool** on a suitable axes to draw its graph.

How many solutions does this equation have? [an infinite number]

Tell me some of the solutions. [e.g. (1, 4), (0, 3), (2, 5), (−1, 2)]

Use the graph to show how you can work out the value of x when you know the value of y.

Now say that you are going to show how to work out the value of x when given a value for y without using the graph.

Write $y = x + 35$ and $x + 35 = y$ on the board. Establish that the two equations are identical. Suppose the value of y is 110. Show pupils how to solve the equation, using a function machine to help. (In this example, numbers have been chosen to encourage pupils to use a formal solution rather than solving the equations informally.)

Example 1: addition

$$x + 35 = 110 \qquad x \rightarrow \boxed{+35} \rightarrow 110$$

subtract 35 $\qquad \underline{x = 75} \qquad\qquad 75 \leftarrow \boxed{-35} \leftarrow 110$

As you write the second line of the solution, say:

I subtract 35 from the left-hand side of the equation. That leaves x.
Then I subtract 35 from the right-hand side of the equation. That leaves 75.
The value of x is 75. I do the same thing to both sides of the equation.

Explain that by doing the same thing to both sides, the equation it is kept in balance. Check the answer by substituting back into the original equation.

Pupils may come across examples where the letters and numbers are reversed so explain that $x + 35 = 110$ is the same $35 + x = 110$. Check by substituting $x = 75$ in both equations.

Repeat for subtraction, multiplication and division, checking each answer by substituting the value for x back into the original equation.

Example 1: subtraction

$$x - 51 = 94 \qquad x \rightarrow \boxed{-51} \rightarrow 94$$
$$\text{add 51} \qquad \underline{x = 145} \qquad 145 \leftarrow \boxed{+51} \leftarrow 94$$

Explain that the equation $51 - x = 94$ is not the same as $x - 51 = 94$. Check by substituting 145 for x in both equations.

Example 2: multiplication

$$23x = 207 \qquad x \rightarrow \boxed{\times 23} \rightarrow 207$$
$$\text{divide by 23} \qquad \underline{x = 9} \qquad 9 \leftarrow \boxed{\div 23} \leftarrow 207$$

Explain that $23 \times x = 207$ is the same as $x \times 23 = 207$. Check by substituting $x = 9$ in both equations. Explain that with multiplication the convention is to write the number first.

Example 3: division

$$x \div 31 = 17 \qquad x \rightarrow \boxed{\div 31} \rightarrow 17$$
$$\text{multiply by 31} \qquad \underline{x = 527} \qquad 527 \leftarrow \boxed{\times 31} \leftarrow 17$$

Explain that $x \div 31 = 17$ is not the same as $31 \div x = 17$. Check by substituting $x = 527$ in both equations. Show pupils how division can be written in different forms, for example:

$$\frac{x}{31} = 17 \ \text{ or } \ x/31 = 17$$

Select individual work from **A4.4 Exercise 2** in the class book (p. 206). Pupils will need graph paper.

Review

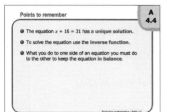

Launch **Equations – challenge 1** and **challenge 2** to set problems involving all four operations.

Ask pupils to discuss in pairs how to match the numbers.

Sum up with the learning points on **slide 2.1**.

SIM

SIM

Homework

Ask pupils to do **A4.4 Task 2** in the home book (p. 81).

3 More linear equations

Learning points

- The equation $y = 3x + 5$ has an infinite number of solutions. Any point (x, y) on its graph is a solution.

- The equation $3x + 5 = 17$ has a unique solution.

- To solve the equation use the inverse function:

	$3x + 5 = 17$	$x \to \boxed{\times 3} \to \boxed{+5} \to 17$
subtract 5	$3x = 12$	$4 \leftarrow \boxed{\div 3} \leftarrow \boxed{-5} \leftarrow 17$
divide by 3	$\underline{x = 4}$	

- What you do to one side of the equation you must do to the other to keep the equation in balance.

Starter

Say that this lesson is again about solving linear equations.

Show **slide 3.1**.

Ask pupils to write equations for each situation on their whiteboards.

Main activity

Write the equation $7x + 9 = 65$ on the board.

Show pupils how to set out a solution to the equation with a function machine to help. (As pupils grow confident they can dispense with the function and its inverse as an aid.)

Example 1: addition

	$7x + 9 = 65$	$x \to \boxed{\times 7} \to \boxed{+9} \to 65$
subtract 9	$7x = 56$	$8 \leftarrow \boxed{\div 7} \leftarrow \boxed{-9} \leftarrow 65$
divide by 7	$\underline{x = 8}$	

As you write the second and third lines of the solution say:

> I subtract 9 from the left-hand side of the equation. That leaves $7x$.
> Then I subtract 9 from the right-hand side of the equation. That leaves 56.

> Now I divide the left-hand side of the equation by 7. That gives x.
> Then I divide the right-hand side of the equation by 7. That gives 8.

> I always do the same to both sides of the equation to keep it in balance.

Always check answers by substituting back into the original equation.

Go through the same process for an equation involving subtraction.

Example 2: subtraction

$$11x - 5 = 72 \qquad x \rightarrow \boxed{\times 11} \rightarrow \boxed{-5} \rightarrow 72$$

add 5 $\qquad 11x = 77 \qquad 7 \leftarrow \boxed{\div 11} \leftarrow \boxed{+5} \leftarrow 72$

divide by 11 $\qquad \underline{x = 7}$

For able pupils, you may wish to show an example involving division.

Example 3: division

$$\frac{x}{5} + 9 = 12 \qquad x \rightarrow \boxed{\div 5} \rightarrow \boxed{+9} \rightarrow 12$$

subtract 9 $\qquad \frac{x}{5} = 3 \qquad 15 \leftarrow \boxed{\times 5} \leftarrow \boxed{-9} \leftarrow 12$

multiply by 5 $\qquad \underline{x = 15}$

$$\frac{x}{7} - 4 = 8 \qquad x \rightarrow \boxed{\div 7} \rightarrow \boxed{-4} \rightarrow 8$$

add 4 $\qquad \frac{x}{7} = 12 \qquad 84 \leftarrow \boxed{\times 7} \leftarrow \boxed{+4} \leftarrow 8$

multiply by 7 $\qquad \underline{x = 84}$

Ask pupils to do **A4.4 Exercise 3** in the class book (p. 208).

Review

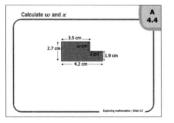

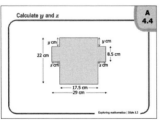

Show **slide 3.2**.

Ask pupils to write equations in w, x, y and z and then to solve them.

Some pupils may be able to work out the values mentally but explain that you want them to form the equations first.

Sum up by asking pupils to remember the points on **slide 3.3**.

Homework

Ask pupils to do **A4.4 Task 3** in the home book (p. 82).

4 Forming equations and formulae

Learning points

- You can use algebra to solve problems.
- Read through the problem carefully and write an equation.
- Solve the equation, then go back and use this to solve the problem.

Starter

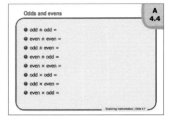

Say that this lesson is about using algebra to model and then solve problems.

Show **slide 4.1**. Ask pupils to work out whether the right-hand side of the equations should be odd or even. Ask them to justify their answers, e.g. by using dot patterns. Establish that:

odd $\pm$ odd = even	odd $\times$ odd = odd
even $\pm$ odd = odd	even $\times$ even = even
even $\pm$ even = even	odd $\times$ even = even
odd $\pm$ even = odd	even $\times$ odd = even

Main activity

Explain that in the last lesson the class used algebra to solve some word and geometric problems. In this lesson, they will use algebra to solve some different problems. Emphasise the importance of defining any letters being used, e.g. 'let x be the length of a line'.

Ask pupils to write on their whiteboards the equations for the statements you give them.

> Let a number be x. Multiply it by 5 then add 32. The answer is 82.
> [$5x + 32 = 82$]

> Let a number be y. Divide it by 3 then subtract 19. The answer is 11.
> [$\frac{y}{3} - 19 = 11$]

> Let a number be n. Multiply it by 8 then subtract 21. The answer is 51.
> [$8n - 21 = 51$]

> Let a number be p. Add 7 to it then multiply the result by 5.
> The answer is 65. [$5(p + 7) = 65$]

Explain that the word 'consecutive' means 'following one another in sequence', e.g. 17, 18 and 19 are three consecutive whole numbers. Ask pupils to give you further examples of three consecutive whole numbers.

> 56 is the smallest of three consecutive whole numbers.
> What are the other two?

> 109 is the largest of three consecutive whole numbers.
> What are the other two?

> 215 is the middle number of three consecutive numbers.
> What are the other two?

Establish that if you know one of the numbers you can work out the other two by adding or subtracting 1 or 2.

> Let n be the smallest of three consecutive whole numbers.
> What are the other two?

Establish that the three numbers are n, $n + 1$ and $n + 2$.

Find three consecutive whole numbers whose sum is 315.

Show pupils how to write this as:

> Let n be the smallest number.
>
> $n + n + 1 + n + 2 = 315$
>
> $3n + 3 = 315$

Ask them to solve the equation and so work out the three numbers.

Ask pupils to do **A4.4 Exercise 4** in the class book (p. 211).

Review
Go through the exercises.

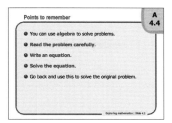

Invite some pupils to write their solutions on the board. Discuss and compare different approaches.

Finish the lesson by reminding pupils of the points on **slide 4.2**.

Homework
Ask pupils to do **A4.4 Task 4** in the home book (p. 83).

5 Equations with brackets

Learning points

◎ To solve a linear equation containing brackets, it is normally best to multiply out the brackets and simplify the equation.

Example:

$$2(x + 4) + 5(3x + 7) = 77$$
$$2x + 8 + 15x + 35 = 77$$
$$17x + 43 = 77$$

Starter

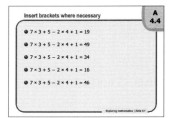

Say that this lesson is about solving equations containing brackets.

Show **slide 5.1**. Remind them that, if there are no brackets, multiplication and division are done before addition and subtraction. Brackets can be inserted to override this rule and change the order of operations.

Do the first example as a demonstration. Ask pupils to discuss in pairs where the brackets should go in the remaining examples.

Take suggestions, checking that other pairs agree, and insert the brackets.

Main activity

Write the equation $4(x + 7) = 48$ on the board. Ask pupils to give you the function for this relationship. The brackets have changed the order of operations so that the function is:

$$x \rightarrow \boxed{\text{add 7}} \rightarrow \boxed{\text{multiply by 4}} \rightarrow y$$

The brackets can be multiplied out to give the equation $4x + 28 = 48$ with associated function:

$$x \rightarrow \boxed{\text{multiply by 4}} \rightarrow \boxed{\text{add 28}} \rightarrow y$$

Explain that there are two different ways of solving this equation. The brackets can be left in the expression or they can be worked out first.

Show pupils how to set out solutions to the equation using a function machine to help them on the right-hand side.

Method 1

	$4(x + 7) = 48$	$x \rightarrow \boxed{+7} \rightarrow \boxed{\times 4} \rightarrow 48$
divide by 4	$x + 7 = 12$	$5 \leftarrow \boxed{-7} \leftarrow \boxed{\div 4} \leftarrow 48$
subtract 7	$\underline{x = 5}$	

Method 2

	$4(x + 7) = 48$	
	$4x + 28 = 48$	$x \rightarrow \boxed{\times 4} \rightarrow \boxed{+28} \rightarrow 48$
subtract 8	$4x = 20$	$5 \leftarrow \boxed{\div 4} \leftarrow \boxed{-28} \leftarrow 48$
divide by 4	$\underline{x = 5}$	

Check that the answers are the same in both cases. Substitute the value of x in the original equation to check that it is correct.

Repeat with similar examples.

Ask pupils to do **A4.4 Exercise 5** in the class book (p. 214).

Review   Show **slide 5.2**.

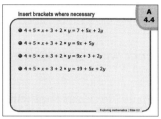

Ask pupils to discuss in pairs how to insert brackets to make the equations correct. After a time, invite pairs to come to the board to insert brackets.

> Does everyone agree that the equation is now correct?

Sum up by showing **slide 5.3**.

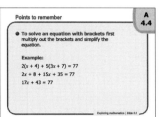

Homework   Ask pupils to do **A4.4 Task 5** in the home book (p. 84).

6 Equations with x on both sides

Learning points

- To solve a linear equation containing brackets, first multiply out the brackets and simplify the equation.

$$2(x + 4) = 26$$
$$2x + 8 = 26$$

- To solve a linear equation that has x terms on both sides, first collect all x terms together on one side of the equation.

$$10x + 3 = 6x + 11$$
$$4x + 3 = 11$$

Starter

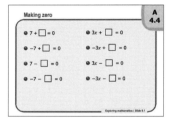

Tell pupils that in this lesson they will learn to solve equations with terms with x on both sides.

Show **slide 6.1**. Ask pupils to give you the numbers that go in the boxes that will make each equation zero.

Main activity

Example 1

Write the equation $3x - 5 = 2x + 1$ on the board. Point out that there are terms in x on both sides of the equation. The first step in the solution is to get all the x terms on one side of the equation while keeping the equation balanced.

Remind pupils that when they have an equation they must always do the same thing to both sides of the equation. In this case they can subtract $2x$ from both sides.

Show pupils how to set out the formal solutions to the equation with the function to help them on the right-hand side.

$$3x - 5 = 2x + 1$$

subtract $2x$ $x - 5 = 1$ $x \rightarrow \boxed{-5} \rightarrow 1$

add 5 $\underline{x = 6}$ $6 \leftarrow \boxed{+5} \leftarrow 1$

Check that the answers are the same in both cases. Substitute the value of x in the original equation to check that it is correct.

Example 2

Write the equation $2x + 7 = 5x - 20$ on the board. Consider what happens if you subtract $5x$ from both sides of the equation. Explain that this would not be incorrect but that they would be working with negative x terms and this would be clumsy. They need to inspect equations first and decide on which side to collect the x terms.

$$2x + 7 = 5x - 20$$

subtract x $7 = 3x - 20$

This is identical to $3x - 20 = 7$ which is a form that pupils can recognise and solve.

For able, confident pupils, you may wish to discuss what to do to get all the terms in x on one side of the equation in two further examples.

Example 3

$3x + 5 = 19 - 4x$ [add $4x$ to get $7x + 5 = 19$]

Example 4

$16 - 3x = 21 - 8x$ [add $8x$ to get $16 + 5x = 21$]

Select individual work from **A4.4 Exercise 6** in the Tier 4 class book (p. 216).

Review

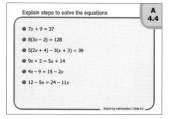

Show **slide 6.2**.

Focus on each equation in turn. Ask pupils to tell you what their first and second steps would be to solve it.

If there is time, ask a pupil to write the solution on the board.

Ask pupils to remember the points on **slide 6.3**.

Round off the unit by referring again to the objectives. Suggest that pupils find time to try the self-assessment problems in **A4.4 How well are you doing?** in the class book (p. 218).

Homework

Ask pupils to do **A4.4 Task 6** in the Tier 4 home book (p. 85).

A4.4 Check up

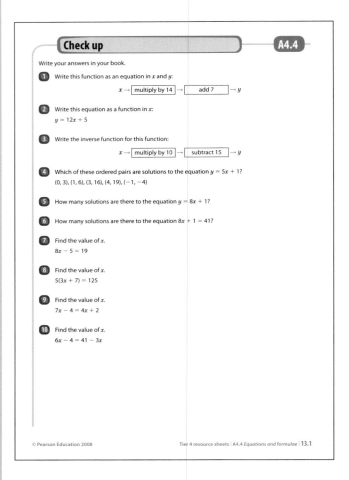

Write your answers in your book.

1. Write this function as an equation in x and y:

   $x \rightarrow$ | multiply by 14 | $\rightarrow$ | add 7 | $\rightarrow y$

2. Write this equation as a function in x:

   $y = 12x + 5$

3. Write the inverse function for this function:

   $x \rightarrow$ | multiply by 10 | $\rightarrow$ | subtract 15 | $\rightarrow y$

4. Which of these ordered pairs are solutions to the equation $y = 5x + 1$?

   $(0, 3), (1, 6), (3, 16), (4, 19), (-1, -4)$

5. How many solutions are there to the equation $y = 8x + 1$?

6. How many solutions are there to the equation $8x + 1 = 41$?

7. Find the value of x.

   $8x - 5 = 19$

8. Find the value of x.

   $5(3x + 7) = 125$

9. Find the value of x.

   $7x - 4 = 4x + 2$

10. Find the value of x.

    $6x - 4 = 41 - 3x$

A4.4 Answers

Class book

Exercise 1

1 a $4 \to 17$
$5 \to 22$
$6 \to 27$
$7 \to 32$
$x \to 5x - 3$

b $4 \to 37$
$5 \to 46$
$6 \to 55$
$7 \to 64$
$x \to 9x + 1$

2 a $y = x + 15$
b $y = x - 8$
c $y = 7x$
d $y = \dfrac{x}{3}$
e $y = 4x + 11$
f $y = 10x - 3$
g $y = \dfrac{x}{2} + 4$
h $y = \dfrac{x}{5} - 1$

3 a $x \to \boxed{\text{add 13}} \to y$

b $x \to \boxed{\text{subtract 21}} \to y$

c $x \to \boxed{\text{multiply by 9}} \to \boxed{\text{add 25}} \to y$

d $x \to \boxed{\text{multiply by 7}} \to \boxed{\text{subtract 1}} \to y$

e $x \to \boxed{\text{divide by 3}} \to \boxed{\text{add 4}} \to y$

f $x \to \boxed{\text{multiply by 8}} \to \boxed{\text{add 19}} \to y$

g $x \to \boxed{\text{multiply by 12}} \to \boxed{\text{subtract 7}} \to y$

h $x \to \boxed{\text{add 2}} \to \boxed{\text{multiply by 10}} \to y$

4 Pupils' graphs

5 Five ordered pairs selected by pupils for each graph in question 4

Extension problem

6 a $x = \dfrac{y}{7} - 15, y = 7(x + 15)$

b $x = \dfrac{y}{6} + 2, y = 6(x - 2)$

Exercise 2

1 a $x \leftarrow \boxed{\text{subtract 52}} \leftarrow y$

b $x \leftarrow \boxed{\text{add 16}} \leftarrow y$

c $x \leftarrow \boxed{\text{divide by 31}} \leftarrow y$

d $x \leftarrow \boxed{\text{multiply by 6}} \leftarrow y$

e $x \leftarrow \boxed{\text{divide by 8}} \leftarrow \boxed{\text{subtract 25}} \leftarrow y$

f $x \leftarrow \boxed{\text{divide by 102}} \leftarrow \boxed{\text{add 15}} \leftarrow y$

g $x \leftarrow \boxed{\text{multiply by 14}} \leftarrow \boxed{\text{subtract 9}} \leftarrow y$

h $x \leftarrow \boxed{\text{multiply by 3}} \leftarrow \boxed{\text{add 0.5}} \leftarrow y$

2 a Pupils' graph
b $y \approx 3$
c $x \approx -1.5$
d $y \approx 9$
e $x \approx 1$
f $y \approx 7.4$

3 a $x = 7$
b $x = 41$
c $x = 44$
d $x = 4.8$
e $x = 10.5$
f $x = -16$
g $x = 19$
h $x = -14$
i $x = 13$

4 $x + 7 = 19$ and $x - 5 = 7$
$x + 4 = 11$ and $x + 9 = 16$
$x + 19 = 25$ and $x + 22 = 28$
$x + 15 = 17$ and $x - 1 = 1$
$x - 7 = 6$ and $x + 16 = 29$
$x - 4 = 5$ and $x + 27 = 36$

5 a $x = 8$
b $x = 14$
c $x = 5$
d $x = 6$
e $x = 36$
f $x = 20$

6 a $p = 30$
b $m = 34$
c $t = 12$
d $a = 72$
e $s = 24$
f $w = 39$

7 a $6p = 180$
b $p = 30$. The angles are 30°, 60° and 90°.

8 a $15q = 360$
b $q = 24$. The angles are 48°, 72°, 96° and 144°.

9 a $x + 19 = 52$
b The car has 33 miles to go.

Extension problems

10 a $x \leftarrow \boxed{\text{subtract 2.5}} \leftarrow \boxed{\text{divide by 0.1}} \leftarrow y$

b $x \leftarrow \boxed{\text{add } -1} \leftarrow \boxed{\text{divide by 2.4}} \leftarrow y$

11 $4x = 28$ and $8x = 56$

$3x = 48$ and $\dfrac{x}{8} = 2$

$\dfrac{x}{4} = 2$ and $5x = 40$

$\dfrac{x}{5} = 3$ and $2x = 30$

$\dfrac{x}{6} = 3$ and $\dfrac{x}{9} = 2$

$9x = 36$ and $5x = 20$

Exercise 3

1 a $x = 4$ b $x = 6$
   c $x = 8$ d $x = 10$
   e $x = 0.5$ f $x = 7$
   g $x = 9$ h $x = 18$
   i $x = 55$

2 $5x - 21 = 24$ and $3x - 4 = 23$
   $5x + 9 = 24$ and $3x + 14 = 23$
   $3x - 2 = 28$ and $4x + 7 = 47$
   $4x + 15 = 43$ and $6x - 3 = 39$
   $7x - 8 = 27$ and $2x + 6 = 16$
   $8x - 2 = 62$ and $2x + 5 = 21$

3 a $h = 5$ b $q = 9$
   c $t = 12$ d $a = 144$
   e $r = 10$ f $b = 2.5$
   g $m = -2$ h $c = -5$

4 a $140x = 3220$
   b $x = 23$. The width of each rectangle is 23 cm.

5 a $3x + 5 = 17$
   b $x = 4$. The sides are 4 cm, 6 cm and 7 cm.

6 a $4x + 69 = 125$
   b $x = 14$. The two sides are 14 cm and 42 cm.

7 a $1500 + 24(x - 100)$
   b £68.04
   c 260 minutes

Extension problem

   d 142 minutes

Exercise 4

1 a $7w + 25 = 67$
   b $\frac{x}{4} + 7 = 13$
   c $9y - 13 = 59$
   d $5(z + 2) = 45$

2 $2x + 15 = 39$, $x = 12$ I am 12 years old.

3 $y + y + 2 + y - 1 + 2y + 4 = 5y + 5 = 50$,
   $y = 9$
   Ravinda is paid £9 per hour, Bradley £11,
   Courtney £8 and Natalie £22.

4 $n + n + 7 + 2(n + 7) = 4n + 21 = 81$, $n = 15$
   There are 15 chocolates in the True Chocs box, 22
   in a box of High Treats and 44 in the Sweethearts
   box.

5 a 76, 77
   b 99, 98
   c 33, 35
   d $n + 1, n + 2, n + 3$ e $n - 1, n - 2, n - 3$
   f $n - 2, n - 1, n + 1, n + 2$

6 a 173, 174
   b 25, 26, 27
   c 24, 26, 28
   d 35, 37

Extension problem

7 Let the three consecutive numbers be $n, n + 1$
   and $n + 2$.
   Then $n + n + 1 + n + 2 = 3n + 3 = 3(n + 1)$.
   Since this expression has a factor of 3 it is
   divisible by 3.

Exercise 5

1 a $6 \times 2 + (7 - 3) \times 5 + 4 = 36$
   b $6 \times 2 + 7 - 3 \times (5 + 4) = -8$
   c $6 \times 2 + 7 - 3 \times 5 + 4 = 8$
   d $6 \times (2 + 7) - 3 \times 5 + 4 = 43$

2 a $x = 5$ b $x = 4$
   c $x = 8$ d $x = 3$
   e $x = 5$ f $x = 1$

3 a $x = 6$ b $x = 1$
   c $x = 18$ d $x = 13$
   e $x = 21$ f $x = -1$

4 a $x = 3$ b $x = 6$
   c $x = 1$ d $x = 4$
   e $x = 2$ f $x = \frac{1}{2}$

5 a $x = 2$ b $x = 3$
   c $x = 5$ d $x = 4$
   e $x = 7$ f $x = 1$

6 There are three matching cards:
   $6(7x + 2) + 4(x + 1)$
   $4(5x + 2) + 2(13x + 4)$
   $4(9x + 5) + 2(5x - 2)$

7 a $p = 5$ b $q = 2$
   c $s = 3$ d $t = 7$
   e $n = 5$ f $b = 6$

Extension problems

8 a $x = 5$ b $x = 8$
   c $x = 19$ d $x = 6$
   e $x = 16$ f $x = -1$

9 a $x = 1$ b $x = 3$
    c $x = 2$ d $x = \frac{1}{2}$
    e $x = 4$ f $x = 1$

Exercise 6

1 a $16 + (\mathbf{-16}) = 0$ b $-16 + \mathbf{16} = 0$
    c $16 - \mathbf{16} = 0$ d $-16 - (\mathbf{-16}) = 0$
    e $7x + (\mathbf{-7x}) = 0$ f $-7x + \mathbf{7x} = 0$

2 a $x = 3$ b $x = 5$
    c $x = 2$ d $x = 6$
    e $x = 4$ f $x = 1$

3 a $x = 2$ b $x = 1$
    c $x = 3$ d $x = 5$
    e $x = \frac{1}{4}$ f $x = -1$
    g $x = 4$ h $x = 8$

4 a $x = 4$ b $x = 2$
    c $x = 3$ d $x = -2$
    e $x = 5$ f $x = 6$
    g $x = -3$ h $x = 1$

5 a $2x + 72 = 3x$
    b $x = 72$; the width of the rectangle is 72 cm.

6 a $72 + 2(48 - x) = 2(2x + 72)$, $x = 4$
    b $36(48 - x) = 72x$, $x = 16$

7 $33x = 15(24 - x)$, $x = 7.5$

Extension problem

8 a $x = 4$ b $x = 5$
    c $x = 6$ d $x = 2$
    e $x = 2\frac{1}{2}$ f $x = 1\frac{1}{4}$
    g $x = -2$ h $x = 3$

How well are you doing?

1 $y = 14x - 9$

2 $x \leftarrow \boxed{\text{divide by 9}} \leftarrow \boxed{\text{add 4}} \leftarrow y$

3 (1, 5) and (0.5, 4)

4 a $k = 4$ b $t = -7$

5 a $3k = 6$, $k = 2$ b $6y = 3$, $y = 0.5$

6 $8x - 66 = 2x$, $x = 11$

Home book

TASK 1

1 a $y \approx 3$ b $y \approx 5$
    c $y \approx 1$ d $y \approx -1$
    e $y \approx 4$ f $y \approx 0$

2 a $y = x + 36$ b $y = x - 23$
    c $y = 24x$ d $y = \frac{x}{15}$
    e $y = 7x + 41$ f $y = 72x - 53$
    g $y = \frac{x}{7} + 32$ h $y = \frac{x}{17.5} - 6$

TASK 2

1 An infinite number

2 One solution, when $x = 4$

3 a $x = 37$ b $x = 31$
    c $x = 14$ d $x = 0.5$
    e $x = 8$ f $x = -2$
    g $x = 12$ h $x = 6$

4 a $x = 3$ b $x = 7$
    c $x = 13$ d $x = 11$
    e $x = 28$ f $x = 48$
    g $x = 38$ h $x = 15$

TASK 3

1 a $3x + 60 = 180$
    b $x = 40$
      The three angles are 40°, 60° and 80°.

2 a $x = 9$ b $x = 0.5$
    c $x = 3$ d $x = 5$
    e $x = 7$ f $x = 0.2$
    g $x = 12$ h $x = 27$

TASK 4

1 a $6w + 31 = 121$; $w = 12$
    b $\frac{x}{3} + 42 = 46$; $x = 12$
    c $14y - 35 = 91$; $y = 9$
    d $8(z + 5) = 96$; $z = 7$

2 Sam is 14 years old.

3 The packets hold 25, 52 and 75 peanuts.

4 Alice gets £18, Daisy £36 and Becka £41.

5 83, 84 and 85

6 No. You can find four even numbers such as 2, 4, 6 and 10 whose sum is not divisible by 4. This is called a counter-example.

TASK 5

1   a $x = 9$ b $x = 11$
     c $x = 27$ d $x = -2$

2   a $x = 4$ b $x = 5$
     c $x = 12$ d $x = 1$

3   a $x = 1$ b $x = 7$
     c $x = 3$ d $x = 2$

4   a $x = 4$ b $x = 6$
     c $x = 0.5$ d $x = -1$

TASK 6

1   a $x = 1$ b $x = 3$
     c $x = 5$ d $x = 2$

2   a $x = 4$ b $x = 1$
     c $x = 6$ d $x = 3$

3   a $x = 2$ b $x = 7$
     c $x = 3$ d $x = 4$

4   a $x = 1$ b $x = 6$
     c $x = 0.5$ d $x = -2$

CD-ROM

Check up

1 $y = 14x + 7$

2 $x \rightarrow$ | multiply by 12 | $\rightarrow$ | add 5 | $\rightarrow y$

3 $x \leftarrow$ | divide by 10 | $\leftarrow$ | add 15 | $\leftarrow y$

4   (1, 6), (3, 16) and (−1, −4)

5   There is an infinite number of solutions.

6   There is one solution, when $x = 5$.

7 $x = 3$

8 $x = 6$

9 $x = 2$

10 $x = 5$

Previous learning

Before they start, pupils should be able to:

- design a data collection sheet or questionnaire to use in a simple survey
- construct frequency tables for discrete data, grouped where appropriate in equal class intervals
- construct and interpret bar-line graphs and frequency diagrams for grouped discrete data
- interpret pie charts
- calculate the mean, including from a simple frequency table
- find the mode, median and range, and the modal class for grouped data, and use them to compare two simple distributions

Objectives based on NC levels 5 and 6 (mainly level 5)

In this unit, pupils learn to:

- identify mathematical features of a context or problem
- conjecture and generalise
- try out and compare mathematical representations
- select appropriate procedures and tools, including ICT
- make accurate diagrams and graphs on paper and on screen
- refine own findings on the basis of discussion with others
- record methods, solutions and conclusions, relating them to the context
- evaluate alternative strategies and approaches

and to:

- compare estimated experimental probabilities with theoretical probabilities
- decide which data to collect to answer a question, and identify possible sources
- plan, construct and use frequency tables with equal class intervals for gathering continuous data
- construct and interpret:
  - bar charts and frequency diagrams for continuous data
  - simple line graphs for time series
- compare two simple distributions using the range and one of the mode, median or mean, relating summary statistics and findings to the questions being explored
- write about and discuss the results of a statistical enquiry, justifying the method used, and using ICT as appropriate.

Lessons

1 **Collecting continuous data**

2 **Processing and representing continuous data**

3 **Analysing and interpreting distributions**

4 **Communicating findings**

5 **Mean, median and range**

6 **Comparing probabilities**

7 **Line graphs for time series**

About this unit

This unit extends data-handling work to consider continuous data for the first time. This is covered through some taught work on grouping data and constructing frequency diagrams plus a project for pupils based on the data-handling cycle. Planning and collecting data is developed further, as is interpretation and comparison of tables and charts. This includes using probability experiments to collect data. The unit also covers calculating the actual mean using an assumed mean and line graphs for time series.

Common errors and misconceptions

Look out for pupils who:

- choose overlapping class intervals when grouping data;
- cannot distinguish between discrete and continuous data;
- have difficulty in choosing and reading a scale for a frequency axis;
- plot continuous data as if it were discrete data.

Key terms and notation

data, information, discrete, continuous

frequency table, frequency diagram, scatter graph, line graph, axis/axes, horizontal axis, vertical axis

mean, median, mode, range, assumed mean

interpret, represent, compare, distribution

Practical resources

30 cm rulers, one per pupil
2-metre rulers or a measuring tape, fixed to the classroom wall as a standing scale to measure height
short length of coloured tape fixed to the floor and a measuring tape
individual whiteboards
graph-plotting software (e.g. Autograph) and presentation software (e.g. PowerPoint) for pupils to use in a computer suite for lessons 3 and 4

calculators
graph paper
squared paper
interlocking cubes, red and blue counters in a bag
for each group: coins, BluTack, red, orange and green counters in bags, dice
data logger with temperature probe (or a stopwatch and thermometer), beaker and hot water (e.g. in a vacuum flask to keep it hot until required)

Exploring maths

Tier 4 teacher's book
Answers for Unit S4.3 , pp. 268–273

Tier 4 CD-ROM
PowerPoint files
    S4.3 Slides for lessons 1 to 7
Excel file
    S4.3 Lesson 7
Tier 4 programs
    Reaction time
    Probability simulation

Tier 4 class book
S4.3, pp. 219–237
S4.3 How well are you doing? p. 236

Tier 4 home book
S4.3, pp. 86–95

Tier 4 CD-ROM
S4.3 Check up
S4.3 Pupil resource sheets
    1.1 One per pupil
    3.1 One per group
    3.2 One per pupil (optional)
    6.1 One per pupil
    7.1 One per pupil

Useful websites

World records
www.guinessworldrecords.com

Census at School
www.censusatschool.ntu.ac.uk

Murphy's law
en.wikipedia.org/wiki/Murphy's_law
www.murphys-laws.com

1 Collecting continuous data

Learning points

○ Discrete data can be collected by counting and takes only integer values. Examples are the number of pupils in a class or the number of weeds on a lawn.

○ Continuous data can be collected by measuring and takes any value within an interval. Examples are quantities such as length, weight, temperature, time and speed.

Starter

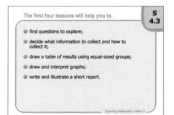

Use **slide 1.1** to discuss the objectives for the first four lessons. Say that this lesson is about discrete and continuous data.

Now ask:

> Who has the largest hand span in the class? Who has the smallest?

> How are the different hand spans distributed across the range of lengths?

> How can we find out?

Discuss with pupils how to measure their hand span. They need to agree that they will all stretch their hands, which hand they will measure and what degree of accuracy they will use.

Ask each pupil to measure their hand span in the agreed manner and to note the measurement for use later in the lesson.

Main activity

Show **slide 1.2**. Ask pupils to discuss the world records on the slide in pairs before asking individuals to contribute to a class discussion.

> What do you notice about the units of measurement?

Pupils should notice that the records are measured to different degrees of accuracy.

> Can you think of any other quantities that might be measured to different degrees of accuracy?

Explain the two types of data: *discrete* and *continuous*. Discrete data can be collected by counting and take only integer values, e.g. the number of kittens in a cat's litter, the number of patients in a hospital at a given time or the number of spelling errors in an essay. Continuous data can be collected by measuring and are never exact. They take any value within an interval, e.g. when someone grows in height from 160 to 161 cm we assume every possible value between 160 and 161 has been attained.

The times and speeds on slide 1.2 are measured to different degrees of accuracy because they are examples of continuous data. Refer pupils to the definitions at the beginning of **S4.3 Exercise 1** in the class book (p. 220).

> What other examples of discrete data can you think of?

> What other examples of continuous data can you think of?

Ask pupils to do **S4.3 Exercise 1A** in the class book (p. 220).

Explain to the class that they are going to do a project later in the unit using continuous data collected about themselves. First, they are going to collect some data and learn how to group it before representing it in a suitable diagram.

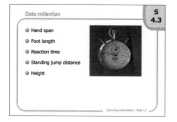

Slide 1.3 shows the data they are going to collect. Discuss and agree with pupils the level of accuracy they need to use for each measurement. Show them how to measure their height using a standing scale set up on the classroom wall. Agree with pupils what constitutes a standing jump keeping two feet together and how to measure it from a line fixed on the classroom floor.

Launch **Reaction time** and follow the onscreen instructions.

SIM

Ask pupils to work in groups of six. Give each group a copy of **S4.3 Resource sheet 1.1**. Refer groups to **S4.3 Exercise 1B** in the class book (p. 221).

RS

Ask pupils to collect the data and to enter it on the resource sheet. Help the class to organise themselves effectively. Collect the data sheets. You will need to collate the data onto one master list for use in subsequent lessons.

Review

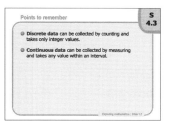

Show pupils the set of hand span data on **slide 1.4**.

What do you notice about this set of data?

How accurately do you think these pupils measured their hand spans?

What variation is there in the hand spans?

How are the sizes of hand span distributed among the group of pupils?

Pupils should be able to make some comments from looking at the data and to pick out the range as a measure of spread. They should be able to give an interval within which most of the hand spans lie. Explain that they will look at other ways of analysing continuous data in the next lesson.

Sum up by stressing the points on **slide 1.5**.

Homework

Ask pupils to do **S4.3 Task 1** in the home book (p. 86).

2 Processing and representing continuous data

Learning points

- In a frequency diagram for continuous data, the bars touch and the horizontal axis is labelled as a scale.
- Groups for continuous data should be of equal width and not overlap.

Starter To check pupils' understanding of place value with decimals, ask them to answer on their whiteboards questions such as:

Which is larger, 8.02 or 8.20?

Which number is halfway between 1.6 and 1.7?

Which number is halfway between 3.9 and 4?

Write down the number that is 0.05 less than 4.7.

Continue this sequence: 0.12, 0.14, 0.16, …

Explore and explain any misunderstandings pupils may have.

Main activity

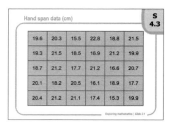

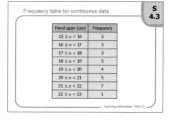

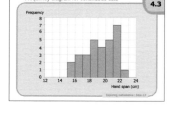

Show **slide 2.1.** Ask the class what they think a bar chart to represent the data would look like. Draw out that, unless they grouped the data, there would be a lot of short bars.

Ask pupils to suggest suitable intervals for grouping the data. Record suggestions. Encourage them to see the need for non-overlapping class intervals. Develop the language from '16 and all the values up to 17 but not including 17' to the formal notation used for class intervals of $16 \leqslant x < 17$.

Show the completed frequency table on **slide 2.2**.

Where would a hand span of 18.5 cm go in the frequency table?

Where would a hand span of 21 cm go in the frequency table?

What does the notation for this class interval mean?

Show the frequency diagram for the hand span data on **slide 2.3**.

What quantity is on the horizontal axis? [hand span]

What is measured on the vertical axis? [frequency]

What do you notice is different about this frequency diagram compared with the ones you have drawn previously for discrete data? Why do you think this is?

Pupils should notice that the bars touch and the horizontal scale is labelled differently. Ensure that they understand why. Pick a bar and ask what the class interval is. Pick a class interval from the previous slide and ask them to identify the corresponding bar.

Ask pupils to do **S4.3 Exercise 2** in the class book (p. 223). They will need graph paper.

Review

Show **slide 2.3** again.

Ask pupils in pairs to discuss and write on their whiteboards a sentence to say what the frequency diagram shows about the distribution of hand spans.

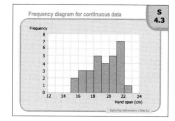

> What can you say about the range of the hand spans?
>
> Which is the modal group or class for hand spans?
>
> What can you say about the shape of the distribution?

Ask pairs of pupils to share what they have written. Develop appropriate phrases for them to use to describe the distribution of hand spans.

Sum up by stressing the lesson's learning points.

Homework

Ask pupils to do **S4.3 Task 2** in the home book (p. 86). Pupils will need graph paper.

3 Analysing and interpreting distributions

Learning points

◎ Scatter graphs are useful for showing connections between two quantities.

◎ Frequency diagrams are useful for showing how a set of data is distributed.

Starter *This and the next lesson preferably need to take place in a computer room, with access from each computer to graph-plotting software for statistical diagrams (e.g. Autograph, Excel, or the Statistics tools) and presentation software (e.g. PowerPoint). A help sheet for any pupils using Autograph is available on Resource sheet 3.2 (see below).*

Tell pupils that they will be completing two small statistical investigations over the next two lessons using the data collected in the two previous lessons.

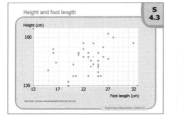

Show **slide 3.1**.

> **What type of graph is this?**
>
> **What quantity is plotted on the horizontal axis? The vertical axis?**
>
> **What does each point represent?**
>
> **What does the graph show?**
>
> **What does the graph tell you about the relationship between height and foot length?**
>
> **What can we use scatter graphs for?**

There is no need at this stage to discuss 'correlation' but pupils should notice that the graph shows that people with larger feet tend to be taller. Stress that scatter graphs are useful for showing connections between two variables.

Main activity Give each pupil a copy of the collated class data collected in lesson 1 of this unit (this is also needed for the homework task in lesson 4). An alternative data set is provided on **S4.3 Resource sheet 3.1**.

Ask pupils in pairs to think of some questions to investigate using this data. They can either look for relationships between variables or look at the distribution for a single variable. Some possibilities are shown on **slide 3.2**.

1 Do tall people jump further?

2 Do most people have similar reaction times?

3 Is there a relationship between foot length and hand span?

4 How does hand span vary in the class?

Ask the pairs to pick a question and discuss how to investigate it. They will need to consider what kinds of tables, graphs and charts to use. Questions 1 and 3 involve the relationship between two variables (requiring the use of a scatter graph); questions 2 and 4 involve investigating the distribution of a single variable (requiring grouping of continuous data).

You can vary the difficulty of the activity by suggesting that certain pairs of pupils work with different parts of the data, for example, height, because it is in whole numbers. Ideally, the groups should answer all the questions between them.

Ask one or two pairs to report back to the class so that you know that they are ready to start their project.

Ask pupils to work on **S4.3 Exercise 3** in the class book (p. 225).

For the rest of the lesson pupils should work on their chosen question, analysing the data, plotting a graph and coming to preliminary conclusions.

Encourage pupils to enter the data and use graph-plotting software for statistical diagrams to draw their graphs and charts for this work. **S4.3 Resource sheet 3.2** contains help for pupils if they are using Autograph for this purpose. Alternatively, pupils could draw their graphs on squared paper.

RS

Review

Show **slide 3.3**. Lead a discussion on the foot lengths of the people shown. Ask pupils to contribute their ideas. Pick out the key features of the distribution.

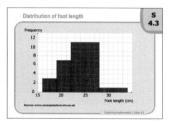

> What length are most people's feet?
>
> Are there many people with feet shorter than this?
>
> Are there many people with feet longer than this?
>
> What is the variation in the length of people's feet?
>
> What is the modal group? What does this mean?

Ask pupils in pairs to write on their whiteboards a sentence describing the foot lengths of this group of people, mentioning as many key features as they can. Ask a few pairs to read their sentence to the class.

Finish by stressing the points on **slide 3.4**.

Homework

Ask pupils to do **S4.3 Task 3** in the home book (p. 89).

4 Communicating findings

Learning points

- The shape of a graph helps you to see important features of a data set.

- Choose a chart or diagram that helps you to answer your question. Explain why you chose it.

- Write down what each chart, diagram or calculation shows you about the data.

- Make sure that you answer the original question.

- In your conclusion, say how accurate you think your results are and how you could improve the project another time.

Starter

This lesson is a continuation of the previous one. It preferably needs to take place in a computer room, with access from each computer to graph-plotting software for statistical diagrams (e.g. Autograph, Excel, or the Statistics tools) and presentation software (e.g. PowerPoint).

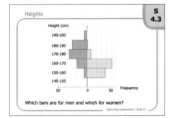

Show **slide 4.1**. Explain that one set of bars shows the heights of 100 men and the other the heights of 100 women.

> Which set of bars is for the men? How do you know?
>
> Describe the distribution of the men's heights.
>
> Describe the distribution of the women's heights.
>
> Are there any differences in the shapes of the two distributions?
>
> Which is the modal class interval for men and which for women?

Main activity

Pupils should spend this part of the lesson putting the final touches to their project from the previous lesson and then producing a short presentation of their findings.

Pupils could prepare a slide using presentation software such as PowerPoint in this part of the lesson. Slides could then be printed and displayed in the classroom.

Alternatively, if they have drawn graphs on paper, they could prepare an overhead projector transparency or a poster.

Ask pupils to work on **S4.3 Exercise 4** in the class book (p. 226).

Review

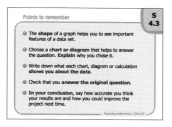

Use a longer review time to invite pairs of pupils to present their findings from this lesson and the previous one.

Involve the whole class in:

- considering how far they can generalise from their results
- comparing and evaluating their solutions.

Ask pupils to remember the points on **slide 4.2**.

Homework

Ask pupils to do **S4.3 Task 4** in the home book (p. 91).

5 Mean, median and range

Learning points

- An assumed mean can help you to calculate the actual mean of a data set.

- You can use the range and one of the mean, median or mode to compare two sets of data.

Starter

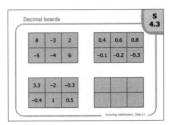

Say that this lesson is about calculating statistics such as the mean and range for a set of data.

Show **slide 5.1**.

> What is the total for the top left set of boxes? [4]
>
> What is the total for the top right set of boxes? [1.2]
>
> What is the total for the bottom left set of boxes? [4]

Ask pupils to share their methods and to explain how they grouped the numbers to work out the answers.

Ask pairs to use their whiteboards to suggest a set of six numbers for the blank set of boxes. For example, you could ask them for six different numbers that add to a certain total with half the numbers negative, or for a set of decimals adding to 0.7. Ask some pairs to come to the board and write their numbers in the blank grid. The class can then check the total for the set of numbers.

Main activity

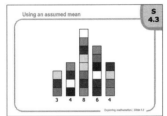

Ask pupils what they can remember about how to find the mean of a set of numbers and what the mean represents.

Write this list of numbers on the board: 1008, 1013, 992, 1005, 992.

> How can we calculate the mean of this list of numbers?

Explain that although we could calculate the mean in the usual way by adding up the numbers and dividing by 5, we can also calculate the mean more easily.

Show **slide 5.2**.

> What is the mean of 3, 4, 8, 6 and 4? [5]

Remind pupils that the mean has the effect of averaging out the number of cubes in each tower. You can demonstrate with interlocking cubes if you wish. Draw a horizontal line on the slide to show a tower height of 5. Indicate how the excess cubes can be moved to make all the towers have this height.

Now move the horizontal line indicating the mean up to 6. This time when you share out the cubes evenly you are five cubes short of reaching the line so each tower is one cube short of the line.

Next move the horizontal line down to 4. Now when you share out the cubes evenly you have five cubes too many so each tower has one cube more than the line.

Return to the original example of finding the mean of 1008, 1013, 992, 1005 and 992.

> Can you make an estimate of the mean?
> What would be a good number to use? [1000]

How far is each number from this assumed mean?
[Write them up on the board as 8, 13, −8, 5, −8.]

What is the total? [10]

If we are out by a total of +10 over the five numbers, how much will each number be out by, on average? [+2]

What is the actual mean? [1002]

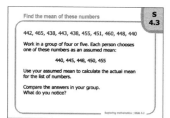

Show **slide 5.3**. Ask pupils to work in groups of four or five on the problem on the slide.

Pupils should all get the same actual mean [448] whatever they use as the assumed mean. Discuss with them how they might choose a good assumed mean for a set of numbers.

Ask pupils to do **S4.3 Exercise 5** in the class book (p. 227).

Review   Show the problem on **slide 5.4** and ask pupils to work in pairs to solve it.

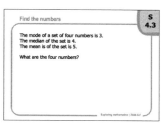

The mode of a set of four numbers is 3.
The median of the set is 4.
The mean is of the set is 5.

What are the four numbers?

Ask pupils to share strategies for solving the problem, then ask them to try to write a problem of their own. Some of these can be shared with the class for others to solve.

Ask pupils to remember the points on **slide 5.5**.

Homework   Ask pupils to do **S4.3 Task 5** in the home book (p. 92). Pupils will need a calculator and should either use the class data collected earlier in the unit or the sample data set provided on **S4.3 Resource sheet 3.1**.

6 Comparing probabilities

Learning points

- A simulation is a way of collecting data about a problem without having to carry out the actual experiment.

- A simulation is an easy-to-do experiment that behaves in the same way as the experiment we are unable to do.

- Probability experiments can be simulated.

Starter

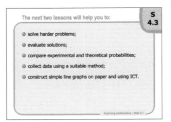

Use **slide 6.1** to discuss the objectives for the next two lessons. Say that this lesson is about collecting data from experiments.

Put four blue counters and eight red counters in a bag in secret. Draw a counter out, note the colour on the board and replace the counter.

What can you say about the colours of the counters in the bag?

Draw some more counters out one at a time, record the colour and then replace the counter.

What can you say about the colours of the counters in the bag now?

What do you think is the probability of getting a blue counter? Why?

Show pupils how many counters of each colour are in the bag.

What is the theoretical probability of getting a blue counter?
Is this the same as we got in the experiment? If not, why not?

Repeat the experiment with other proportions of red and blue counters. Encourage pupils to consider both the theoretical and experimental probabilities each time.

Main activity

Ask pupils if they have heard of Murphy's law. State this as 'Anything that can go wrong will go wrong'. See if they can come up with any examples. Some examples are:

- A slice of buttered bread, when dropped, will always land butter-side down.

- When you need an item that is in a pile, it will always be the one at the bottom.

- Buses take ages to arrive, but when they do they always arrive three at a time.

- The day you forget your umbrella, it pours with rain.

- When caught in a traffic jam, the lane that you are in will always be the slowest to move.

You can find more of these on en.wikipedia.org/wiki/Murphy's_law and www.murphys-laws.com.

Explain to pupils that they are going to try out some experiments to see if Murphy's law is true. What they are going to do is *simulate* the problems, which means making up an easy-to-do experiment that will behave like the situation we are trying to find out about. For example, if we wanted to simulate picking one sweet at random from a box containing six different sweets, we could allocate a number to each type of sweet and roll a dice to find out which sweet was picked.

Ask pupils to work in pairs on **S4.3 Exercise 6** in the class book (p. 230). They will each need a copy of **S4.3 Resource sheet 6.1**. Start by having all pupils do the buttered toast experiment together as a class as an example.

RS

Review

Launch **Probability simulation** and run a simple simulation of a horse race. Explain that the program will roll two dice and add the scores to give a total. Allocate a number from 2 to 12 to each of eleven pupils to be the number of their horse.

SIM

> Why can't you choose horse number 1?

> Which horse do you think will win?

Choose two dice and display the total. Run the program a trial at a time so that the pupils with the horse numbers can tally the results as you go.

> Which horse won? Why?

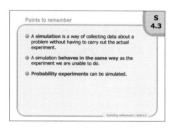

Pupils should recognise that they have looked at combining two events previously in unit S4.1. They should remember that 7 is the most likely outcome when adding the scores on two dice because you can make 7 in the greatest number of ways.

Sum up with the points on **slide 6.2**.

Homework

Ask pupils to do **S4.3 Task 6** in the home book (p. 93).

7 Line graphs for time series

Learning points

- Data can be collected from experiments.
- A line graph is a useful way of displaying continuous data against time.

Starter Use a data logger or improvise with a stopwatch and thermometer to collect some data with the class. Pupils are likely to have done this or a similar experiment in science.

> **How does the temperature of hot water change over time?**
>
> **How long will it take for a beaker of boiling water to cool down to room temperature?**
>
> **What do you think the graph of temperature against time will look like?**
>
> **Is the data discrete or continuous?**
>
> **What sort of graph should you draw? Why?**

Ask pupils to sketch their graphs on their whiteboards and to show them to you. Discuss the need for a line graph as a good way of displaying time series data because it is continuous. Make sure that pupils put time on the horizontal axis.

Main activity Pour some very hot water into a beaker and record the temperature every 15 seconds for 30 minutes. If you use a data logger you will be able to display the data in real time as it is collected.

While the experiment is running, ask pupils to do **S4.3 Exercise 7** in the class book (p. 233). They will need **S4.3 Resource sheet 7.1** and some graph paper.

Stop pupils when the experiment has finished to discuss the findings.

> **Was your prediction for the shape of the graph correct?**
>
> **Can you describe how the temperature changes over time?**
>
> **What will happen over a longer period of time?**

Help pupils to develop appropriate language for describing the shape of the graph and predicting its behaviour as the temperature of the hot liquid approaches room temperature.

A set of real data from this experiment is provided in the spreadsheet file **S4.3 Lesson 7** on the 'Cooling' worksheet. This can either be displayed in Excel or imported into graph-plotting software.

Pupils can then continue with the exercise.

Review   Show pupils the 'Review' worksheet in the spreadsheet file **S4.3 Lesson 7**.
Explain that the table shows the average temperature each month for
Bangkok and Kabul.

XL

> What do you notice about the temperature in the two cities?
>
> What type of graph could you use so that you can compare the
> temperatures in the two cities more easily?
>
> Why is a line graph a good choice?

Encourage pupils to recognise that the temperature data is continuous and that
the monthly average temperature changes gradually between months so that
the points can be joined to show the trend. Two line graphs on the same set of
axes allow data to be compared more easily. Scroll down the page and show
pupils the line graph.

> Which line is for Kabul and which is for Bangkok? Why?
>
> Describe the differences in the average temperature in the two cities.

Ask pupils to work in pairs on this last question using a whiteboard to draft and
develop their work. Ask a few pupils to share their work with the class.

Finish by asking pupils to remember the points on **slide 7.1**.

Round off the unit by referring again to the objectives. Suggest that pupils find
time to try the self-assessment problems in **S4.3 How well are you doing?** in the
class book (p. 236).

Homework   Ask pupils to do **S4.3 Task 7** in the home book (p. 94). They will need graph
paper.

S4.3 Check up and resource sheets

Check up
S4.3

Write your answers in your book.

1 A teacher asked her pupils how much time they spent on their homework over the weekend. The results are in the table.

Time spent on homework (minutes)	Frequency
$0 \leqslant x < 30$	3
$30 \leqslant x < 60$	7
$60 \leqslant x < 90$	10
$90 \leqslant x < 120$	12
$120 \leqslant x < 150$	6
$150 \leqslant x < 180$	5
$180 \leqslant x < 210$	2

a How many pupils were asked?

b Why is the data grouped?

c Draw a frequency diagram to illustrate the data. Use a scale of 2 cm to 30 minutes from 0 to 210 minutes on the horizontal axis. Use a scale of 1 cm per person on the vertical axis.

2 The exact number of raisins in each of 15 small boxes is:

31, 29, 34, 27, 33, 34, 28, 26, 27, 27, 29, 30, 31, 32, 33

a Choose a number to take as the assumed mean. Explain your choice.

b Calculate the actual mean using the value you have suggested for the assumed mean. Show all the stages in your workings.

3 Increasing levels of carbon dioxide (CO_2) in the atmosphere indicate global warming. This data is from air bubbles in the Antarctic ice core and from air samples collected in Hawaii. The CO_2 figure is parts per million.

Year	1899	1909	1915	1927	1935	1943	1953	1963	1973	1983	1993	1999
CO_2	296	299	301	306	307	308	313	319	330	343	357	368

Data from k12s.phast.umass.edu/~warming/.

a Draw a horizontal axis for the years from 1899 to 1999, using a scale of 1 cm for every 10 years.
Draw a vertical axis for the CO_2 (parts per million) from 290 to 370, using a scale of 1 cm for every 10 parts.
Draw a line graph to illustrate the data.

b Describe the shape of the graph.

c Do you think that graph shows evidence for global warming? Explain your answer.

Resource sheet 1.1
S4.3

Person number	Hand span	Foot length	Reaction time	Standing jump	Height

Resource sheet 3.1
S4.3

Sample data set

Person	Height (cm)	Foot length (cm)	Hand span (cm)	Reaction time (s)	Standing jump (cm)
1	165	21	19	0.51	111
2	155	25	20	0.59	117
3	165	25.5	18.2	0.48	135
4	145	21	17	0.65	99
5	134	20	16	0.59	145
6	140	20	18	0.53	133
7	145	19	15	0.59	151
8	154	23	17	0.60	109
9	157	22	20	0.59	127
10	156	25	18	0.59	108
11	175	26	20	0.61	112
12	148	22	17	0.50	131
13	159	25	20	0.53	123
14	170	25	15	0.63	144
15	162	24	20	0.56	120
16	170	30	23	0.52	119
17	147	24	18	0.54	121
18	150	23	18.4	0.65	122
19	140	30	20	0.64	161
20	176	27	22	0.59	134
21	159	20	19	0.78	113
22	161	23	19	0.43	131
23	169	28	19	0.55	130
24	165	23.5	19	0.49	147
25	174	25	18	0.59	177
26	165	24	16	0.50	103
27	147	23	13	0.54	134
28	159	20.5	27.5	0.54	133
29	169	24	22	0.38	128
30	145	24	19	0.62	121

Data source for height, foot length and hand span: www.censusatschool.ntu.ac.uk

Resource sheet 3.2 — S4.3

Help sheet for producing statistical graphs in Autograph

1. Click on 'file' and choose 'New 1D Statistics Page'.

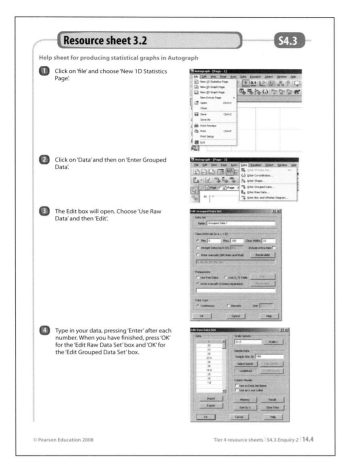

2. Click on 'Data' and then on 'Enter Grouped Data'.

3. The Edit box will open. Choose 'Use Raw Data' and then 'Edit'.

4. Type in your data, pressing 'Enter' after each number. When you have finished, press 'OK' for the 'Edit Raw Data Set' box and 'OK' for the 'Edit Grouped Data Set' box.

Resource sheet 3.2 [continued]

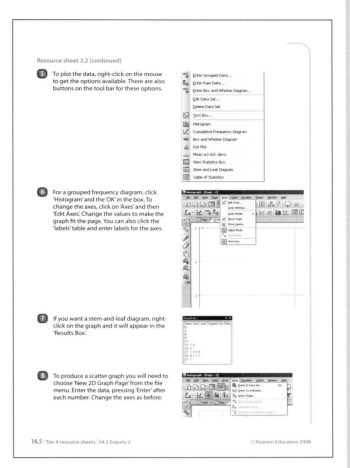

5. To plot the data, right-click on the mouse to get the options available. There are also buttons on the tool bar for these options.

6. For a grouped frequency diagram, click 'Histogram' and the 'OK' in the box. To change the axes, click on 'Axes' and then 'Edit Axes'. Change the values to make the graph fit the page. You can also click the 'labels' table and enter labels for the axes.

7. If you want a stem-and-leaf diagram, right-click on the graph and it will appear in the 'Results Box'.

8. To produce a scatter graph you will need to choose 'New 2D Graph Page' from the file menu. Enter the data, pressing 'Enter' after each number. Change the axes as before.

Resource sheet 6.1 — S4.3

Write your answers on the sheet.

Experiment 1

No BluTack

	Tally	Frequency
Heads		
Tails		

Experimental probability of a head =

Experimental probability of a tail =

BluTack on 'tails' side

	Tally	Frequency
Heads		
Tails		

Experimental probability of a head =

Experimental probability of a tail =

Experiment 2

Dice score	Counter R/O/G	Dice score	Counter R/O/G	Dice score	Counter R/O/G	Dice score	Counter R/O/G	Dice score	Counter R/O/G

Number of times the lights are red and I am in a hurry =

Experimental probability of the lights being red and me being in a hurry =

Experiment 3

Write the rules for the two dice here:									

Die 1	Die 2	Die 1	Die 2	Die 1	Die 2	Die 1	Die 2	Die 1	Die 2

Resource sheet 7.1 — S4.3

Write your answers on the sheet.

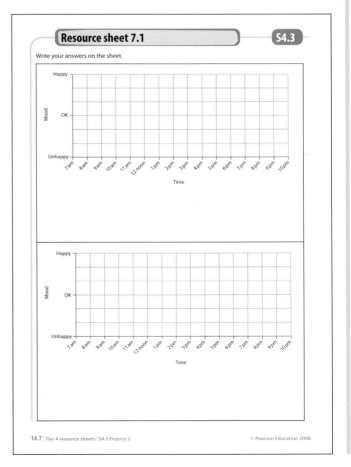

Class book

Exercise 1A

1 Pupil's age to different degrees of accuracy

2 a 13 to 14 cm
  b 13.6 cm
  c 13.62 cm
  d 13.622 cm

Exercise 1B

This is a class investigation from S4.3 Resource sheet 1.1.

Exercise 2

1 a

Height (cm)	Frequency
$130 \leqslant x < 140$	1
$140 \leqslant x < 150$	4
$150 \leqslant x < 160$	9
$160 \leqslant x < 170$	8
$170 \leqslant x < 180$	7
$180 \leqslant x < 190$	1

b

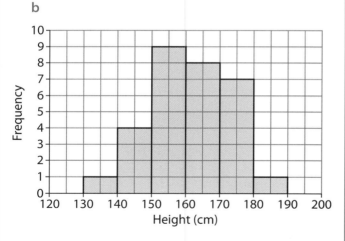

2 a For example, 18.7 cm, 19.5 cm and 19.9 cm
  b $22 \leqslant x < 24$
  c $28 \leqslant x < 30$

d

Foot length (cm)	Frequency
$18 \leqslant x < 20$	2
$20 \leqslant x < 22$	7
$22 \leqslant x < 24$	6
$24 \leqslant x < 26$	8
$26 \leqslant x < 28$	5
$28 \leqslant x < 30$	1
$30 \leqslant x < 32$	1

e

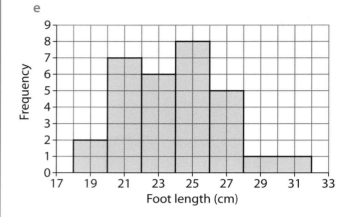

3 a

Wrist circumference (mm)	Frequency
$110 \leqslant x < 130$	3
$130 \leqslant x < 150$	3
$150 \leqslant x < 170$	11
$170 \leqslant x < 190$	11
$190 \leqslant x < 210$	2

b

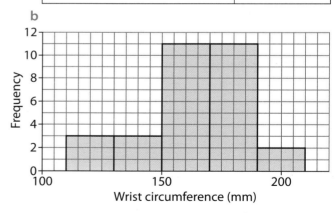

Exercise 3

These answers are based on the sample data set on S4.3 Resource sheet 3.1.

Exercise 4

1 Do tall people jump further?

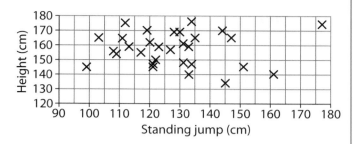

The graph shows little connection between height and standing jump.

2 Do most people have similar reaction times?

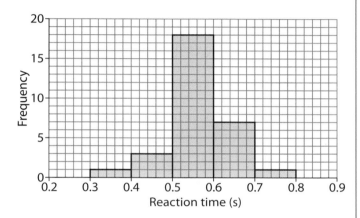

Yes, most people had a reaction time of between 0.5 and 0.6 seconds.

3 Is there a relationship between foot length and hand span?

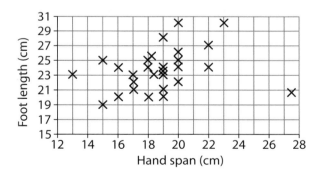

The graph shows a slight relationship between foot length and hand span. Generally, people with bigger feet had larger hand spans.

4 How does hand span vary in the class?

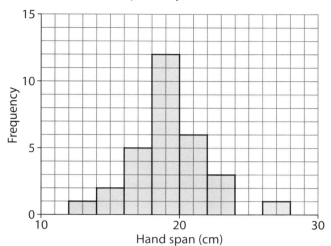

There are only a few people with small hand spans. The number of people increases so that the modal group is for hand spans of 18 cm up to but not including 20 cm. The number of people then decreases making the graph almost symmetrical. Only one person has a very large hand span.

Exercise 5

1 14.1

2 £2.27

3 1005

4 70.2 kg

5 2 cm

6 Set 1: mean 12.6, range 10
Set 2: mean 12.6, range 7
Both data sets have the same mean but the range is less for set 2 so that data must be more closely grouped together.

7 a Girls: mode 6, range 5
Boys: mode 8, range 5
b The most common shoe size for girls is 6 compared to 8 for the boys. Overall, the girls have smaller feet.
c The mean is likely to be a decimal value, which is less useful with shoe sizes which are whole numbers.

8 **a** Type A: mean 4.5, range 5, mode 2 and 7
Type B mean 3.375, range 4, mode 4

    b Type A is the best type because it has the highest mean.

    c Type B is the best type because the range is smaller so the type is more consistent in the number of courgettes it produces.

9 **a** Girls: range 13 cm, median 139 cm
Boys: range 16 cm, median 147 cm

    b There is more variation in the boys' heights than the girls'. Half the girls are less than 139 cm tall and half the boys are less than 147 cm tall. The boys are generally taller.

Extension problem

10 For example: The order for the mean height of the men, tallest first is: Netherlands, USA, UK, Germany and Italy, France, Japan and China

The order for the mean height of the women, tallest first is: Netherlands, USA, UK and Germany, Italy, France, Japan, China

The order is the same, so the country with the tallest men on average also has the tallest women and the country with the shortest men has the shortest women.

The mean height for the men is always more than the mean height of the women.

Exercise 6

1 **a** The piece of toast

    b The butter

    c Butter-side-down

    d Pupils' answer

    e $\frac{1}{2}$ The Blu-Tack is likely to make the coin land 'butter-side-down' more often.

    f Pupils' answer. Whether or not a pupil thinks this is realistic depends on whether they think buttering the toast on one side can be modelled by a piece of Blu-Tack on one side of a coin.

2 **a** Pupils' answer

    b $\frac{1}{2}$

    c Pupils' answer

    d $\frac{2}{5}$

    e The events do not affect one another. The lights are not more likely to be red if you are in a hurry.

    f Pupils' answer. They may mention that some traffic lights work on sensors, that the traffic light sequence could be better modelled or

they may say that it is quite realistic because the lights only seem more likely to be red when you are in a rush.

3 **a** Pupils' answer

    b No

    c Perhaps, by taking weather data and counting up how many days it rains in a month or a year.

    d No, the two dice do not affect one another. Forgetting your umbrella is unaffected by the chance of it raining.

    e Pupils' answer. The simulation assumes that the likelihood of rain is unconnected to the chance of you having your umbrella is unlikely to be realistic as many people either check the weather forecast or make a judgement about the likely weather before deciding to take their umbrella with tem or not. Because you can't work out the theoretical probably of forgetting your umbrella and it is different for each person, this simulation is unlikely to be realistic.

Exercise 7

1–2 Pupils' mood graphs

3 **a**

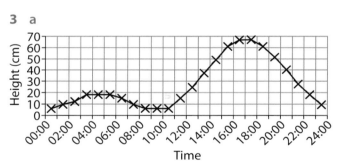

    b The graph shows a small peak between 03:00 and 0:500 and then a dip before reaching a much higher peak between 16:00 and 17:00.

4 **a**

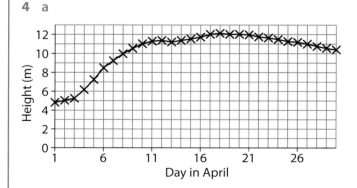

b The floodwater rises slowly at first and then more quickly before flattening off and then decreasing slowly.

c Horizontal line indicated at 5.5 m; exceeded on 4 April.

d 18 April

5 a

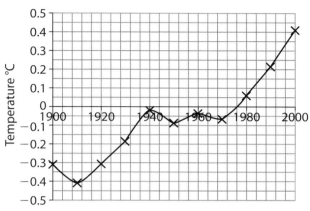

b The graph dips at first before making a rise between 1910 and 1940. It then dips and rises a little before starting to rise steadily from 1960 onwards.

c Pupils' answers

How well are you doing?

1 75.5

2 a

Neck circumference (cm)	Frequency
$30 \leqslant x < 35$	1
$35 \leqslant x < 40$	3
$40 \leqslant x < 45$	6
$45 \leqslant x < 50$	7
$50 \leqslant x < 55$	11
$55 \leqslant x < 60$	2

b

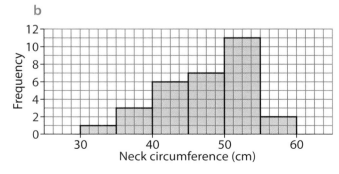

3 a £30.00

b 4-5 years old

Home book

TASK 1

This is an experiment.

TASK 2

1 a

Time (min : s)	Frequency
$2:10 \leqslant x < 2:15$	3
$2:15 \leqslant x < 2:20$	4
$2:20 \leqslant x < 2:25$	10
$2:25 \leqslant x < 2:30$	5
$2:30 \leqslant x < 2:35$	2

b

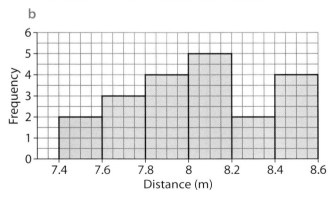

2 a

Distance (m)	Frequency
$7.40 \leqslant x < 7.60$	2
$7.60 \leqslant x < 7.80$	3
$7.80 \leqslant x < 8.00$	4
$8.00 \leqslant x < 8.20$	5
$8.20 \leqslant x < 8.40$	2
$8.40 \leqslant x < 8.60$	4

b

TASK 3

Frequency table for album 1:

Length of track (m : s)	Frequency
$1{:}00 \leqslant x < 2{:}00$	1
$2{:}00 \leqslant x < 3{:}00$	2
$3{:}00 \leqslant x < 4{:}00$	3
$4{:}00 \leqslant x < 5{:}00$	4
$5{:}00 \leqslant x < 6{:}00$	1
$6{:}00 \leqslant x < 7{:}00$	0
$7{:}00 \leqslant x < 8{:}00$	1

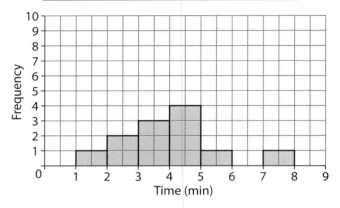

Frequency table for album 2:

Length of track (m : s)	Frequency
$0{:}00 \leqslant x < 1{:}00$	1
$1{:}00 \leqslant x < 2{:}00$	0
$2{:}00 \leqslant x < 3{:}00$	0
$3{:}00 \leqslant x < 4{:}00$	9
$4{:}00 \leqslant x < 5{:}00$	1
$5{:}00 \leqslant x < 6{:}00$	0
$6{:}00 \leqslant x < 7{:}00$	1

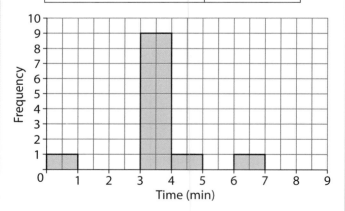

Graph for album 2

For album 1 there is more variation in the lengths of the tracks than for album 2. In album 2 most of the tracks are of similar length, between 3 and 4

minutes. The modal group is higher on the second album. Both albums have one very short track and one very long track.

TASK 4

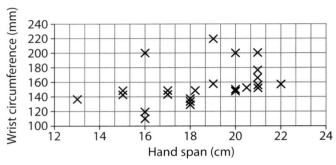

The graph shows very little connection between hand span and wrist size. You cannot say that people with larger hand spans will usually have bigger wrists.

TASK 5

1 and 2

	Height (cm)	Foot length (cm)	Hand span (cm)	Reaction time (s)	Standing jump (cm)
Mean	157.5	23.8	18.8	0.6	128
Median	159	24	19	0.575	127.5
Range	42	11	14.5	0.4	78

3 The mode is not generally sensible because the values are very often all different for data on height or hand span, for example.

TASK 6

Pupils' answers other than
2 a 8 possibilities

TASK 7

1

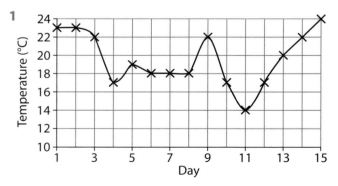

2 It is warm to start with then the temperature drops for most of the period other than on the 9th day when it is warmer again. The temperature then rises again at the end of the period.

3 The temperature in Winchester is higher than that in Belfast for the whole period except for one day. The general shape is the same, other than the peak on day 9 for Winchester.

CD-ROM

Check up

1 a 45

  b Because the answers are likely to have been different

  c

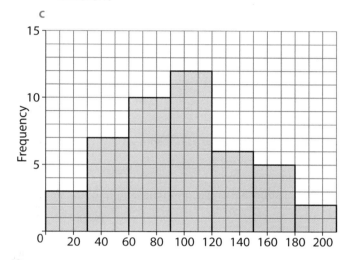

2 a 30 is probably a good choice.

  b 30

3 a

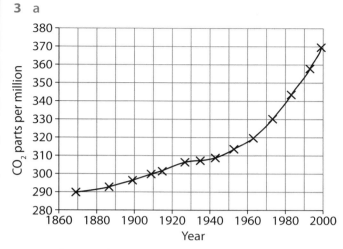

  b The graph rises and seems to get steeper towards the end.

  c Pupils' answer

Constructions

Previous learning

Before they start, pupils should be able to:

- measure and draw lines to the nearest millimetre
- measure and draw angles to the nearest degree
- construct a triangle given two sides and the included angle (SAS) or two angles and the included side (ASA)
- construct simple nets of 3D shapes
- use coordinates in all four quadrants.

Objectives based on NC levels 5 and 6 (mainly level 5)

In this unit, pupils learn to:

- identify the mathematical features of a problem or context
- make connections with related contexts
- select appropriate procedures and tools, including ICT
- make accurate mathematical constructions on paper and on screen
- visualise and manipulate dynamic images
- use logical argument to establish the truth of a statement
- record methods, solutions and conclusions

and to:

- use straight-edge and compasses to construct:
  - the midpoint and perpendicular bisector of a line segment
  - the bisector of an angle
  - the perpendicular from a point to a line
- use ruler and compasses to construct a triangle, given the lengths of the three sides (SSS)
- use ICT to explore constructions
- make scale drawings
- use bearings to specify direction
- find simple loci, both by reasoning and by using ICT, to produce shapes and paths.

Lessons

1 **Drawing arcs and circles**

2 **Constructing midpoints and bisectors**

3 **Constructing triangles on paper**

4 **Constructing triangles using ICT**

5 **Making shapes on pinboards**

6 **Scale drawings**

7 **Using bearings**

8 **Exploring loci**

9 **Using ICT to explore loci**

About this unit

This unit develops pupils' construction skills, which have a wide range of applications in mathematics and other subjects, at school and beyond. To make accurate drawings, pupils need to use and apply their increasing knowledge of properties of shapes and to apply their reasoning skills. Their use of ICT to construct and draw should help them to appreciate how mathematical skills are linked to ICT skills in the workplace.

Assessment

This unit includes:

- a self-assessment section (*G4.4 How well are you doing?* class book p. 262);
- a set of questions to replace or supplement questions in the exercises or homework tasks, or to use as an informal test (*G4.4 Check up*, CD-ROM).

Common errors and misconceptions	Look out for pupils who:

Common errors and misconceptions

Look out for pupils who:

- use a ruler to measure when a 'straight-edge' and compasses should be used;
- confuse 'perpendicular to' with 'vertical to';
- think that increasing the scale of a drawing increases the size of the drawing;
- don't appreciate the significance of the angle or side being included in SAS and ASA triangle constructions;
- confuse interior and exterior angles when they construct shapes using Logo.

Key terms and notation

problem, solution, method, pattern, relationship, represent, solve, explain, justify

locus, loci, construct, plan, straight-edge, ruler, compasses, perpendicular to ($\perp$), parallel to (//), equidistant, bearing, degree (°), and compass directions

circle, circumference, radius, diameter, arc, chord, segment, sector

acute, obtuse, reflex, vertex, vertices, congruent, side-angle-side (SAS), angle-side-angle (ASA), side-side-side (SSS), and names of shapes

ratio, unitary ratio, scale, scale factor, units of measurement and notation $a:b$

Practical resources

plain paper and squared dotty paper
measuring instruments: rulers, compasses, protractors, set-squares
individual whiteboards
straws or thin strips of paper and scissors
small cones or similar as markers

metre stick and long measuring tape
chalk or tape
dynamic geometry software (e.g. The Geometer's Sketchpad; lesson 4) and Logo software (e.g. MSW Logo; lesson 9) for pupils to use in a computer suite

Exploring maths

Tier 4 teacher's book
Answers for Unit G4.4 , pp. 296–299

Tier 4 CD-ROM
PowerPoint files
    G4.4 slides for lessons 1 to 9
The Geometer's Sketchpad files (optional)
    G4.4 Triangles
MSW Logo file
    G4.4 Polygon (optional)
Tools and prepared toolsheets
    Ruler tool
    Compasses tool
    Line segment tool
    Line tool
    Protractor tool
    Image bank tool
Tier 4 programs
    Pinboard
    Bearings

Tier 4 class book
G4.4, pp. 238–263
G4.4 How well are you doing? p. 262

Tier 4 home book
G4.4, pp. 96–105

Tier 4 CD-ROM
G4.4 Check up
G4.4 Pupil resource sheets
    4.1 One per pair
    4.2 One per pair
    7.1 One per pair
    7.2 One per pupil
    8.1 One per pupil
    9.1 One per pair

Useful websites

Islamic patterns based on circles
www.askasia.org/teachers/lessons/plan.php?no=65&era=&grade=&geo=
Construction www.mathsnet.net/campus/construction/index.html
Bisecting lines lgfl.skoool.co.uk/keystage3.aspx?id=65
Canoeing uk.knowledgebox.com/index.phtml?d=23376
Bearings
www.bbc.co.uk/schools/ks3bitesize/maths/shape_and_space/angles_2_3.shtml
MSW Logo for free download www.softronix.com/logo.html

1 Drawing arcs and circles

Learning points

- The circumference of a circle is the distance all the way round its edge.
- The radius is the line joining the centre to any point on the circumference.
- The diameter is the distance across the circle through the centre.
- An arc is part of the circumference of a circle.

Starter

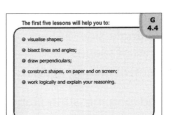

Use **slide 1.1** to discuss the objectives for the first five lessons of this unit. Say that this lesson is about using compasses to draw arcs and circles.

Each pupil will need compasses, a ruler and a sharp pencil. Demonstrate how to draw a circle and let pupils practise until they can draw a circle accurately.

Ask pupils to name the parts of a circle: circumference, radius, diameter, arc.

Demonstrate how to draw this design, using the **Ruler** and **Compasses tools**.

Draw the central circle first, then a circle with centre anywhere on the circumference of the first circle. Use the intersection points of circles with the original circle as subsequent centres. The circles all have the same radius.

Ask pupils to copy the diagram on plain paper using compasses set to approximately 5 cm.

Now ask pupils to use a ruler and coloured pencil to join some of the points of intersection to see what polygons they can make. Ask them to name the polygons and to justify their properties.

For example, this shape is a rhombus.

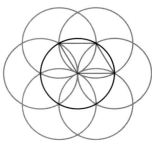

All the sides are the same length because they are all radii of circles with the same radius.

The acute angle that the rhombus makes where it meets the circumference of the central circle is 60° because six equal angles fit round a point.

Main activity

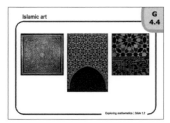

Show **slide 1.2**. Give pupils a couple of minutes to look at the patterns and to discuss in pairs the shapes and patterns that they can see.

What shapes can you see?

How are the shapes arranged to make each design?

Can you see any underlying patterns or arrangements of shapes, such as circles or hexagons?

Show pupils how to draw a regular hexagon using a single circle and arcs (rather than full circles), as for the first part of the exercise to follow.

Ask pupils to do **G4.4 Exercise 1** in the class book (p. 239).

Review   Return to the basic construction of a hexagon using compasses and ruler.

> **How do we know that the constructed hexagon is a regular one?**

> **What properties does a regular hexagon have?**
> [equal sides, equal angles]

Construct the hexagon, using the **Ruler**, **Compasses** and **Line segment tools**. Use red lines to join the vertices of the hexagon to the centre of the circle.

> **What do you know about the lengths of the red line segments? Why?**

Use black lines to join the vertices of the hexagon.

> **What do you know about the lengths of the green line segments? Why?**

Establish that this means that all the sides of the hexagon are the same length.

> **What do you know about the red and the black line segments? Why?**
> [they are all of equal length]

> **What do you know about the triangles that make up the hexagon? Why?**
> [they are identical equilateral triangles]

> **What can you deduce about the angles in the hexagon?**
> [they are all equal to 120°]

Sum up by reminding pupils of the names of the parts of a circle on **slide 1.3**.

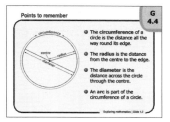

Homework   Ask pupils to do **G4.4 Task 1** in the home book (p. 96). They will need a ruler, protractor and sharp pencil.

2 Constructing midpoints and bisectors

Learning points

- Constructions using a straight-edge and compasses are more accurate than those done by measuring with rulers and protractors.

- Leave construction lines on the diagram.

- Any point on an angle bisector is the same perpendicular distance from each of the two arms of the angle.

- Any point on the perpendicular bisector of a line segment is the same distance from each end of the line.

Starter   Say that this lesson is about constructing angles and lines.

Start with a visualisation activity. Ask pupils to imagine a square and then to imagine using one straight cut to cut off a corner. Ask them to describe the shape that is left.

Repeat with two corners, then three corners.

Now ask pupils to imagine cutting off four corners, not necessarily symmetrically. This time they should discuss their answers with a partner and make sketches on their whiteboards before responding.

>   **When you cut off four corners, can you make an octagon? How?**

>   **Can you make a hexagon? How?**

Repeat with a kite, square, rectangle and trapezium.

Main activity   Show the class some constructions using straight-edge and compasses. Explain that these constructions are very accurate since no measuring is involved.

Draw the constructions using the **Ruler** and **Compasses tools**.

Construct the bisector of an angle. Explain that you are opening your compasses to any radius and keeping them fixed.

- With centre O, draw an arc crossing both arms of the angle. Label the crossing points A and B.

- With centre A, draw a second arc in the middle of the angle.

- With centre B, draw another arc to cross the second arc. Label this point X.

- Join OX. The line OX is the angle bisector.

Explain that any point on an angle bisector is the same perpendicular distance from each of the two arms of the angle.

> Ask pupils to do **G4.4 Exercise 2A** in the class book (p. 242).

Construct the midpoint and perpendicular bisector of a line AB.

- ⊙ Draw a line segment AB of any length. Set compasses to any radius greater than half the length of AB. With centre A, draw an arc above and below AB.

- ⊙ With compasses set at the same radius, and with centre B, draw another arc to cut the first arc at C and D.

- ⊙ Join C and D to cut AB at X. The line CD is the perpendicular bisector of the line AB. X is the midpoint of the line AB.

Explain that any point on the perpendicular bisector of a line segment is the same distance from each end of the line.

> Ask pupils to do **G4.4 Exercise 2B** in the class book (p. 243).

Review   Draw a sketch of an acute-angled triangle on the board. Ask pupils to draw a similar triangle in the centre of a page of their books and then to construct the perpendicular bisector of each side.

What do you notice?

You could if you wish use dynamic geometry software to construct a triangle with the perpendicular bisectors of its three sides.

Draw the circumcircle.

Observe the effect of dragging the vertices of the triangle. Point out that the three perpendicular bisectors of the sides always meet at a point.

Ask pupils to remember the points on **slide 2.1**.

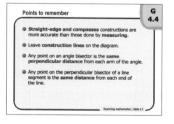

Homework   Ask pupils to do **G4.4 Task 2** in the home book (p. 97). They will need a ruler, protractor, compasses and sharp pencil.

3 Constructing triangles on paper

Learning points

○ Triangles that are constructed using these methods are unique:
  — side-side-side (SSS);
  — angle-side-angle (ASA);
  — side-angle-side (SAS).

Starter

Say that this lesson is about constructing triangles using the lengths of the three sides.

Give each group of four a few straws (or thin strips of paper) and scissors. Then give each group a set of three numbers. Ask them to cut the straws to size and to see if they can make a triangle with those lengths. Some suitable sets of lengths are:

6, 8, 10	5, 5, 9	3, 7, 13	5, 6, 15	2, 9, 4	5, 5, 7	6, 6, 4
6, 6, 12	8, 8, 8	7, 7, 5	8, 4, 3	6, 3, 12	8, 8, 10	2, 12, 7
7, 6, 3	3, 4, 5	4, 4, 4	5, 6, 9	4, 4, 8	7, 3, 5	

Which sets of three numbers produce triangles?

What different types of triangle can you make?

What is special about those sets of numbers that produce triangles?

Pupils should notice that there are sets that produce right-angled triangles (3, 4, 5 and 6, 8, 10), isosceles triangles and equilateral triangles. One set produces a straight line (4, 4, 8). Those sets where the sum of the two smaller numbers is greater than the third will produce a triangle, since the sum of the lengths of the two shortest sides of a triangle must always be greater than the length of the longest side.

Main activity

Ask pupils how they think they could draw a triangle when they know only the lengths of the sides. Take suggestions and try them on the board. Pupils should be able to start by drawing a line of a given length for one of the sides. Encourage them to consider how work in previous lessons might help them.

Demonstrate how to draw a triangle from SSS with side lengths 10 cm, 8 cm and 6 cm using the **Ruler**, **Compasses** and **Line tools**.

○ Draw a line segment of length 10 cm.

○ Set compasses to a radius of 8 cm. With centre at one end of the line segment, draw an arc.

○ Set compasses to 6 cm. With centre at the other end of the line segment, draw a second arc to cut the first.

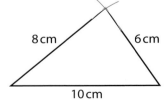

○ Where the two arcs cross is the third vertex of the triangle. Join the ends of the line segment to the new vertex.

TO

Ask pupils to do **G4.4 Exercise 3A** in the class book (p. 245). They will need a ruler, compasses and sharp pencil.

Ask pupils to compare their constructions in groups of three or four.

> Are your answers the same?

Pupils should notice that SSS constructions give the same triangle. Remind them that triangles that are exactly the same size and shape are called *congruent*.

Explain that triangles can also be constructed using other types of information, such as two sides and the included angle (SAS) and two angles and the included side (ASA). Some pupils will have met these constructions previously, but instructions and practice are given in the class book and they are also explored in the next lesson. You may need to demonstrate these constructions to the class.

Ask pupils to do **G4.4 Exercise 3B** in the class book (p. 247). They will need a ruler, protractor and sharp pencil.

Review

Write these angles and lengths on the board:

35°, 75°, 60°, 5 cm, 7 cm, 8 cm

Ask pupils to pick any three measurements from the six and use them to draw an accurate triangle.

> Do the three pieces of information produce a unique triangle?

> How can you pick information that leads to a unique triangle?

Lead a discussion based on pupils' ideas and drawings. They should note that SSS produces a unique triangle, but AAA does not. If they pick a combination of angles and sides they need to consider where the sides are in relation to the angles. SAS (two sides and the included angle) produces a unique triangle as does ASA (two angles and the included side). Not specifying the relationship may lead to different triangles satisfying the same conditions.

Ask pupils to remember the points on **slide 3.1**.

Homework

Ask pupils to do **G4.4 Task 3** in the home book (p. 98). They will need a ruler, protractor, compasses and sharp pencil.

4 Constructing triangles using ICT

Learning points

- Triangles that are constructed using these methods are unique:
  - side-side-side (SSS);
  - angle-side-angle (ASA);
  - side-angle-side (SAS).

Starter

This lesson preferably needs to take place in a computer room, with access from each computer to dynamic geometry software (e.g. The Geometer's Sketchpad). A help sheet for any pupils using The Geometer's Sketchpad is available on Resource sheet 4.1 (see below).

Tell pupils that the lesson is about using a computer to draw triangles.

Use dynamic geometry software to make a triangle by connecting line segments.

Ask a pupil to drag the vertices and make some different triangles.

What different types of triangle can you make?

What are the different properties of each type?

Main activity

Demonstrate how to use dynamic geometry software to construct triangles using SSS, SAS and ASA.

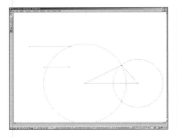  

If you are using The Geometer's Sketchpad there is a basic help sheet on **G4.4 Resource sheet 4.1**. Instructions for the activity are on **Resource sheet 4.2**. If necessary, adapt the sheets for your own dynamic geometry software.

A sample file **G4.4 Triangles** for The Geometer's Sketchpad is provided.

Select individual work from **G4.4 Exercise 4** in the class book (p. 249).

RS

GSP

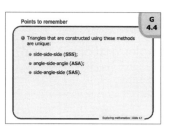
Review Pick some of the questions from the exercise that require reasoning skills and discuss them with the class. Suitable questions are those where the SAS and ASA constructions are used to make equilateral and isosceles triangles.

Use dynamic geometry software to create examples.

GSP

Launch **G4.4 Triangles** to help you if you wish. Ask pupils to suggest how they know why the triangles are isosceles or equilateral.

Finish by reiterating the points on **slide 4.1**.

Homework Ask pupils to do **G4.4 Task 4** in the home book (p. 99). They will need a ruler, protractor and sharp pencil.

5 Making shapes on pinboards

Learning points

- You can use the properties of shapes to help you to make shapes on pinboards.

- You can find the area of a pinboard shape by dividing it into squares, rectangles or triangles, and thinking of triangles as halves of rectangles.

Starter

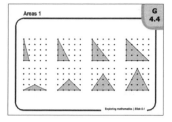

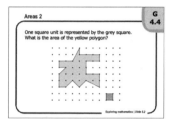

Say that this lesson is about solving problems by constructing polygons on pinboards. Give out squared dotty paper.

Show **slide 5.1**.

> **Without using the formula for the area of a triangle, how can you work out the area of each triangle in square units?**

Sketch the surrounding rectangles on the whiteboard. In the first row, the triangles can be considered as half a rectangle. In the second row, each triangle can be divided into two triangles, each of which is half a rectangle. In each row, the areas are 2, 4, 6 and 8 square units respectively.

Show **slide 5.2**. Ask pairs to work out the area of the yellow polygon [21 square units].

> **On your dotty paper, draw a letter W so that it has an area of 7 square units.**

> **Draw three different shapes each with an area of 16 square units.**

Main activity

SIM

Launch **Pinboard**. Choose a square grid and set the board to its maximum size of 20 by 14 pins.

> **How many different sizes of squares can you construct on a 3 by 3 pinboard?**

Stress that each square must have a pin at each corner. Explain that each square will have four equal sides and four right angles and that it will help to think of different ways to make right angles on the pinboard. Explain that squares that are same size but in different positions don't count as 'different'.

Establish with the class that three different sizes of squares are possible.

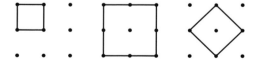

> **How do you know that each shape you have made is a square?**

> **If one small square on the pinboard is 1 square unit, what is the area of each of the three squares?** [1, 4 and 2 square units]

Make sure that pupils understand that the square of area 2 square units is made up of four small squares halved across their diagonals.

Ask pupils to use their dotty paper and to use 4 by 4 dots each time to represent 4 by 4 pinboards. Ask them to work in pairs to sketch different squares.

How many different sizes of squares can you construct on a 4 by 4 pinboard? [five]

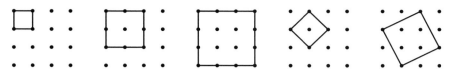

How do you know that each shape you have made is a square?

What is the area of each of the five squares?
[1, 4, 9, 2 and 5 square units]

Stress that areas can be found by subdividing the inside of the shape into squares, rectangles and triangles, and that each triangle can be thought of as half a rectangle.

If pupils want to try 5 by 5 pinboards, they can make all the squares that can be made on 4 by 4 pinboards, plus three more squares with areas 16, 8 and 10 square units.

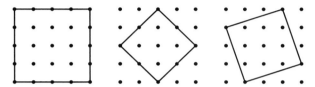

Select further investigations for pupils to work on in pairs from **G4.4 Exercise 5** in the class book (p. 250).

Review

Invite pairs of pupils to describe the results of their investigations to the class.

Launch **Pinboard**. Set 5 by 5 pins. Challenge pupils to construct triangles from the information you give them. For example, draw one side of a triangle and ask them to construct an isosceles triangle with the given side as a base. Then ask them to construct an isosceles triangle with the given side as one of the two equal sides.

SIM

Is it possible to make an acute-angled triangle on this pinboard? Why not?

What about isosceles, right-angled, equilateral and scalene triangles?

Can you make a right-angled isosceles triangle?

Sum up by stressing the points on **slide 5.3**.

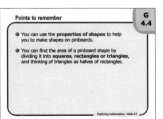

Homework

Ask pupils to do **G4.4 Task 5** in the home book (p. 100). They will need some squared dotty paper.

6 Scale drawings

Learning points

- A scale drawing is a smaller drawing of an actual object.
- The scale gives the relative size of the drawn length to the actual length.
- State the scale next to the drawing.
- Corresponding measurements in the actual object and the scale drawing are all in the same ratio.

Starter

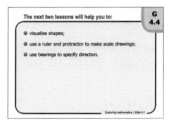

Use **slide 6.1** to discuss the objectives for this and the next lesson. Say that this lesson is about making scale drawings. Each pupil will need a ruler, protractor and sharp pencil for this lesson.

> **What properties of a rectangle do we use when we make an accurate drawing of a rectangle?**
> [opposite sides are equal and parallel; all four angles are right angles]

Use the **Ruler**, **Protractor** and **Line tools** to remind pupils of the procedure for constructing a 5 cm by 8 cm rectangle using a ruler and protractor.

Draw a line segment 8 cm long. Label it AB. Draw right angles at A and B to form angle BAX and angle ABY.

On AX, extended if needed, mark off a point D 5 cm from A. On BY, extended if needed, mark off a point C 5 cm from B.

ABCD is the required rectangle.

Check by measuring that side CD is 8 cm.

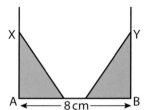

Main activity

Explain that architects and builders need scale plans when they design and construct buildings. A scale plan shows actual measurements drawn to a smaller scale, e.g. a length of 1 cm on a drawing might represent a length of 20 m in a building. This is written as a scale of 1 cm : 20 m. Where a scale is given without units, we assume that the units are the same; a scale of 1 : 20 for a model car means that 1 cm on the model represents 20 cm on the actual car.

Corresponding measurements in the actual building and the scale drawing are all in the same ratio. For example:

a roof section with these actual dimensions

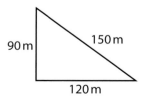

has these dimensions in a plan using a scale of 1 cm : 30 m.

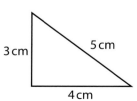

Show that the ratios of 3 : 90, 4 : 120 and 5 : 150 are all equivalent.

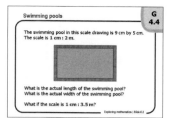

Show **slide 6.2**. Ask pupils to work out the true dimensions of the swimming pool.

Now ask pupils to use rulers and protractors to draw plans for pools measuring 5 m by 8 m and 9 m by 4 m using a scale of 1 cm : 1 m. Get them to measure the diagonal of the swimming pool and to state its true length [first pool: 9.4 m; second pool: 10.2 m].

Select individual work from **G4.4 Exercise 6** in the class book (p. 252).

Review Show **slides 6.3 and 6.4**. For each slide, say that the dimensions of the real building are shown on the left. Some possible scale drawings are shown on the right. Ask:

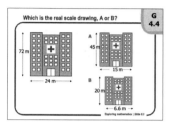 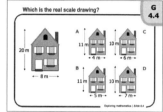 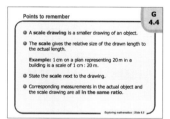

Which is the real scale drawing? Explain why.

What scale has been used for the drawing?

Finish by stressing the points on **slide 6.5**.

Homework Ask pupils to do **G4.4 Task 6** in the home book (p. 101). They will need a ruler, protractor and sharp pencil.

7 Using bearings

Learning points

- A distance 'as the crow flies' is the shortest distance between two points, measured as a straight line.
- A bearing is the direction that you travel in to go straight to the object.
- Bearings are measured clockwise from north in degrees.
- Bearings always have three figures.

Starter

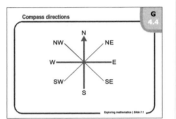

Say that this lesson is about using directions. Pupils should know from geography lessons that north on a map is marked using an arrow.

Use **slide 7.1** to review the eight compass directions: north (N), north-east (NE), east (E), south-east (SE), south (S), south-west (SW), west (W) and north-west (NW).

Blank out the slide. (Right-click on the slide and choose Screen > Black. Click again on the slide to restore it.) Ask pupils to visualise and to answer on their whiteboards.

> I am facing east. I turn 90 degrees clockwise.
> What direction am I facing now? [S]
>
> I am facing north. I turn anticlockwise through a right angle.
> What direction am I facing now? [W]
>
> I am facing west. I turn clockwise to face east.
> Through how many degrees have I turned? [180°]
>
> I face south-west. I turn through 180 degrees anticlockwise.
> What direction am I facing now? [NE]
>
> I face north-east. I turn clockwise through 135 degrees.
> What direction am I facing now? [S]
>
> I face south-west, then I turn anticlockwise through three right angles.
> What direction am I facing now? [NW]
>
> I am facing north-west. I turn clockwise until I face east.
> Through how many degrees have I turned? [135°]
>
> I am facing south-east. I turn anticlockwise until I face south.
> Through how many degrees have I turned? [315°]

Main activity

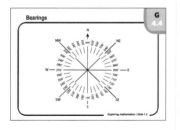

Remind the class that:

- angles on a straight line sum to 180°;
- angles around a point sum to 360°;
- where a transversal crosses a pair of parallel lines, alternate angles are equal and corresponding angles are equal.

Use **slide 7.2** to discuss bearings. A bearing is the direction that you travel in to go straight to an object 'as the crow flies'. It is measured clockwise from north in degrees. It is always given using three digits and is referred to as a 'three-figure bearing'. For example, the bearing for north-east is 045 degrees (a bearing of zero four five).

Explain that ships and planes use bearings for navigation purposes. Bearings are also used in sports such as orienteering.

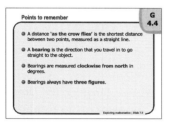

Show **slide 7.3**. Explain how to find the bearing of Leeds from Manchester and the bearing of Manchester from Leeds. These are often referred to as 'back bearings'.

- The bearing of Leeds from Manchester is 050°.

- To find the bearing of Manchester from Leeds, use the dashed line to find the alternate angle of 50° and then add 180°. The bearing is 230°.

- The difference between the two bearings is 180°.

Show **slide 7.4**. Discuss the two questions and ask pupils to explain why the bearing of A from B is 220°.

Give out copies of **G4.4 Resource sheet 7.1** for pupils to work on in pairs. Take feedback and discuss strategies. Answers are on p. 299.   [RS]

> Select individual work from **G4.4 Exercise 7** in the class book (p. 257).

Review Launch **Bearings**. Use it to construct and discuss different examples of bearings.

Ask pupils to remember the points on **slide 7.5**.   [SIM]

Homework Ask pupils to do **G4.4 Task 7** in the home book (p. 102). They will need a ruler, protractor and sharp pencil, and a copy of **G4.4 Resource sheet 7.2**.   [RS]

8 Exploring loci

Learning points

- A locus is the set of points, or path, that follows a rule.
- All the points the same distance from a fixed point form a circle.
- All the points equidistant from two fixed points lie on the perpendicular bisector of the line joining the points.
- All the points equidistant from two lines forming an angle lie on the angle bisector.

Starter

Use **slide 8.1** to discuss objectives for this and the next lesson. Say that this lesson is about exploring the path of points that follow a rule.

Show **slide 8.2**, diagrams of a random wiggly line, a parabola and an arc of a circle. Say that each diagram shows the path, or track, of something that is moving. For each diagram, ask:

> **What path or track could this be? Why?**

Encourage pupils to make a range of suggestions. For example, the parabola could be the path of a ball in the air or the path of a jet of water coming out of a fountain. The arc could be the path of the end of a single windscreen wiper blade or of a swinging searchlight. The wiggly line could be the path of a child playing chase or the tip of a sparkler waved in the air.

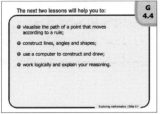

Main activity

The best way to do this part of the lesson is to take the class to a large space like the playground or the school hall. You will need two small cones or other markers for points on the floor, some chalk or tape, a metre stick and a long measuring tape. Alternatively you could use the **Image bank tool** to select counters to place on the whiteboard.

Use one of the cones to mark a point in the middle of the floor. Ask a pupil to come and stand two metres from the marker. Ask some more pupils to do the same:

> **Where are all the points two metres from the marker?**
>
> **What shape do they make?** [circle]
>
> **What would we use to draw this shape?**

Explain that the *locus* of the points is a circle. A locus is a set of points, or path, that follows a rule.

> **What is the rule for this set of points?** [2 m from a point]

Now put two markers on the floor about four metres apart. Ask a pupil to come and stand equidistant from the two markers. Then ask some more pupils to do this. You can ask them to check where they are standing using the measuring tape.

> **Where are all the points equidistant from the two markers?**
> [on a straight line]

What is special about this straight line?
[it is the perpendicular bisector of the line joining the two markers]

What is the rule for this set of points? [equidistant from two points]

Use the chalk or tape to mark out an acute angle on the floor. Ask a pupil to come and stand equidistant from the two lines. Then ask some more pupils to do this. You can ask them to check where they are standing using the measuring tape.

Where are all the points equidistant from the two lines?
[on a straight line]

What is special about this straight line? [it bisects the angle]

What is the rule for this set of points? [equidistant from two lines]

On returning to the classroom, ask pupils to sketch the three loci they have been working on. You can use **G4.4 Resource sheet 8.1** to support them with this.

RS

Ask pupils to do **G4.4 Exercise 8** in the class book (p. 259). They will need a ruler, compasses and sharp pencil.

Review   Ask pupils to imagine two fixed points A and B 10 cm apart. Now ask them to imagine a point P which is in a position such that the total of its distance from A and B is 20 cm. Now ask them to imagine some more points where the distance from A and the distance from B totals 20 cm.

What shape is the locus of the points? [ellipse]

How does the locus change if A and B are moved closer together?
[the ellipse becomes more like a circle]

How does the locus change if A and B are moved further apart?
[the ellipse becomes more elongated]

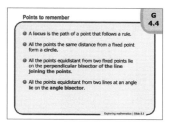

Use a long length of string and some BluTack to demonstrate to pupils that an ellipse is formed.

Ask pupils to remember the points on **slide 8.3**.

Homework   Ask pupils to do **G4.4 Task 8** in the home book (p. 103). They will need a ruler, protractor and sharp pencil.

9 Using ICT to explore loci

Learning points

- In Logo the turtle follows instructions, or rules, to produce a path.
- You can use Logo to explore rules using angles and lengths.

Starter   *This lesson preferably needs to take place in a computer room, with access from each computer to a version of Logo (e.g. MSW Logo). A help sheet for any pupils using MSW Logo is available on Resource sheet 9.1 (see below).*

You need computers (one per pair of pupils) for this lesson. Tell pupils that they will be using the computers to draw loci.

Ask one pupil to pretend to be a robot. This pupil should stand at the front of the class and follow sets of instructions such as:

     forward 2 paces, left 90°, forward 2 paces, left 180°, back 3 paces

Ask pupils to predict the final position of the robot. Also ask them to predict the direction the robot is facing.

Main activity   Demonstrate how to use Logo. The help sheet on **G4.4 Resource sheet 9.1** and instructions are for MSW Logo, for which a free download is available, but similar instructions would work for other versions of Logo.

Explain that the 'turtle' is indicated by the arrow on the screen and works like the robot in the lesson starter activity because it follows exactly the instructions it is given. Demonstrate some sets of instructions like the ones in the starter activity.

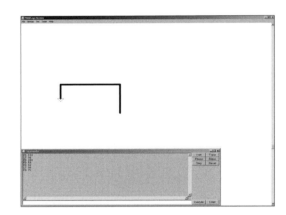

Throughout the lesson encourage pupils to imagine what will happen to the turtle before activating the instructions. Explain that the turtle follows instructions, or rules, to produce a path.

Ask pupils to work in pairs on **G4.4 Exercise 9** in the class book (p. 261) with a computer with MSW Logo. They will also need **G4.4 Resource sheet 9.1**.

Explore the polygon procedure with pupils. Either load the file **G4.4 Polygon** into MSW Logo using the 'file' and 'load' menus or click on 'Edall' and type in the commands yourself. Note the spaces in the instructions.

TO POLYGON :LENGTH :SIDES
REPEAT :SIDES [FD :LENGTH RT 360/:SIDES]
END

Click the 'file' menu in the editor and 'save and exit' when you finish.

Type some sets of commands into the input line with pupils and explore what the procedure does. For example:

POLYGON 100 3

POLYGON 100 4

POLYGON 200 5

What does the first number in the procedure do?
[sets the length of the side]

What does the second number in the procedure do?
[sets the number of sides]

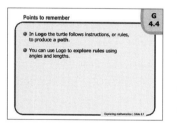

Make some patterns with pupils using the procedure.

Ask pupils to remember the points on **slide 9.1**.

Round off the unit by referring again to the objectives. Suggest that pupils find time to try the self-assessment problems in **G4.4 How well are you doing?** in the class book (p. 262).

Homework

Ask pupils to do **G4.4 Task 9** in the home book (p. 104). They will need a ruler, protractor and sharp pencil.

G4.4 Check up and resource sheets

Check up

Write or draw your answers in your book.
You will need a ruler, compasses, protractor and sharp pencil.

1 *2002 level 5 [adapted]*

Here is a plan of a ferry crossing.

Complete an accurate scale drawing of the ferry crossing using a scale of 1 cm to 20 m.

What is the length of the ferry crossing on your diagram?

Work out the length of the real ferry crossing.

ferry port
ferry crossing 80°
river
30°
ferry port 210 m office

Not drawn accurately

2 Points A and B mark the location of two water taps in a large field. The two taps are 100 m apart.

The farmer wants to know which parts of the field are nearer to one tap than the other.

Make a sketch of the field. Use a scale of 1 cm to 10 m to mark the taps the correct distance apart.

a Use compasses and a ruler to construct accurately the locus of the points equidistant from each tap.

b Shade in the area nearer to tap B than to tap A.

c The farmer has a hose of length 40 m. Shade in the region he can reach with the hose if he connects it to tap B.

|← 100 m →|
A   B

Diagram not to scale

3 A tower is 40 m high. It casts a shadow of 15 m on the ground. Construct a triangle to scale to represent this. Using a protractor, measure the angle that the light from the sun makes with the ground.

4 Paula and Freda are going orienteering. This is the first part of their course instructions.

Use a scale of 1 cm to 10 m to make an accurate scale drawing of their route.

What is the bearing from their start point to their finish point?

Go 100 m on a bearing of 075°.
Now go 70 m on a bearing of 210°. Next go 60 m on a bearing of 305°

Resource sheet 4.1

Help sheet for getting started with The Geometer's Sketchpad

This is the basic screen.

The **toolbox** is down the left-hand side. From the top the tools are:

- selection arrow tool;
- point tool;
- compass tool;
- straight-edge tool;
- text tool;
- custom tool.

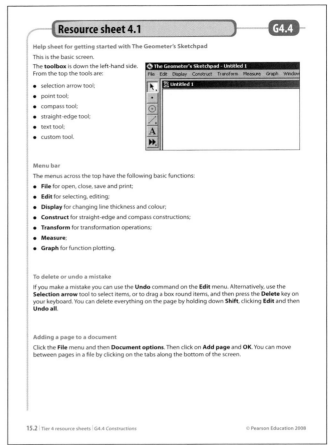

Menu bar

The menus across the top have the following basic functions:

- **File** for open, close, save and print;
- **Edit** for selecting, editing;
- **Display** for changing line thickness and colour;
- **Construct** for straight-edge and compass constructions;
- **Transform** for transformation operations;
- **Measure**;
- **Graph** for function plotting.

To delete or undo a mistake

If you make a mistake you can use the **Undo** command on the **Edit** menu. Alternatively, use the **Selection arrow** tool to select items, or to drag a box round items, and then press the **Delete** key on your keyboard. You can delete everything on the page by holding down **Shift**, clicking **Edit** and then **Undo all**.

Adding a page to a document

Click the **File** menu and then **Document options**. Then click on **Add page** and **OK**. You can move between pages in a file by clicking on the tabs along the bottom of the screen.

Resource sheet 4.2

Using The Geometer's Sketchpad to construct triangles

Constructing a triangle using side-side-side (SSS)

Use the **straight-edge** tool to draw three line segments on the screen. Put one of the line segments further away from the other two to form the base of the triangle. If you hold and drag the straight-edge tool button to the right you will see that there are several different tool options. Make sure you use the line segment tool.

Change to the **selection arrow** tool. Click on one end of base and on one of the other line segments. Click on the **Construct** menu and choose **Circle by Center+Radius**.

Now select the other end of the base and the remaining line segment. Construct another circle in the same way.

Select both circles, click on the **Construct** menu and select **Intersections**. Now click on three points forming a triangle, choose the **Construct** menu and then choose **Segment**.

Drag the ends of the line segments to see how the triangle changes as the side lengths change. Click on a line segment and then on **Measure** and **Length** so you can measure the length of the segment.

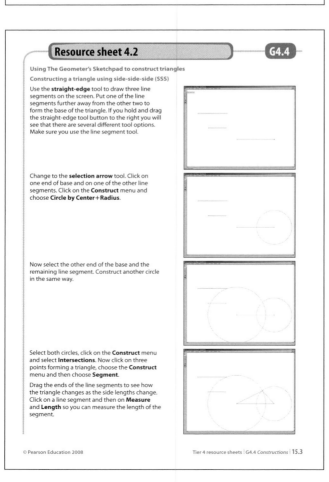

Resource sheet 4.2 [continued]

Constructing a triangle using side-angle-side (SAS)

Use the **straight-edge** tool to draw two line segments from the same point.

Change to the **selection arrow** tool. Click on the line segments and then on **Measure** and **Length** to measure the length of the segments. Click on the three points in the order B, A, C so that the angle being measured is selected. Then click on **Measure** and **Angle** to get a measurement for the angle made by the line segments.

Select points B and C and then choose **Construct** and **Segment** to complete the triangle. Drag the ends of the line segments to see how the triangle changes as the side lengths and included angle change.

Constructing a triangle using angle-side-angle (ASA)

Use the **straight-edge** tool to draw a line segment. Change the straight-edge tool from the line segment option to the **ray** option by holding the mouse down on the tool and moving it to the right. The ray option is the third one along. Draw a ray from each end of the line segment.

Change to the **selection arrow** tool. Click on the line segment and then on **Measure** and **Length** to measure the length of the segment. Click on the points in the order X, A, B so that the angle being measured is selected. Then click on **Measure** and **Angle**. Repeat for the other angle by clicking on the points in the order Y, B A.

Drag the points X, Y, A and B to see how the triangle made by the line segment and two rays changes as the angles and included side length change.

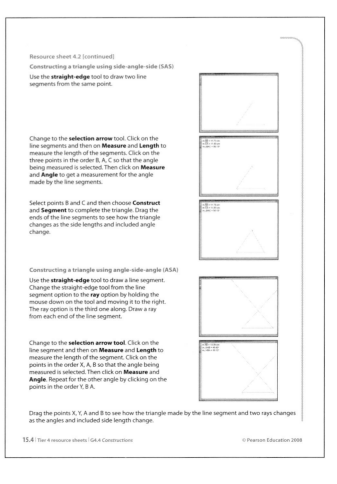

Resource sheet 7.1 — G4.4

Write your answers in your book.
Work with a partner to answer these questions.

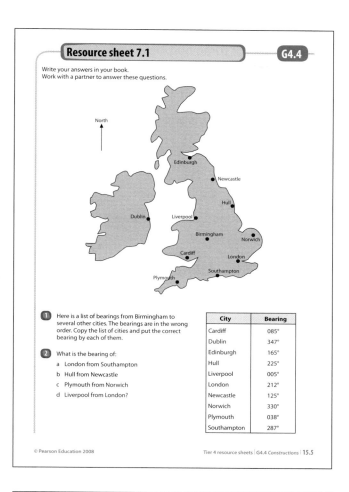

North

Edinburgh

Newcastle

Hull

Dublin

Liverpool

Birmingham

Norwich

Cardiff

London

Plymouth

Southampton

1 Here is a list of bearings from Birmingham to several other cities. The bearings are in the wrong order. Copy the list of cities and put the correct bearing by each of them.

2 What is the bearing of:
a London from Southampton
b Hull from Newcastle
c Plymouth from Norwich
d Liverpool from London?

City	Bearing
Cardiff	085°
Dublin	347°
Edinburgh	165°
Hull	225°
Liverpool	005°
London	212°
Newcastle	125°
Norwich	330°
Plymouth	038°
Southampton	287°

Resource sheet 7.2 — G4.4

Write your answers in your book.
You will need a ruler, protractor and sharp pencil for this task.

Some people like to look at views from the tops of hills. Sometimes there is a **topograph**, which tells you which direction places are in and how far away they are.

Here is a topograph for Haydown Hill in Hampshire.
The distances are all measured 'as the crow flies'.

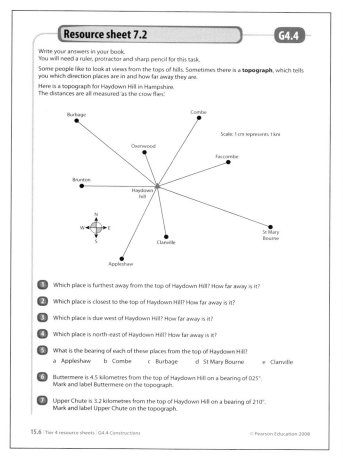

Burbage

Combe

Scale: 1 cm represents 1 km

Oxenwood

Faccombe

Brunton

Haydown hill

N
W — E
S

St Mary Bourne

Clanville

Appleshaw

1 Which place is furthest away from the top of Haydown Hill? How far away is it?

2 Which place is closest to the top of Haydown Hill? How far away is it?

3 Which place is due west of Haydown Hill? How far away is it?

4 Which place is north-east of Haydown Hill? How far away is it?

5 What is the bearing of each of these places from the top of Haydown Hill?
a Appleshaw   b Combe   c Burbage   d St Mary Bourne   e Clanville

6 Buttermere is 4.5 kilometres from the top of Haydown Hill on a bearing of 025°. Mark and label Buttermere on the topograph.

7 Upper Chute is 3.2 kilometres from the top of Haydown Hill on a bearing of 210°. Mark and label Upper Chute on the topograph.

Resource sheet 8.1 — G4.4

Write your answers on the sheet.

1 The locus of all the points 3 cm from
point A is a ....

A •

2 The locus of all the points equidistant
from points A and B is a
....

A •

B •

3 The locus of all the points equidistant
from the two intersecting lines is a
....

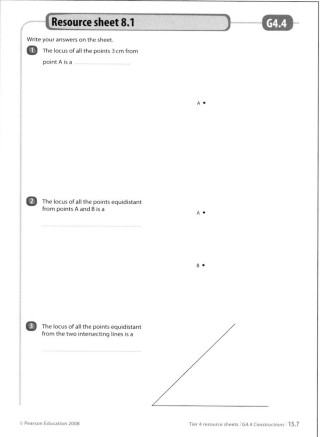

Resource sheet 9.1 — G4.4

Help sheet for using MSW Logo

When you load MSW Logo the screen
looks like this.

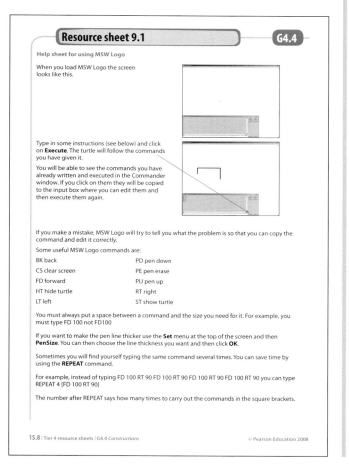

Type in some instructions (see below) and click
on **Execute**. The turtle will follow the commands
you have given it.

You will be able to see the commands you have
already written and executed in the Commander
window. If you click on them they will be copied
to the input box where you can edit them and
then execute them again.

If you make a mistake, MSW Logo will try to tell you what the problem is so that you can copy the
command and edit it correctly.

Some useful MSW Logo commands are:

BK back	PD pen down
CS clear screen	PE pen erase
FD forward	PU pen up
HT hide turtle	RT right
LT left	ST show turtle

You must always put a space between a command and the size you need for it. For example, you
must type FD 100 not FD100

If you want to make the pen line thicker use the **Set** menu at the top of the screen and then
PenSize. You can then choose the line thickness you want and then click **OK**.

Sometimes you will find yourself typing the same command several times. You can save time by
using the **REPEAT** command.

For example, instead of typing FD 100 RT 90 FD 100 RT 90 FD 100 RT 90 FD 100 RT 90 you can type
REPEAT 4 [FD 100 RT 90]

The number after REPEAT says how many times to carry out the commands in the square brackets.

G4.4 Answers

Class book

Exercise 1

1 Pupil's construction

2 Pupil's construction

3 Pupil's construction

Extension problem

4 Pupil's construction

Exercise 2A

1 Pupil's construction

2 Pupil's construction

3 Pupil's construction

4 Pupil's construction

Exercise 2B

1 Pupil's construction

2 Pupil's construction

3 Pupil's construction

Extension problems

4 Pupil's construction

5 a Pupil's construction
   b Pupil's construction

Exercise 3A

1 Pupil's construction

2 Pupil's construction

3 Pupil's construction

Exercise 3B

1 Pupil's construction

2 Pupil's construction

3 Pupil's constructions using ASA
   Triangle C has the greatest perpendicular height.

Exercise 4

1 Not all sets of three numbers work. The sum of two of the numbers must be greater than the third number.

2 Pupils' constructions and reasoning

3 Pupils' constructions and reasoning

Exercise 5

1 a Three different non-square rectangles can be made on a 4 by 4 pinboard.

   b The rectangles have areas:
      1st diagram: 2, 3 square units
      2nd diagram: 6 square units
      3rd diagram: 4 square units

2 a Eight different non-square rectangles can be made on a 5 by 5 pinboard. Four of these are the same as the rectangles that can be made on a 4 by 4 pinboard.

   b The rectangles have areas:
      1st diagram: 2, 3, 4 square units
      2nd diagram: 6, 8 square units
      3rd diagram: 12 square units
      4th diagram: 4 square units
      5th diagram: 6 square units

3 Here are some different polygons with an area of 2 square units that can be made on a 3 by 3 pinboard.

There are these five symmetrical shapes:

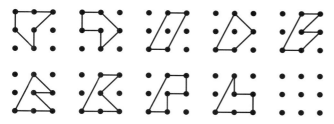

and these shapes and reflections of them:

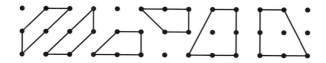

4   Six different trapeziums can be made on a 3 by 3 pinboard, including three pairs of reflections.

Extension problems

5   It is possible to make many different hexagons on a 3 by 3 pinboard. Here are some examples of hexagons that will tessellate.

6   It is possible to make several different heptagons on a 3 by 3 pinboard. Here are two examples of heptagons that will tessellate.

7   It is not possible to make an octagon on a 3 by 3 pinboard, though pupils should reach this conclusion for themselves after trying. The shape with the greatest number of sides that can be made on a 3 by 3 pinboard is a heptagon.

Exercise 6

1   a   1 : 50   b   1 : 5000
    c   1 : 25 000

2   a   7 m wide   b   9 cm long

3   a   2 m tall   b   15 m wide

4

Part	Model plane	Actual plane
length of wing	1 m	**10 m**
length of plane	**2 m**	20 m
height of tail	15 cm	**1.5 m**
width of door	**9 cm**	90 cm
height of door	20 cm	**2 m**
number of seats	**60**	60

5   a   24 km   b   20 cm

6   Pupil's scale drawing
    9.4 km from starting point (to 1 d.p.)

7   Pupil's scale drawing
    1.7 m up the wall (to 1d.p.)

8   Pupil's scale drawing

9   Pupil's scale drawing
    34° (to the nearest degree)

Extension problem

10 Pupil's scale drawing
    153 m (to the nearest metre)

Exercise 7

1   a   NE   b   SE   c   NW
    d   270°   e   225°   f   000°

2   a   285°   b   130°
    c   222°   d   044°

3   a   070°   b   250°

4   a   125°   b   305°

5   a   245°   b   065°

6   Pupil's scale drawing
    North Star was 34.6 km (to 1 d.p.) from the *Princess Margaret* on a bearing of 120°.

Extension problem

7   a   Scale: 1 : 5 000 000
    b   060°
    c   147 km (to nearest km)
    d   Bearing: 035°
        Distance: 302 km (to nearest km)

Exercise 8

1 Pupil's constructions showing:
   a perpendicular bisector
   b circle with centre A
   c the intersections of the two

2 Pupil's construction showing semicircle

3 Pupil's construction showing angle bisector with half nearest the wall shaded

4 Pupil's construction showing borders for goat parallel along the bar and semicircular at the two ends

Extension problem

5 Pupil's construction showing a rectangle with a circle missing from the centre

Exercise 9

1 Pentagon

2 Pupils' polygons and instructions

3 Letter 'H'

4 Pupils' letters and instructions

5 A square spiral

Extension problem

6 Pupils' spirals and instructions.

How well are you doing?

1 Pupil's construction

2 Pupil's construction

3 Pupil's construction

4 Pupil's construction

5 a Pupil's scale drawing
   b Pupil's scale drawing

6 a FORWARD 10
      TURN RIGHT 120°
      FORWARD 10
      TURN RIGHT 120°
      FORWARD 10

   b FORWARD 8
      TURN RIGHT 45°
      FORWARD 6
      TURN RIGHT 135°
      FORWARD 8
      TURN RIGHT 45°
      FORWARD 6

7 a 20 metres
   b 18 centimetres

8 a 5.5 cm
   b 110 km
   c 050°
   d 235°

Home book

TASK 1

1 $a = 34°, b = 146°, c = 53°, d = 161°, e = 71°, f = 306°, g = 244°$

2 Pupil's drawings

TASK 2

1 Pupil's construction

2 Pupil's construction

3 Pupil's construction
   The bisectors of the angles of the triangle meet at a point.

TASK 3

1 Pupil's construction

2 Pupil's construction checked by making tetrahedron

TASK 4

1 a 60°   b 90°   c 108°
   d 120°   e 128.6°   f 135°

2 Pupil's constructions

TASK 5

1 Two different parallelograms can be made on 3 by 3 pinboard.

2 Their areas are 1 and 2 square units respectively.

3 Ten different parallelograms can be made on 4 by 4 pinboard.

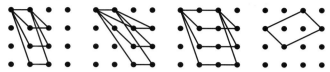

4 Their areas are:
1st diagram: 1, 2 and 3 square units
2nd diagram: 1, 2 and 3 square units
3rd diagram: 2, 4 and 6 square units
4th diagram: 3 square units

TASK 6

1 **a** 1 : 500   **b** 1 : 200 000

2 **a** 60 cm   **b** 14 m

3 Pupil's scale drawing
3.1 m (to 1 d.p.)

4 Pupil's scale drawing
43 m (to nearest metre)

TASK 7

1 St Mary Bourne: 8 km

2 Oxenwood: 2.5 km

3 Brunton: 5 km

4 Combe: 5.5 km

5 **a** Appleshaw: 205°
    b Combe: 030°
    c Burbage: 310°
    d St Mary Bourne: 110°
    e Clanville: 170°

6 Pupil's scale drawing

7 Pupil's scale drawing

TASK 8

1 Pupil's construction with concentric circles
The shape is a ring, or annulus.

2 Pupil's construction with three overlapping circles of different radii

TASK 9

1 RT 90 FD 42 RT 45 FD 40

2 LT 90 FD 120 RT 90 FD 80 RT 45 FD 84 RT 90 FD 84 RT 45 FD 80

3

CD-ROM

Check up

1 Pupil's scale drawing
Scaled distance: 5.4 to 5.7 cm
Actual distance: 110 to 114 m (calculated distance: 111 m)

2 **a** Pupil's construction
    b Shading indicating the region on the right-hand side of the perpendicular bisector
    c Shading indicating the area enclosed by a circle of radius 4 cm with centre A

3 Pupil's construction
68° to 71°

4 Pupil's construction
Approximately 058°

G4.4 Resource sheet 7.1

1

City	Bearing
Cardiff	225°
Dublin	287°
Edinburgh	347°
Hull	038°
Liverpool	330°
London	125°
Newcastle	005°
Norwich	085°
Plymouth	212°
Southampton	165°

2 **a** London from Southampton 055°
    b Hull from Newcastle 143°
    c Plymouth from Norwich 237°
    d Liverpool from London 317°

Using algebra

Previous learning

Before they start, pupils should be able to:

- simplify linear algebraic expressions by collecting like terms
- construct and solve simple linear equations with whole-number coefficients (unknown on one side only)
- recognise straight-line graphs parallel to the x-axis or y-axis.

Objectives based on NC levels 5 and 6 (mainly level 5)

In this unit, pupils learn to:

- try out and compare representations in algebraic or graphical form
- select appropriate procedures and tools, including ICT
- visualise and manipulate dynamic images and explore the effect of varying values
- draw accurate graphs on paper and on screen
- manipulate algebraic expressions and equations
- use logical argument to interpret the mathematics in a given context or to establish the truth of a statement
- explain own findings and approaches after discussion with others
- evaluate the efficiency of alternative strategies and approaches
- relate the current problem and structure to previous situations

and to:

- multiply a single term over a bracket
- simplify or transform linear expressions by collecting like terms
- construct and solve linear equations with integer coefficients (unknown on either or both sides, without and with brackets)
- derive and substitute integers into simple formulae and expressions, including examples that lead to an equation to solve
- generate points in all four quadrants and plot graphs of linear functions (y given explicitly in terms of x), on paper and using ICT
- construct linear functions arising from real-life problems, and plot and interpret their corresponding graphs
- use graphs and set up equations to solve simple problems involving direct proportion.

Lessons

1 **Simplifying expressions**
2 **Factorising expressions**
3 **Solving linear equations**
4 **Sketching linear graphs**
5 **Drawing and interpreting linear graphs**
6 **Interpreting real-life graphs 2**
7 **Word problems**
8 **Geometrical problems**

About this unit

This unit brings together work done in earlier algebra units in this tier. It aims to build pupils' confidence and motivation by giving them opportunities to use what they have learned to solve problems. They gain familiarity and flexibility with expressions, equations and graphs, consolidating their understanding through practice and exploration. Importantly, they make connections within mathematics. They also begin to see the relevance of algebra by working with real-life applications in mathematics and across the curriculum.

Assessment

This unit includes:

- a self-assessment section (*A4.5 How well are you doing?* class book p. 284);
- a set of questions to replace or supplement questions in the exercises or homework tasks, or to use as an informal test (*A4.5 Check up*, CD-ROM).

Common errors and misconceptions

Look out for pupils who:

- do not understand the meaning of the word 'term';
- try to combine unlike terms;
- forget that a number outside a bracket indicates multiplication of all terms within the bracket;
- cannot accept that answers to problems can be algebraic expressions;
- think that letters are abbreviations for words;
- think that letters of the alphabet stand for the numerical position within the alphabet.

Key terms and notation

problem, solution, solve, formulate, simplify, substitute, evaluate, factorise, sketch

term, like terms, expression, factor, common factor, highest common factor, HCF, ratio, proportion, direct proportion, $\propto$

formula, formulae, equation, linear equation, algebra, algebraic, symbol, operation, function

axes, x-axis, y-axis, coordinates, (x, y), graph, linear graph

Practical resources

basic calculators for pupils
individual whiteboards

graph paper
graphing software such as *Autograph*

Exploring maths

Tier 4 teacher's book
Answers for Unit A4.5, pp. 319–323

Tier 4 CD-ROM
PowerPoint files
  A4.5 Slides for lessons 1 to 8
Tools and prepared toolsheets
  Coordinates and functions tools
Tier 4 programs
  Factorise
  Straight-line graphs
  Distance-time graphs

Tier 4 class book
A4.5, pp. 264–285
A4.5 How well are you doing? p. 284

Tier 4 home book
A4.5, pp. 106–113

Tier 4 CD-ROM
A4.5 Check up
A4.5 Pupil resource sheets
  2.1 One per pair, cut up

Useful websites

How many eggs
www.nrich.maths.org; April 1999

Straight-line graphs
www.emaths.co.uk/InterSoW/background.htm

Planet hop
www.bbc.co.uk/education/mathsfile/gameswheel.html

Solving linear equations
www.adamzone.co.uk/linear.ht

Algebra topics
swgfl.skoool.co.uk/keystage3.aspx?id=65#24_30

Challenging maths problems
www.nrich.maths.org.uk/public/leg.php

1 Simplifying expressions

Learning points

- If there are no brackets, do multiplication and division before addition and subtraction.
- You can simplify an algebraic expression by collecting like terms.
- After multiplying out brackets, simplify if you can.

Starter

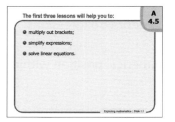

Use **slide 1.1** to discuss objectives for the first three lessons. Say that this lesson is about simplifying expressions.

Show **slide 1.2** to remind pupils about the order of operations: if there are no brackets, multiplication and division take precedence over addition and subtraction. In the expression $4 + 3 \times 5 - 2 \times 7 + 1$, underline each term to make the calculation easy to do like this:

$$4 + \underline{3 \times 5} - \underline{2 \times 7} + \underline{1} = 4 + 15 - 14 + 1 = 6$$

Explain that you can put in brackets to change the order of operations and get different answers. For example:

$(4 + 3) \times 5 - 2 \times 7 + 1 = 22$
$(4 + 3) \times 5 - 2 \times (7 + 1) = 19$
$4 + 3 \times (5 - 2) \times 7 + 1 = 68$

Ask pupils to see if they can get a larger or smaller number by inserting brackets.

Main activity

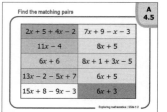

Revise the meaning of the words *term* and *like terms*. Show pupils how to combine like terms in expressions such as:

$3x + 2x + x + 3 + 5$
$x + 9 + x - 4 + 5y$
$15x + 2y + y + 9x - 4$

Use **slide 1.3** to check that pupils can combine like terms.

Remind pupils how to multiply out brackets, if necessary using grids like these.

$6(2x + 3)$

$\times$	$2x$	$+$	3
6	$12x$	$+$	18

$7(5x - 4)$

$\times$	$5x$	$-$	4
7	$35x$	$-$	28

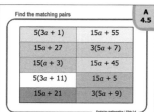

Use **slide 1.4** as a check that they know what to do.

If pupils are confident, show them how to multiply out brackets in a more complex expression and then simplify the expression by collecting together like terms. For example:

- $3(5x + 1) + 7(2x + 4)$

Select individual work from **A4.5 Exercise 1** in the class book (p. 265).

Review

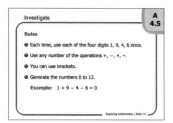

Show **slide 1.5**. Ask pupils to work in pairs and to use the four digits 1, 9, 4, 6, the four operations $+$, $-$, $\times$, $\div$ and brackets to get all the whole numbers from 0 to 12. Explain that they must use each digit but only once. They can use any number of operations and brackets.

There may be several different ways of getting the numbers 0 to 12. Here are some examples.

$1 \times (6 + 4 - 9) = 1$ $\qquad$ $6 + 4 + 1 - 9 = 2$ $\qquad$ $9 \div (4 - 1) = 3$

$(1 + 9 + 6) \div 4 = 4$ $\qquad$ $(9 + 1) \div (6 - 4) = 5$ $\qquad$ $(9 - 6) + (4 - 1) = 6$

$9 - 6 + 5 - 1 = 7$ $\qquad$ $1 + 9 + 4 - 6 = 8$ $\qquad$ $(9 - 6) \times (4 - 1) = 9$

$9 + 6 - 4 - 1 = 10$ $\qquad$ $(9 + 6 - 4) \div 1 = 11$ $\qquad$ $1 + 6 + 9 - 4 = 12$

If time is short, give pairs a specific number to find rather than all the numbers.

Sum up the lesson with the reminders on **slide 1.6**.

Homework

Ask pupils to do **A4.5 Task 1** in the home book (p. 106).

2 Factorising expressions

Learning points

- The factors of a number are all the numbers that divide into it exactly.

- When an expression contains brackets, you can multiply them out.

- You can factorise an expression by finding the highest common factor of each term.

- Factorising is the opposite to multiplying out brackets.

Starter

Say that this lesson is about factorising expressions.

Remind pupils that the factors of a number are all the numbers that divide into it exactly, e.g. the factors of 10 are 1, 2, 5 and 10. Ask pupils to write on their whiteboards all the factors of: 5, 8, 36, 50.

Now ask pupils to write on their whiteboards the common factors (excluding 1) of these pairs of numbers: 6 and 15, 10 and 22, 24 and 30.

This time ask them to write the highest common factor (HCF) of: 30 and 48, 28 and 70, 60 and 45.

Main activity

Write the term $2x$ on the board. Ask pupils to consider all its factors [1, 2, x, $2x$]. Do the same for the terms:

- $3x$ [1, 3, x, $3x$]

- $6x$ [1, 2, 3, 6, x, $2x$, $3x$, $6x$]

- $10x$ [1, 2, 5, 10, x, $2x$, $5x$, $10x$]

- $2xy$ [1, 2, x, y, $2x$, $2y$, xy, $2xy$]

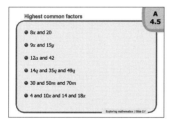

Write the terms $2x$ and 4 on the board. Ask pupils to give you their common factor other than 1 [2]. Do the same for the terms $5x$ and $15z$ [5].

Show **slide 2.1**. Ask pupils to write on their whiteboards the highest common factor for each set of terms.

Write the expression $3x + 15$ on the board. Ask pupils for the HCF of the two terms in the expression [3]. Show them how to *factorise* the expression by taking the HCF outside a bracket: $3(x + 5)$.

Repeat with $7x + 21$, $8x + 20$, $18 + 42x$.

Work through enough examples to make sure that all pupils understand and are able to factorise simple expressions.

Launch **Factorise**, which shows the question 'Factorise $4a + 12$'. Drag all the factors of $4a$ and 12 into their factor boxes. Click on '$a - 100a$' to show values between a and $100a$ in the 100-square.

If 1 and $4a$ are a pair of factors of $4a$, what are the other pairs?
[2 and $2a$, 4 and a]

Repeat for 12.

What is the largest factor that is in both boxes? [4]

Drag the factor 4 into the space furthest left of the answer. To change it, drag in a new answer or drag it out.

What goes inside the bracket? [a] **Why?** [Because $4 \times a = 4a$]

Drag a into position and repeat for the other inside term. Click 'Check' to check the answer.

To create your own questions click 'Reset' to clear the factor boxes and brackets. Select the type of value you want to drag using the options for the 100-square across the bottom of the screen. Drag values for the first and second term from the grid into the question. Click on the sign in the question to change between $+$ and $-$.

Questions could include: $14b + 21$, $2a - 4ab$.

Ask pupils to do **A4.5 Exercise 2** in the class book (p. 267). Question 9 is a game for two or more players; each group will need a dice and a copy of **A4.5 Resource sheet 2.1** cut into cards.   ◀ RS

Review

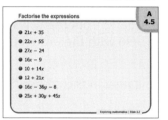

Show **slide 2.2**. Ask pupils to factorise the expressions on the slide and write their answers on their whiteboards.

Sum up by reminding pupils how to multiply out a bracket and then factorise an expression to show how they are linked. Stress the points on **slide 2.3**.

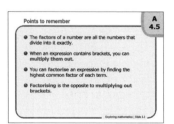

Homework   Ask pupils to do **A4.5 Task 2** in the home book (p. 107).

3 Solving linear equations

Learning points

You can:

- multiply out brackets and then simplify by collecting like terms;
- factorise an expression by finding the highest common factor;
- solve linear equations by using inverse operations.

Starter   Say that this lesson is about solving linear equations.

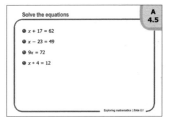

Show **slide 3.1**. Ask pupils to solve the four equations, writing their answers on their whiteboards. Go through each one and ask pupils to explain their solutions. Reinforce the idea of using inverse operations and ensure that all pupils are confident with these simple examples before moving on. Show pupils the different ways of writing the last equation $x \div 4 = 12$ as $^{x}/_{4} = 12$ or $\frac{x}{4} = 12$. Do further examples if necessary.

Main activity   Remind pupils how to solve linear equations. Some pupils will be confident in using the method of 'doing the same to both sides of the equation' but many will continue to need to set out the function and its inverse to help with the order of steps to be taken.

These are examples of equations pupils have encountered earlier in the course.

Example 1
No simplification or rearrangement needed before solving:

$$7x + 9 = 65$$

subtract 9 $\qquad 7x = 56$

divide by 7 $\qquad \underline{x = 8}$

$$x \rightarrow \boxed{\times 7} \rightarrow \boxed{+9} \rightarrow 65$$
$$8 \leftarrow \boxed{\div 7} \leftarrow \boxed{-9} \leftarrow 65$$

Example 2
No simplification or rearrangement needed before solving:

$$\frac{x}{7} - 4 = 8$$

add 4 $\qquad \frac{x}{7} = 12$

multiply by 7 $\qquad \underline{x = 84}$

$$x \rightarrow \boxed{\div 7} \rightarrow \boxed{-4} \rightarrow 8$$
$$84 \leftarrow \boxed{\times 7} \leftarrow \boxed{+4} \leftarrow 8$$

Example 3
An equation with a single bracket can either be solved directly or the brackets can be multiplied out first:

Method 1

$$4(x + 7) = 48$$

divide by 4 $\qquad x + 7 = 12$

subtract 7 $\qquad \underline{x = 5}$

$$x \rightarrow \boxed{+7} \rightarrow \boxed{\times 4} \rightarrow 48$$
$$5 \leftarrow \boxed{-7} \leftarrow \boxed{\div 4} \leftarrow 48$$

Method 2

$$4(x + 7) = 48$$

$$4x + 28 = 48$$

subtract 28 $\quad 4x = 20$

divide by 4 $\quad \underline{x = 5}$

$$x \rightarrow \boxed{\times 4} \rightarrow \boxed{+28} \rightarrow 48$$

$$5 \leftarrow \boxed{\div 4} \leftarrow \boxed{-28} \leftarrow 48$$

Example 4

Equations with two or more brackets, which must be multiplied out first and the equation simplified before solving:

$$5(x + 2) + 7(x + 8) = 102$$

$$5x + 10 + 7x + 56 = 102$$

$$12x + 66 = 102$$

subtract 66 $\quad 12x = 36$

divide by 12 $\quad \underline{x = 3}$

$$x \rightarrow \boxed{\times 12} \rightarrow \boxed{+66} \rightarrow 102$$

$$3 \leftarrow \boxed{\div 12} \leftarrow \boxed{-66} \leftarrow 102$$

Example 5

Equations with x terms on both sides must be rearranged so that all the x terms are on one side and numbers on the other.

$$3x - 5 = 2x + 1$$

subtract $2x \quad x - 5 = 1$

add 5 $\quad \underline{x = 6}$

$$x \rightarrow \boxed{-5} \rightarrow 1$$

$$6 \leftarrow \boxed{+5} \leftarrow 1$$

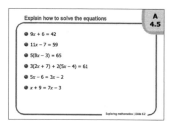

Show **slide 3.2**. Ask pupils to explain what steps they need to take to solve each equation. Emphasise the need to inspect an equation carefully before attempting a solution.

Select individual work from **A4.5 Exercise 3** in the class book (p. 270).

Review Show **slide 3.3**. Ask pupils to match the words on the left to the symbolic representation on the right. Discuss the meaning of the words as you go.

Ask pupils to remember the points on **slide 3.4**.

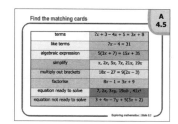

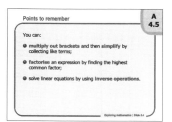

Homework Ask pupils to do **A4.5 Task 3** in the home book (p. 108).

4 Sketching linear graphs

Learning points

- A sketch of a graph is a neat drawing using a pencil and ruler.

- When you sketch a graph, look at the equation. Base your sketch on what you know about similar graphs.

- The graph of $y = ax + b$ is a straight line.

- The gradient of the graph is a and the intercept on the y-axis is $(0, b)$.

Starter

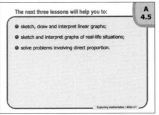

Use **slide 4.1** to discuss what pupils will learn in the next three lessons. Say that this lesson is about sketching straight-line graphs.

Show **slide 4.2**. Inspect the axes and ask pupils to give the coordinates of some points along them. Make sure that pupils read the coordinates in the correct order (x, y).

What are the equations of the axes?

Ask pupils for the equations of the lines marked (a) to (h). It may help to ask them to give a number of coordinates on the lines first.

Main activity

Remind pupils that a sketch is a neat drawing based on knowledge. A sketch of a graph can be done by recognising features of an equation. When they sketch graphs pupils should use a pencil and ruler and mark any points on the graphs that they can see from the equation.

With less-confident pupils use the **Function graph tool** to help them to remember what the graphs look like.

Show **slide 4.3**. Ask pupils to come to the board and sketch the set of graphs:

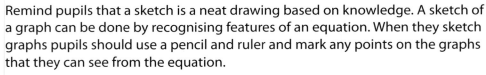

$y = x, y = x + 1, y = x + 2, y = x + 3, y = x + 4, y = x - 1, y = x - 2$, and so on.

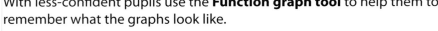

Discuss the properties of the graphs such as:

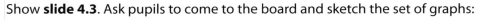

- they are all straight lines;

- they are all parallel to each other;

- the number indicates the point where they cross the y-axis;

- the coefficient of x is always 1.

Start again with a blank grid and ask pupils to sketch the set of graphs:

$y = x, y = 2x, y = 3x, y = 4x, y = 5x, y = 0.5x$, and so on.

Discuss the properties of the graphs, such as:

- they all pass through the origin;
- they are all straight lines;
- the larger the coefficient of x, the steeper the graph.

Repeat for $y = -x, y = -2x, y = -3x, y = -4x$, and so on.

Explain that we use the word *gradient* to describe the steepness of the graph. When an equation is in the form $y = ax + b$, the number a stands for the gradient of the line and $(0, b)$ is the point of intersection of the line with the y-axis.

Now ask pupils to sketch these linear graphs, each time using a new blank grid:

$y = 2x + 1, y = 3x + 4, y = 3x - 1, y = -2x + 5, y = -0.5x - 4$, and so on.

Ask pupils to explain how they know what to draw. Ask them to mark known points such as the intersection on the y-axis.

> Ask pupils to do **A4.5 Exercise 4** in the class book (p. 274).

Review

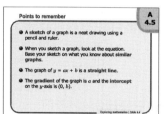

Discuss the work that pupils have done in the exercise. Where appropriate, use the **Function graph tool** to confirm solutions.

Finish by emphasising the points on **slide 4.4**.

TO

Homework

Ask pupils to do **A4.5 Task 4** in the home book (p. 109).

5 Drawing and interpreting linear graphs

Learning points

- To draw a straight-line graph accurately, plot three coordinate pairs.
- A sketch of a graph is a neat drawing that shows some of its features.

Starter

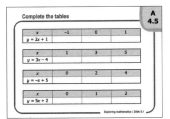

Say that this lesson is about drawing and interpreting straight-line graphs.

Show **slide 5.1**. Ask pupils to come to the board and complete the tables. Ask them to explain how they work out the missing numbers. Remind pupils that these are linear relationships.

Main activity

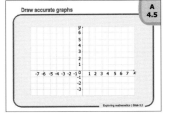

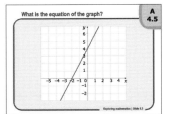

Explain that to draw an accurate graph of a linear equation you need to plot three points. Two points define the line and the third point acts as a check that the two are correct. Mathematicians do not like to waste time and effort so they only do the minimum number of calculations. Graphs of non-linear relationships need more points.

Show **slide 5.2**. Ask pupils to draw accurately the graphs of the equations on slide 17 by plotting the points and joining them with a board ruler. Make sure that they draw the line through the points to the edge of the axes. Remind them that the axes are of infinite length and that the picture on the slide only shows a part of the line.

Show **slide 5.3**. Inspect the graph.

Where does the graph cross the y-axis?

Where does the graph cross the x-axis?

Give the coordinates of some points on the line.

How steep is the line? (What is the gradient of the line?)

What is the equation of the line?

Give the equation of a line parallel to this one.

How many solutions are there to the equation $y = 2x + 4$?

What is the solution of the equation $2x + 4 = 6$?
[look at the value of x when $y = 6$]

Ask pupils to do **A4.5 Exercise 5** in the class book (p. 276). Pupils will need graph paper.

Review

Launch **Straight-line graphs**. This shows a graph of $y = x$. The straight line can be moved by dragging its end points. Make a horizontal line above the x-axis.

SIM

> **What do you think the equation is? Why?**
>
> **What values could be in a table of (x, y) values?**

Click 'Show table of values'.

> **Do you still agree with your first answer? Why or why not?**

Click on 'Show equation' to confirm the answer. Click 'Hide equation' and 'Hide table of values' and repeat for other lines.

Use **slide 5.4**. Inspect the two graphs.

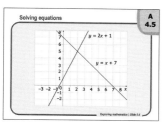

> **How many solutions are there to the equation $y = 2x + 1$?**
> [an infinite number]
>
> **Give some of the solution pairs.**
> [any coordinate pairs on the line]
>
> **How many solutions are there to the equation $y = -x + 7$?**
> [an infinite number]
>
> **Give some of the solution pairs.**
> [any coordinate pairs on the line]
>
> **Which coordinate pair is a solution to both equations?**

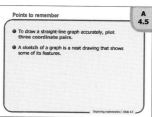

Sum up the lesson with the points on **slide 5.5**.

Homework

Ask pupils to do **A4.5 Task 5** in the home book (p. 110). They will need some graph paper.

6 Interpreting real-life graphs 2

Learning points

⊙ When you draw or interpret graphs of real situations, take care with the scales on the axes.

Starter

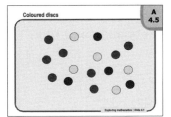

Say that this lesson is about interpreting graphs of real situations.

Show **slide 6.1**. Ask questions such as:

How many coloured discs are there on the slide? [17]

What is the ratio of yellow discs to red discs? [5 : 8]
Of blue discs to red discs? [4 : 8]
Of yellow discs to blue discs? [5 : 4]
Of yellow discs to all discs? [5 : 17]
Of red discs to all discs? [8 : 17]
Of blue discs to all discs? [4 : 17]
Of yellow discs to red and blue discs? [5 : 12]
Of red discs to yellow and blue discs? [8 : 9]
Of blue discs to red and yellow discs? [4 : 13]

What fraction of discs is yellow? [$\frac{5}{17}$]

What percentage of discs is blue? [23.5%]

Main activity

Ask pupils to sketch then describe the graphs of $y = x$, $y = 2x$, $y = 3x$ and so on. Ascertain that all of the graphs are straight lines that pass through the origin. Explain that in all of these cases y is *directly proportional* to x. The notation for this is $y \propto x$ or $y = kx$. Explain that you are going to look at some practical examples of these relationships.

Launch **Distance-time graphs**, which shows a journey from London to Nottingham and back. First the journey is shown, then a distance-time graph. Click 'Play' to start and 'Pause' to stop, or control the animation manually by dragging the 'Playback control'. Question pupils about the graph, relating questions to the journey.

What does the graph look like up to point A? Why?
[sloping upwards, positive gradient, moving away from London]

How long does it take the car to get to point A? [2 hours]
How far has the car travelled? [90 miles]

What does the graph look like between A and B? What is happening?
[a horizontal line; car has stopped, not getting any further from London]

For how long does the car stop? [30 minutes]

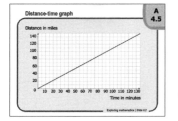

Explain that on another journey a car is travelling at constant speed.

Time in minutes	20	50	120
Distance in miles	22	55	132

Use **slide 6.2**. Show pupils how the graph can be drawn by plotting the three points. You know that the graph is a straight line because the car is travelling at constant speed. We say that the distance is proportional to the time and write distance ∝ time. The equation of the graph is distance = speed × time or $d = st$.

Ask pupils to use the graph to answer these questions.

Estimate how long it took for the car to travel 100 miles.

Estimate how far the car travelled in 60 minutes.

Estimate the car's speed in miles per hour.

The car uses a gallon of petrol to travel 33 miles. How much petrol was used in four hours?

Ask pupils to do **A4.5 Exercise 6** in the class book (p. 277). They will need graph paper.

Review

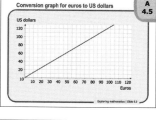

Show **slide 6.3**. Inspect the axes. Ask pupils to work out the scales.

Estimate how many dollars there are to 40 euros.

Estimate how many euros there are to 100 US dollars.

Estimate the exchange rate for one dollar in euros.

Draw up this table and ask pupils to use the graph to estimate the amounts.

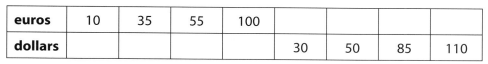

euros	10	35	55	100				
dollars					30	50	85	110

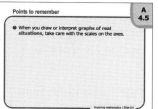

Ask pupils to remember the points on **slide 6.4**.

Homework

Ask pupils to do **A4.5 Task 6** in the home book (p. 110). They will need graph paper.

7 Word problems

Learning points

- Read the question carefully.
- Define any letters you will use.
- Form and solve an equation, showing your working.
- Check that your answer fits the problem.

Starter

Use **slide 7.1** to discuss what pupils will learn in the next two lessons. Say that this lesson will help them to use algebra to solve word problems.

Show **slides 7.2** and **7.3**. The expressions in each cell are the result of adding the expressions in the two cells beneath it. Ask pupils to copy and complete each grid. Ask individual pupils to complete the grid on the board as they explain their thinking.

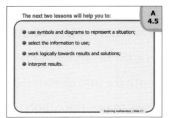
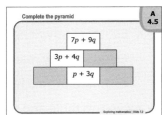
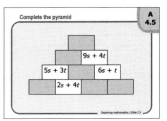

Main activity

Explain that maths is used to solve many different problems. Encourage pupils to imagine that they are working like detectives looking for clues and seeking solutions to puzzles.

Say that algebra is useful when there is a number or quantity that is unknown. First you have to read and understand the problem. Then you have to break the problem down, decide what the unknown quantity is and give it a letter. Next you form an equation, which you solve. Finally, you return to the problem and interpret your results in terms of the original problem, checking that your answer is sensible.

Do several problems with pupils to demonstrate how to define a letter as a symbol and form an equation which they can solve. Some examples are on **slides 7.4** and **7.5**.

I am thinking of a number. Let that number be n.
I multiply the number by 3 and add 4 to get 31.
What is the number? $[3n + 4 = 31; n = 9]$

I am thinking of a number. Let the number be m.
I double the number, add 3 and multiply by 5 to get 85.
What is the number? $[5(2m + 3) = 85; m = 7]$

The sum of four consecutive whole numbers is 510.
Let the smallest whole number be p. What are the four numbers?
$[p + p + 1 + p + 2 + p + 3 = 4p + 6 = 510;$
the four numbers are 126, 127, 128, 129]

The mean of seven consecutive whole numbers is 18.
Let the smallest number be q. What are the seven numbers?
[$7q + 21 = 126$; the numbers are 15, 16, 17, 18, 19, 20, 21]

A shop has to calculate prices for goods with 17.5% VAT.
Write a formula to calculate the price on goods worth £x.

[price $= 1.175x$ or $\dfrac{117.5x}{100}$]

Ask pupils to calculate the sale price for goods worth different prices.

Ask pupils to do **A4.5 Exercise 7** in the class book (p. 279).

Review

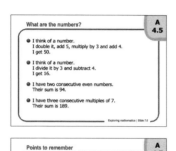

Show **slide 7.6**. Encourage pupils to define a letter and form an equation for each example, then ask them to solve the equations and answer the questions. Use the examples to summarise how pupils should set out their solutions. Don't let them guess answers!

Summarise the problem solving process with the points on **slide 7.7**.

Homework

Ask pupils to do **A4.5 Task 7** in the home book (p. 111).

8 Geometrical problems

Learning points

- Take time to read questions carefully.
- Identify and define any letters you use.
- Form an algebraic expression, equation or formula.
- Set out each step of working.
- Go back and make sure you have answered the original problem.
- Check that your answers are sensible.

Starter

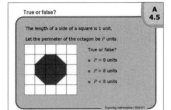

Say that this lesson is about using algebra to solve measurement problems.

Show **slide 8.1**. Ask pupils how to work out the perimeter of an octagon. Confirm that the perimeter is the sum of the lengths of the sides.

Ask pupils to read the three statements and interpret the symbols.

> **Are the statements true or false?**

Invite them to explain why the perimeter is greater than 8 units by referring to the length of a diagonal of a square.

Main activity

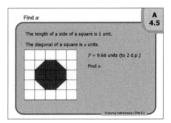

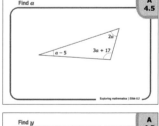

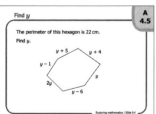

Say that when problems involve geometrical shapes, you should first inspect the shape and remind yourself of its properties, e.g. the formulae for the area or perimeter, properties of the sum of interior or exterior angles, equal or parallel sides, etc.

Show **slide 8.2**. Ask pupils to form an equation in x and then solve the equation to find the length of the diagonal of a square [1.415].

Show **slide 8.3**, a scalene triangle with angles $2a$, $3a + 17$ and $a - 5$.

> **What is the angle sum of any triangle?**

Ask pupils to form an equation in x and then solve the equation.

Remind them that finding the value of x is not the end of the problem. They have to go back and work out the value of each angle. They should then check to see that their answers are sensible.

Show **slide 8.4**, an irregular hexagon with sides of length y, $y + 4$, $y - 6$, $2y$, $y + 5$ and $2y - 1$. Tell pupils that the perimeter of the hexagon is 22 cm. Ask them to form an equation in y and solve it to work out the six lengths.

Ask pupils to do **A4.5 Exercise 8** in the class book (p. 281).

Review

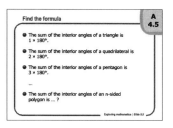

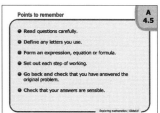

Show **slide 8.5**. Ask pupils to find the formula for the sum of the interior angles of an n-sided polygon [$(n - 2) \times 180°$].

Show them how to break the problem down and start with triangles, quadrilaterals and so on. Ask them to look at the sequence of numbers and form the general term. Use this example to illustrate the power of algebra in generalising a situation.

Ask pupils to remember the points on **slide 8.6**.

Round off the unit by referring again to the objectives. Suggest that pupils find time to try the self-assessment problems in **A4.5 How well are you doing?** in the class book (p. 284).

Homework

Ask pupils to do **A4.5 Task 8** in the home book (p. 112).

A4.5 Check up and resource sheets

Check up

Write your answers in your book.

1. Simplify these expressions by collecting together like terms.
   a $7x + 4x + 13 + 9x + 2$
   b $10x - 7 + 12x - 8$
   c $2x + 3y + 5 + 3x - y - 8$

2. Multiply out these brackets.
   a $3(4x + 5)$
   b $7(5x - 6)$

3. Factorise these expressions.
   a $10x + 35$
   b $12x - 44$

4. Find the value of x in the equation $7x + 8 = 50$.

5. Find the value of x in the equation $6(5x + 7) = 312$.

6. Find the value of x in the equation $9x - 8 = 5x + 8$.

7. At what point does the graph of $y = 3x + 4$ cross the y-axis?

8. What is the gradient of the graph of the equation $y = 0.5x - 8$?

9. Jo earns £20 a week for delivering papers.
   He spends twice as much on computer games as he spends on sweets.
   He puts £5 a week into a savings account.
   How much does Jo spend on computer games?

10. The five interior angles of a pentagon measured in degrees are $4x$, $5x$, $6x$, $7x$ and $8x$.
    Work out their measurements.

Resource sheet 2.1

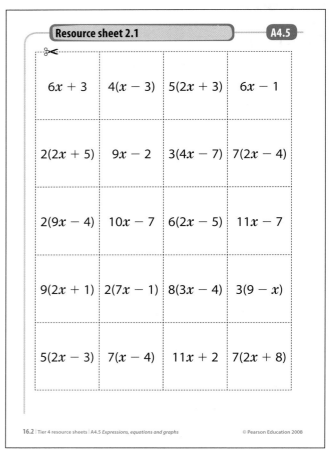

$6x + 3$	$4(x - 3)$	$5(2x + 3)$	$6x - 1$
$2(2x + 5)$	$9x - 2$	$3(4x - 7)$	$7(2x - 4)$
$2(9x - 4)$	$10x - 7$	$6(2x - 5)$	$11x - 7$
$9(2x + 1)$	$2(7x - 1)$	$8(3x - 4)$	$3(9 - x)$
$5(2x - 3)$	$7(x - 4)$	$11x + 2$	$7(2x + 8)$

A4.5 Answers

Class book

Exercise 1

1 a $3 + 5 \times (6 - 2 + 4) = 43$
   b $(3 + 5) \times 6 - 2 + 4 = 50$
   c $(3 + 5) \times (6 - 2) + 4 = 36$
   d $3 + (5 \times 6 - 2) + 4 = 35$

2 a $13x + 4$
   b $11y + 5$
   c $8p + 6$
   d $7q + 5$
   e $9s + 2r + 11$
   f $16t - 2$
   g $x + y + 6$
   h $21ab + 3a + 5$

3 $3x + 6 + 5x + 9$ and $10x + 7 - 2x + 8$
   $8x + 9 + x - 8$ and $2x - 1 + 7x + 2$
   $13x + 9 - 7x - 3$ and $x + 12 + 5x - 6$
   $7x + 2 + 6x + 8$ and $15x + 4 - 2x + 6$
   $x + 3 + x - 7$ and $4x + 1 - 2x - 5$
   $2x + 7 + x - 8$ and $x - 10 + 2x + 9$

4 a

		$13a + 12b$		
	$8a + 4b$		$5a + 8b$	
$5a + 3b$		$3a + b$		$2a + 7b$

   b

		$14n + 6m$		
	$8n + 4m$		$6n + 2m$	
$4n + 3m$		$4n + m$		$2n + m$
$n + 2m$	$3n + m$		n	$n + m$

5 a $5x + 40$ b $4y - 28$
   c $27x - 18$ d $50a + 70$
   e $56 + 48t$ f $60x - 45$
   g $24a + 15b$ h $36p - 24q + 12r$

6 a $9x + 22$ b $8y + 50$
   c $14s + 102$ d $12p + 112$
   e $36a + 19$ f $75x + 5$
   g $150t - 128$ h $142b - 47$

7 $5(x + 3) + 7(2x + 1)$ and $19x + 22$
   $8(5x + 3) - 6(3x + 4)$ and $22x$
   $10(2x + 9) + 4(7x - 5)$ and $48x + 70$
   $7(6x + 1) + 8(3x - 9)$ and $66x - 65$
   $6(7x + 4) - 2(5x - 8)$ and $32x + 40$

Extension problems

8

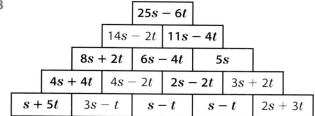

				$25s - 6t$				
			$14s - 2t$		$11s - 4t$			
		$8s + 2t$		$6s - 4t$		$5s$		
	$4s + 4t$		$4s - 2t$		$2s - 2t$		$3s + 2t$	
$s + 5t$		$3s - t$		$s - t$		$s - t$		$2s + 3t$

9 a $5x + 22$ b $5y + 17$
   c $11s - 5$ d $6p + 36$
   e $43a - 123$ f $36x - 43$
   g $-6t + 3$ h $55b - 67$

Exercise 2

1 a 1, 2, 3, 4, 6, 12   b 1, 2, 4, 5, 10, 20
   c 1, 2, 3, 6, 9, 18   d 1, 5, 7, 35
   e 1, 3, 17, 51   f 1, 3, 9, 11, 33, 99

2 a 2, 3, 6   b 2, 5
   c 3, 5, 15   d 2, 3, 6
   e 7   f 2, 4, 8

3 a 6   b 8   c 15
   d 5   e 7   f 6

4 a $1, 3, x, 3x$ b $1, 7, p, 7p$
   c $1, 2, 4, y, 2y, 4y$ d $1, a, b, ab$
   e $1, 2, x, y, 2x, 2y, 2xy$ f $1, 13, p, 13p$

5 a x b 2
   c 3 d $7, t, 7t$
   e $2, 5, 10, s, 2s, 5s, 10s$ f $3, m, 3m$

6 a 10 b x
   c $6p$ d $15q$
   e $14m$ f $12t$

7 a $5(x + 3)$ b $6(y + 3)$
   c $7(m - 7)$ d $9(n + 4)$
   e $3(2s + 7)$ f $4(3a - 5)$
   g $10(2t - 3)$ h $2(7v + 11)$
   i $8(3x + 5y)$

8 $3(2x + 5)$ and $6x + 15$
   $2(x + 8)$ and $2x + 16$
   $3(x + 2)$ and $3x + 6$
   $7(3x + 2)$ and $21x + 14$
   $2(4x + 7)$ and $8x + 14$
   $7(x + 1)$ and $7x + 7$

9 This is a game.

Extension problem

10 a $3(2x + 3y + z)$ **b** $4(7a - 2b + 2)$
   c $6(8 + 2m - 3n)$ **d** $5(5w - 6x - 4y)$
   e $7a(2x + 5y)$ **f** $10b(3p - 4q)$

Exercise 3

1 a $x = 7$ **b** $x = 15$
   c $x = 47$ **d** $x = 4.8$
   e $x = 9.3$ **f** $x = -1$
   g $x = 28$ **h** $x = 16$
   i $x = 15$

2 $x + 6 = 11$ and $x - 1 = 4$
$x + 3 = 19$ and $x - 7 = 9$
$x + 14 = 22$ and $x + 19 = 27$
$x + 12 = 13$ and $x + 44 = 45$
$x - 3 = 9$ and $x - 5 = 7$
$x + 10 = 16$ and $x + 16 = 22$

3 a $x = 7$ **b** $x = 11$
   c $x = 7$ **d** $x = 4$
   e $x = 5$ **f** $x = 5$
   g $x = 30$ **h** $x = 7.5$
   i $x = 2$

4 $5x = 40$ and $\frac{x}{2} = 4$
$\frac{x}{7} = 5$ and $\frac{x}{5} = 7$
$7x = 35$ and $9x = 45$
$6x = 54$ and $\frac{x}{3} = 3$
$2x = 28$ and $\frac{x}{7} = 2$
$9x = 27$ and $12x = 36$

5 a $p = 47$ **b** $m = 82$
   c $t = 8$ **d** $z = -33$
   e $s = 8$ **f** $w = 10$
   g $x = 8$ **h** $a = 7$
   i $b = 20$ **j** $c = -2$

6 $9x - 8 = 19$ and $4x - 5 = 7$
$7x + 12 = 47$ and $8x + 15 = 55$
$4x - 6 = 22$ and $3x + 17 = 38$
$8x + 11 = 43$ and $5x + 13 = 33$
$12x - 9 = 15$ and $10x - 7 = 13$
$5x + 6 = 1$ and $3x + 8 = 5$

7 a $x = 3$ **b** $x = 5$
   c $x = 7$ **d** $x = 4$
   e $x = 6$ **f** $x = 2$
   g $x = 8$ **h** $x = 9$

Extension problems

8 a $x = 2$ **b** $x = 1$
   c $x = 4$ **d** $x = 6$
   e $x = 3$ **f** $x = 2.5$

9 a $x = 1$ **b** $x = 3$
   c $x = 4$ **d** $x = 5$
   e $x = 6$ **f** $x = 2$

Exercise 4

1 a   **i** $y = 5$ **ii** $x = 4$ **iii** $y = 2$
    iv $x = 1$ **v** $x = 2$ **vi** $y = -3$
  b   **i** $y = -1$ **ii** $x = -1$
  c   **i** $y = 3.5$ **ii** $x = 2.5$
  d $y = 4$
  e $x = -2$

2 a $(0, 0)$ or the origin
  b $45°$
  c 1
  d (i), (iv)
  e (ii), (iv)
  f $(0, 21)$

3 a $(0, 4)$
  b $(-4, 0)$
  c 1

4 Pupils' sketches of graphs

5 Pupils' sketches of graphs

Exercise 5

1 Pupils' accurate graphs

Extension problems

2 a $(0, -5)$
  b Any three points on the graph
  c 4
  d $y = 4x - 5$
  e 11

3 a $y = x + 5$
  b $y = 5x - 3$

Exercise 6

1. a About 45 miles
   b Approximately 4 hours
   c 14:30 or 2:30 pm
   d About 45 miles per hour.
   e About 15:30 or 3:30 pm

2. a About 4.5 gallons
   b About 4.5 litres to a gallon
   c About 11 gallons
   d About 528 miles
   e About 25 pints
   f 10 litres is greater than 2 gallons.

3. a About £270
   b About £430
   c About 7.5 metres

4. a Pupils' graphs
   b About £9
   c About £84
   d About £17

5. a Pupils' graphs
   b £13.75
   c 250

Exercise 7

1. a 2.5   b 7
   c 28   d 60
   e 1   f 3

2. a 211, 212, 213
   b 15, 16, 17, 18, 19
   c 200, 201, 202, 203, 204, 205, 206

Extension problems

3. Alex saved £27.

4. Ramesh spends £3 a week.

5. The maximum number of boxes is 42

6. Nicki is 13.

7. Amber spent £25, Jade spent £33 and Eva spent £66.

8. Zak travels 0.5 miles, David 2.5 miles and Paul 7.5 miles.

9. a 132, 134
   b 51, 54, 57
   c 7

Exercise 8

1. 15.5 cm

2. 4.5 cm

3. 8.2 cm

4. 9.5 cm

5. a 45°, 60° and 75°
   b 50°, 75° and 55°
   c 45°, 46° and 89°
   d 26°, 51° and 103°

6. 7 cm, 14 cm, 21 cm, 16 cm, 20 cm, 11 cm

7. 19 cm

8. $2x = 36°, 4x = 72°, 5x = 90°, 9x = 162°$

9. 18 cm and 6 cm

10. The base is 12 cm. The two equal sides are 36 cm.

Extension problems

11. 36°, 48°, 72°, 120°, 84°

12. 54°, 81°, 216°, 189°, 162°, 135°, 135°, 108°

13. The height of the triangle is 8 cm.

How well are you doing?

1. $3(3x - 8)$

2. $8x + 31$

3. $n = 0.5$

4. $y = 6.5$

5. 11

6. $m = 50°$

7. a $x = 8$ b $y = x + 7$ c $y = x - 1$

8 a 3 hours, 50p

b They charge £10 each month, with no extra charges

Home book

TASK 1

1 a

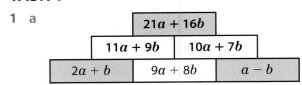

b

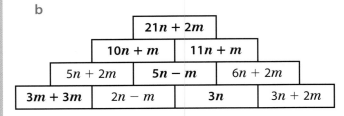

2 a $19x$ **b** $6y + 5$
c $19p + 8$ **d** $4q + 12$
e $11s + r$ **f** $14t + 17$
g $5x + 10$ **h** $12w - 4$

TASK 2

1 $5(3x + 8)$ and $15x + 40$
$7(2x + 9)$ and $14x + 63$
$4(8x + 11)$ and $32x + 44$
$9(5x + 9)$ and $45x + 81$
$3(7x + 6)$ and $21x + 18$
$8(6x + 10)$ and $48x + 80$

2 a $4(3x + 5)$ **b** $7(2y + 5)$
c $5(8m - 11)$ **d** $3(6n + 7)$
e $2(5s + 7)$ **f** $6(5a - 8)$
g $8(2t - 5)$ **h** $11(3v + 7)$

TASK 3

1 a $x = 6$ **b** $x = 7$
c $x = 12$ **d** $x = -1$
e $x = 9$ **f** $x = 2$
g $x = 1$ **h** $x = 5$

2 a $x = 1$ **b** $x = 3$
c $x = 2$ **d** $x = 4$
e $x = 5$ **f** $x = 7$
g $x = 6$ **h** $x = 8$

TASK 4

1 Pupils' sketches

2 b and d

3 $y = 7x + 4$

TASK 5

1 Pupils' accurate graphs

2 a $y = 3x + 4$ **b** $y = 2x + 9$
c $y = 5x - 6$ **d** $y = 7x - 8$
e $y = -x - 2$ **f** $y = -3x - 6$

TASK 6

1 a 39 mph
b 3.5 hours
c 12 mph (excluding the stop for coffee)

2 a About 16 km
b About 15 miles
c About 330 miles
d About 9.6 hours

TASK 7

1 47

2 23

3 54

4 31, 32, 33

5 10, 11, 12, 13, 14

6 7

7 12

8 £32, £47, £94

TASK 8

1 8.6 cm

2 9 cm

3 4.2 cm

4 24 cm and 15 cm

5 14 cm

CD-ROM

Check up

1 a $20x + 15$
  b $22x - 15$
  c $5x + 2y - 3$

2 a $12x + 15$
  b $35x - 42$

3 a $5(2x + 7)$
  b $4(3x - 11)$

4 $x = 6$

5 $x = 9$

6 $x = 4$

7 (0, 4)

8 0.5

9 £10

10 72°, 90°, 108°, 126°, 144°

Solving problems

Previous learning

Before they start, pupils should be able to:

- understand place value in whole numbers and decimals
- understand the order of operations
- calculate with whole numbers and decimals mentally, on paper and with a calculator, as appropriate
- estimate and check results.

Objectives based on NC levels 5 and 6 (mainly level 5)

In this unit, pupils learn to:

- identify mathematical features of a context or problem
- relate the current problem and structure to previous situations
- conjecture and generalise
- use logical argument to interpret the mathematics in a given context or to establish the truth of a statement
- calculate accurately, selecting mental methods or a calculator as appropriate
- give accurate solutions appropriate to the context or problem
- refine own findings and approaches on the basis of discussion with others
- recognise efficiency in an approach
- relate the current problem and structure to previous situations
- record methods, solutions and conclusions

and to:

- recognise some of the historical and cultural roots of mathematics.

Lessons

1 **Place value puzzles**

2 **Early history of numbers and counting**

3 **Missing digits and operations**

About this unit

This unit provides opportunities for pupils to use and apply their mathematical knowledge and skills to investigate and solve problems. It also offers a chance for pupils to learn more about the history of mathematics.

The first lesson is adapted from a lesson in the Secondary Strategy's *Year 8 intervention pack*.

Assessment

This unit includes:

- an optional mental test that could replace part of a lesson (p. 333);
- a self-assessment section (*N4.5 How well are you doing?* class book p. 293);
- a set of questions to replace or supplement questions in the exercises or homework tasks, or to use as an informal test (*N4.5 Check up*, CD-ROM).

Common errors and misconceptions

Look out for pupils who have difficulty in:

- breaking problems into smaller parts;
- identifying what mathematical knowledge could be useful in helping to solve a problem.

Key terms and notation	problem, investigation, conjecture, pattern, predict, represent, solve, explain, justify, generalise, verify, prove, disprove, counter-example, method, solution, systematic
	positive, negative, odd, even, multiple, factor, prime, square, square root, factor, consecutive numbers
	calculate, calculation, operation, add, subtract, multiply, divide, sum, total, difference, product, quotient, greater than, less than, inverse

Practical resources

calculators for pupils
individual whiteboards

one 1−6 die per pair of pupils
set of 0−9 digit cards per pupil

Exploring maths

Tier 4 teacher's book
N4.5 Slide commentary, p. 330 (lesson 2)
N4.5 Mental test, p. 333
Answers for Unit N4.5, pp. 337–339

Tier 4 CD-ROM
PowerPoint files
   N4.5 Slides for lessons 1 to 3
   N4.5 History of counting (lesson 2)
Tools and prepared toolsheets
   Dice tool
   Calculator tool

Tier 4 class book
N4.5, pp. 286–294
N4.5 How well are you doing? p. 293

Tier 4 home book
N4.5, pp. 114–116

Tier 4 CD-ROM
N4.5 Check up
N4.5 Pupil resource sheets
   1.1 One per pair

Useful websites

History of mathematics
www-gap.dcs.st-and.ac.uk/~history/HistTopics/

Button beach challenge
www.amblesideprimary.com/ambleweb/mentalmaths/buttons.html

Number puzzles
nlvm.usu.edu/en/nav/category_g_3_t_1.html

Mini-max
www.nrich.maths.org; September 1999

Year 8 intervention lessons and resources
www.standards.dfes.gov.uk/keystage3/respub/ma_l3_5

1 Place value puzzles

Learning points

When you solve problems, remember to:

- be systematic;
- keep a careful record of your findings as you work;
- look for patterns in your findings;
- explain and justify your conclusions.

Starter

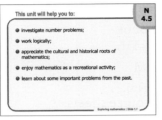

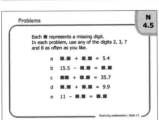

Use **slide 1.1** to discuss the objectives for this unit. Say that this lesson is about solving calculation problems.

Show **slide 1.2**. Ask pupils to work in pairs, using the digits 2, 3, 7 and 8 as often as they like, to make the number sentences correct.

☐.☐ + ☐.☐ = 5.4   [e.g. 2.2 + 3.2 = 5.4]

15.5 − ☐.☐ = ☐.☐   [e.g. 15.5 − 7.2 = 8.3]

☐☐ + ☐.☐ = 35.7   [e.g. 32 + 3.7 = 35.7]

☐.☐ + ☐.☐ = 9.9   [e.g. 7.7 + 2.2 = 9.9]

11 − ☐.☐ = ☐.☐   [e.g. 11 − 7.3 = 3.7]

Discuss the strategies used and alternative solutions.

Main activity

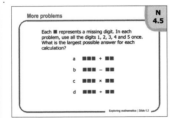

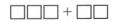

Show **slide 1.3**. Refer pupils to the first problem.

> **Using each of the digits 1, 2, 3, 4, 5 once, what is the largest sum you can make?**
>
> ☐☐☐ + ☐☐
>
> **Which digit will you place first? Which one next? ... Why?**

Establish that using knowledge of place value and addition helps to make decisions. Develop a solution [e.g. 541 + 32 = 573]. Point out that the 4 and 3 are interchangeable, as are the 1 and 2.

> **How would you approach the problem if addition were changed to subtraction?**

Ask pairs to work on the other three problems on the slide. Give them several minutes to work on the problems. Take feedback, drawing out the knowledge that they have used to solve the problems.

[Solution: largest difference 543 − 12 = 531; largest product 531 × 42 = 22 302; largest quotient 543 ÷ 12 = 45.25.]

Play this game. Write on the board:

$$\square\square\square \times \square\square$$

Explain that the aim is for each pupil to make the largest possible product.

Launch the **Dice tool**. Choose one 1–8 die. Roll it, and call out the digit. Allow 10 seconds for pupils to decide what they think is the best position for it. Continue until five digits are placed. What is the largest product?

Give each pair a 1–6 die and a copy of **N4.5 Resource sheet 1.1** to play the game.

TO

RS

Select further work for pupils to do individually or in pairs from **N4.5 Exercise 1** in the class book (p. 287).

Review

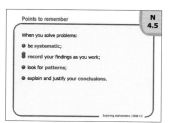

Discuss the solutions to the problems that pupils have tackled, stressing that systematic working and careful recording help to solve problems.

Ask pupils to remember the points on **slide 1.4**.

Homework

Ask pupils to do **N4.5 Task 1** in the home book (p. 114). They will need a set of cards from 1 to 9 (e.g. playing cards or home-made from paper).

2 Early history of numbers and counting

Learning points

◉ You can often work out complex calculations by breaking them into simpler calculations.

◉ When you calculate, try to choose the most efficient method.

Starter Say that this lesson is about the early history of numbers, counting and calculating.

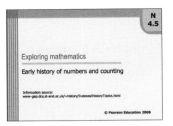

Display the title slide of **N4.5 History of counting**. Use **N4.5 Slide commentary** (p. 330) as background notes while you show **slides 1** to **13**.

As you reach slide 13, show pupils how to write one or two numbers using Roman numerals. Get them to write a few numbers, starting with 106 (CVI). Change this to 206 (CCVI), then 266 (CCLXVI) then 466 (CDLXVI), etc. Suggest that they write their birth date in Roman numerals, or the number of pupils in the school, or any other large numbers of interest to them.

Where have you seen Roman numerals being used in school or locally?
[e.g. book preface pages or chapter numbers, watches or clocks, foundation stones of buildings, statues, monuments, old gravestones, …]

Main activity Write powers of 2 on the board: 1, 2, 4, 8, 16, 32, 64, 128, 256, 512, …

Explain that every number can be written as the sum of powers of 2.

Take a two-digit number such as 85. Take the largest power of 2 below 85, which is 64. Subtract this from 85, leaving 21.

Take the largest power of 2 below 21, which is 16. Subtract this from 21, leaving 5.

Take the largest power of 2 below 5, which is 4. Subtract this from 5, leaving 1, which is a power of 2.

$$\begin{array}{r} 85 \\ -64 \\ \hline 21 \\ -16 \\ \hline 5 \\ -4 \\ \hline 1 \end{array}$$

So $85 = 64 + 16 + 4 + 1$.

Repeat with a three-digit number, such as 237. Repeatedly subtract the largest possible power of 2 to show that $237 = 128 + 64 + 32 + 8 + 4 + 1$.

Write two or three numbers on the board for pupils in pairs to express as powers of 2, e.g. 47, 782, 150.

Say that the ancient Egyptians used an interesting method for multiplication that is shown in the Rhind papyrus. This method is based on doubling.

Assume that we want to multiply 59 by 41. We take the larger number, 59, and double it repeatedly, keeping a record of how many times we have doubled it.

Explain that, since $59 \times 64 > 59 \times 41$, there is no need to double beyond 59×32.

59×41	
$59 \times 1 =$	59
$59 \times 2 =$	118
$59 \times 4 =$	236
$59 \times 8 =$	472
$59 \times 16 =$	944
$59 \times 32 =$	1888

Now express 41 as a sum of powers of 2:
41 = 32 + 8 + 1.

$$41 - 32 = 9$$
$$9 - 8 = 1$$

Now take the products above corresponding to 32, 8 and 1, and add them.

$$59 \times 1 = 59$$
$$59 \times 8 = 472$$

$$59 \times 32 = 1888$$
$$59 \times 41 = 2419$$

We see that the answer to 59 × 41 is 2419.

To reinforce the method, ask:

> How would you work out 59 × 18? And 59 × 48?

> How could you check the answer?
> [e.g. by reversing the factors and doubling 41]

Work this out as a check. Point out that an approximation of 60 × 40 = 2400 is also a good indication that the answer is correct.

Select individual work from **N4.5 Exercise 2** in the class book (p. 289).

Review Discuss the Egyptian doubling-and-addition multiplication method with the class.

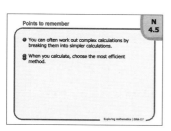

> Did you find this method easy? Long-winded? Efficient?

> Do you think you could teach it to someone else?

> Would it still work with much larger numbers?

Invite one or two pupils up to the board to show their workings for one of the problems.

Finish by reminding pupils of the points on **slide 2.1**.

Homework Ask pupils to do **N4.5 Task 2** in the home book (p. 115).

3 Missing digits and operations

Learning points

- Decide which information, given or needed, may be useful in solving the problem.

- Look for patterns and relationships in the information that you are given or find out.

- Use your knowledge of number facts and place value to help to solve missing-digit or missing-operation problems.

Starter

Say that this lesson is about using relationships between numbers to solve puzzles and problems.

Write on the board: $16 \times 28 = 448$. Say that you bought 16 bottles of lemonade at 28p each for a party. Confirm with the **Calculator tool** that the cost was £4.48. Now ask questions for pupils to answer on whiteboards. After each question, clarify how the answer was worked out.

> **What is the cost of 17 bottles of lemonade? Of 32 bottles? Of 8 bottles?**
>
> **What is the cost of the 16 bottles of lemonade at 56p each? At 29p each? At 30p each?**
>
> **How would you work out the cost of 26 bottles of lemonade at 28p each? Of 16 bottles at 38p each?**
>
> **28 packets of crisps for the party cost £4.48. What does one packet of crisps cost?**

Ask pupils to do questions 1–3 of **N4.5 Exercise 3** in the class book (p. 290).

Main activity

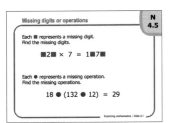

Show the first problem on **slide 3.1**.

> Each box represents a missing digit.
> Find the missing digits.
>
> $\square 2\square \times 7 = 1\square 7\square$

Ask the class to work in pairs to discuss how to approach the problem. Take feedback.

> **What can you tell me about this problem that would get us started?**
> [the hundreds digit in the first number must be 1 or 2]
>
> **Why?**
> [if it were 3 or more, the product would be at least $300 \times 7 = 2100$, which is too big]
>
> **Can we eliminate either 1 or 2 as the hundreds digit of the first number?**
> [it can't be 1, because the first number would then be less than 130, and $130 \times 7 = 910$, which is too small]

Write a digit 2 into the hundreds place of the first number. Ask the pairs to use their calculators to find the solution [225 × 7 = 1575]. Explain that working systematically through the possibilities for the third digit of the first number is a better way to proceed than a random approach.

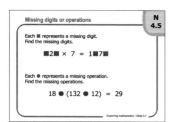

Show the second problem on **slide 3.1**.

> Each circle represents a missing operation.
> Find the missing operations.
>
> 18 ○ (132 ○ 12) = 29

Discuss the difference between missing-operation and missing-digit problems. Remind pupils about the order of operations. Ask the pairs to find a solution. Take feedback, asking pairs to explain their strategies. The solution is 18 + (132 ÷ 12) = 29.

Select individual work from questions 4–7 of **N4.5 Exercise 3** in the class book (p. 291).

Review Take feedback. Select some of the problems and discuss methods and solutions.

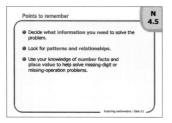

Sum up the lesson with the points on **slide 3.2**.

Round off the unit by referring again to the objectives. Suggest that pupils find time to try the self-assessment problems in **N4.5 How well are you doing?** in the class book (p. 293).

Homework Ask pupils to do **N4.5 Task 3** in the home book (p. 116).

Early history of numbers and counting

Stone Age

Slide 1

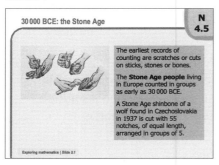

The earliest records of counting are from scratches or cuts on sticks, stones or bones. For example, the **Stone Age people** living in Europe had devised a system of tallying by counting in groups as early as 30 000 BCE. A shinbone of a young wolf was found in Czechoslovakia in 1937. It is 18 cm long and is engraved with 55 deeply cut notches, of about equal length, arranged in groups of 5.

Counting in groups of two

Slide 2

We probably count in tens because we have ten fingers. Nowadays most of the world counts in groups of 10, 100, 1000 and so on. But some tribes count in much smaller groups. For example, a tribe of **Aboriginal hunters** in Australia still counts in groups of two. Their word for 'one' is *enea*, and for 'two' is *petcheval*. They don't have a word for 'three', but say *petcheval-enea*, or 'two-one'. For four they say *petcheval-petcheval*.

The Incas of Peru

Slide 3

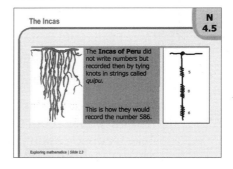

The **Incas of Peru** were from many different ethnic groups and spoke about 20 different languages. They had no written records but they developed a method of recording numbers that involved tying knots in strings called *quipu*.

A number was represented by knots in the string, based on a place-value system and groups of 10. If the number 586 was to be recorded on the string then six touching knots were placed near the free end of the string, a space was left, then eight touching knots for the 10s, another space, and finally 5 touching knots for the 100s.

The ancient Egyptians

Slide 4

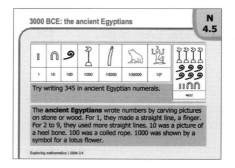

About 5000 years ago, the **ancient Egyptians** used to write by carving pictures on stone or wood. To write 1, they made a straight line, as we do, a simple picture of a finger. To write numerals from 'two' to 'nine', they used more straight lines. 'Ten' was a picture of a heel bone. 'One hundred' was a coiled rope. 'One thousand' was shown by a symbol for a lotus flower.

Slide 5

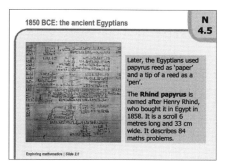

Later, the Egyptians used flattened sheets of dried papyrus reed as 'paper' and the tip of a reed as a 'pen'. The 'paper' was fragile but two papyrus documents dealing with mathematics have survived. One of them, the **Rhind papyrus**, is in London in the British Museum. It is named after the Scottish Egyptologist, Henry Rhind, who bought it in Egypt in 1858. The papyrus is a scroll about 6 metres long and 33 cm wide, written around 1650 BCE by the scribe Ahmes, who was copying a document 200 years older. It contains 87 problems, some involving numbers and some involving shapes.

The Babylonians

Slide 6

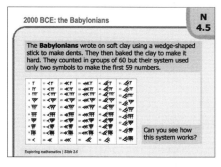

Around 4000 years ago, the **Babylonians** in the Middle East counted in groups of 60. We still use a sixty-in-a-group system when we measure time, since there are 60 seconds in a minute and 60 minutes in an hour. The Babylonians wrote on soft clay using a wedge-shaped stick to make dents. They then baked the clay to make it hard. The Babylonians had no symbol for zero. To translate into our notation, they could not distinguish between 307 and 37, so people had to work out from the context what was intended. The Babylonians managed for over 1000 years without a zero. It was not until 400 BCE that they introduced two wedge symbols to represent zero.

We still use context to interpret numbers today. If we go on a bus and are told that the fare is 'two fifty', we know it means £2.50. If we ask what time the bus leaves and are told at 'two fifty', we know it means at ten minutes to three. If we ask a travel agent the price of a flight from London to Rome and are told 'two fifty' we know it means £250.

The Chinese

Slide 7

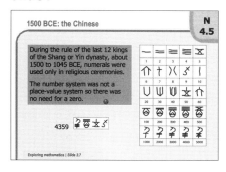

In 1899 a major discovery was made at a Chinese village in the province of Henan. Thousands of bones and tortoise shells were discovered inscribed with ancient Chinese characters. The last 12 kings of the Shang (or Yin) dynasty ruled here from about 1500 to 1045 BCE. The bones and shells had been used as part of religious ceremonies. The inscriptions had a lot of numerical information about numbers of men lost in battle, prisoners taken, animals killed on hunts, and so on. The **Chinese number system** was not a place-value system so there was no need for a zero.

Slide 8

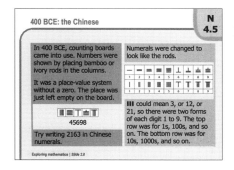

A **second form of Chinese numerals** was used from about 400 BCE when counting boards came into use. The board had rows and columns. Numbers were represented by little rods made from bamboo or ivory. A number was formed in a row with the units placed in the far right column, the tens in the next column to the left, the hundreds in the next column to the left, and so on. It was a place-value system but there was still no need for a zero. The place was just left empty on the board. Numerals were written using a stroke to represent the little rod, and were generally written from top to bottom.

Slide 9

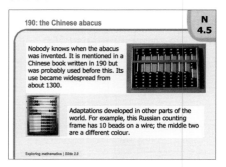

Nobody knows for certain when the **Chinese abacus** was invented. It is mentioned in *Supplementary Notes on the Art of Figures* written by Xu Yue in 190 but it was probably in use earlier than this.

Slide 10

Different forms of the abacus or counting frame started to be used in other parts of the Far East and Asia and are still in use today. The Russian abacus has 10 beads on each wire. The middle two beads are a different colour. The Japanese soroban is a bit like the Chinese abacus but it has one bead in the top row and four beads in the bottom row.

The ancient Greeks, Romans and Jews

Slide 11

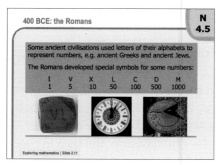

The **ancient Greeks** began their contributions to mathematics around the time that zero was

coming into use in Babylonian numerals. However, the Greeks didn't adopt a place-value number system. They used letters of their alphabet to stand for numbers.

The **ancient Jews** used the letters of the Hebrew alphabet in a similar way.

About the same time, the **ancient Romans** developed special symbols for numbers:

I	V	X	L	C	D	M
1	5	10	50	100	500	1000

If they put a smaller number to the right of a larger one, it meant that they should be added. So VIII means five plus three, or eight. If they put a smaller number to the left of a larger one, it meant that it should be subtracted. So XL meant fifty minus ten, or forty.

Slide 12

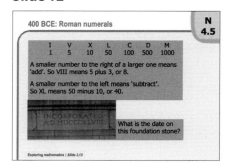

Roman numerals are still seen today on clocks and watches, sundials, pages of books, chapter headings, foundation stones, old gravestones, and so on.

Acknowledgement

The information in this commentary is based on the information in www-gap.dcs.st-and.ac.uk/~history/HistTopics/

N4.5 Mental test

Read each question aloud twice.

Allow a suitable pause for pupils to write answers.

1 Write in figures the number that is one less than one million. *2006 KS3*

2 What is the next prime number after seven? *2006 KS3*

3 When a number is divided by seven, the answer is three remainder four. What is the number? *2007 KS3*

4 What number is six less than minus two? *2006 KS3*

5 I am thinking of a two-digit number that is a multiple of eight. The digits add up to six. What number am I thinking of? *2003 KS3*

6 Eighteen multiplied by twenty-two is three hundred and ninety-six. What is three thousand nine hundred and sixty divided by eighteen? *2007 KS3*

7 What is six point two multiplied by one thousand? *2005 KS3*

8 The first even number is two. What is the hundredth even number? *2003 KS3*

9 I am thinking of two numbers that add to ten. The two numbers multiply together to make twenty-one. What are my two numbers? *2005 KS3*

10 A yogurt costs forty-five pence. How many yogurts can be bought for five pounds? *2003 KS3*

11 What is eighteen multiplied by nine? *2005 KS3*

12 What is the remainder when you divide three hundred by twenty-nine? *2004 KS3*

Key:

KS3 Key Stage 3 test
All questions are at level 5

Answers

1	999 999	**2**	11
3	25	**4**	−8
5	24	**6**	220
7	6200	**8**	200
9	3 and 7	**10**	11 yogurts
11	162	**12**	10

N4.5 Check up and resource sheets

Check up   N4.5

Write your answers in your book.

Solving problems (no calculator)

1   Mark's garden has 84 rows of cabbages. There are 57 cabbages in each row. Which is the best way to estimate how many cabbages there are altogether?

    A $100 \times 50 = 5000$ B $90 \times 60 = 5400$

    C $80 \times 60 = 4800$ D $80 \times 50 = 4000$

2   A teacher has written on the board $34 \times 56 = 1904$.
    What is 35×56?

3   Work out the number that is halfway between 27×38 and 33×38.
    Show your working.

4   *2006 level 5*

    a I am thinking of a number. My number is a multiple of 4.
       Which of these three statements is the correct one?

       My number must be even.
       My number must be odd.
       My number could be odd or even.

       Explain how you know.

    b I am thinking of a different number. My number is a factor of 20.
       Which of these three statements is the correct one?

       My number must be even.
       My number must be odd.
       My number could be odd or even.

       Explain how you know.

5   *2006 level 5*

    k stands for a whole number.
    $k + 7$ is greater than 100.
    $k - 7$ is less than 90.
    Write all the numbers that k could be.

Solving problems (calculator allowed)

6   *2004 level 5*

    Work out the number that goes in each box.

    a $\square \div 21.7 = 37.5$

    b $100 - (22.75 + 19.08) = \square$

Check up [continued]

7   Here are some digit cards.

    | 2 | | 4 | | 6 | | 8 |

    a Write all the three-digit numbers less than 500 that you can make using the cards.

    b Arrange the four cards to make a product like this.

       $\square\,\square \times \square\,\square$

       What is the largest product you can make?

Resource sheet 1.1   N4.5

You need a $1 - 6$ die to play this game.
Play several times to see if you can improve your strategy.

Rules
_____

▶ The aim of the game is to make the largest product.

▶ Take turns.

▶ Roll a die. Decide where to place the number in your calculation.

▶ After each player completes their calculation, the player with the largest product wins.

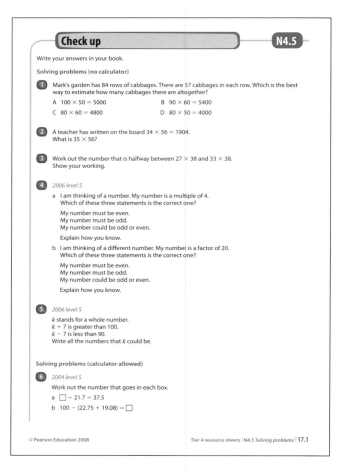

Game	Player A	Player B
1	$\square\square\square \times \square\square$	$\square\square\square \times \square\square$
2	$\square\square\square \times \square\square$	$\square\square\square \times \square\square$
3	$\square\square\square \times \square\square$	$\square\square\square \times \square\square$
4	$\square\square\square \times \square\square$	$\square\square\square \times \square\square$

Class book

Exercise 1

1 a

b

c

d

2 This is a game.

3 For example, 572, 693 and 814

Exercise 2

1 a i 2352   ii 2025   iii 5184
  b 1702
  c Pupil's preference and explanation

2 a 773
  b 723
  c Pupil's preference and explanation

3 a 177
  b 285
  c Pupil's preference and explanation

4 Eight different numbers:
  333, 338, 383, 388, 833, 838, 883, 888.

Exercise 3

1 a 3420
  b 34 200
  c 34 200
  d 34.2
  e 3.42
  f 323

2 a 2016
  b 4032
  c 504
  d 252
  e 1036
  f 1044

3 a 143
  b 91
  c 77
  d $0.7 \times 1.1 \times 1.3 = 1.001$, which is > 1
  e $456 \times 7 \times 11 \times 13$
    $= 456 \times (1000 + 1)$
    $= 456\,000 + 456$
    $= 456\,456$

4 a **2**23 + **9**3 = 316
  b **7**73 − **5**4 = 719
  c **1**9 × 1**2** = 228
  d (3**4**)^2 = 11**5**6
  e 93 × 8**6** = 7**99**8
  f **1**32 × **4**5 = 5940

5 a (78 + 45) × 37 = 4551
  b (1430 ÷ 65) + 78 = 100
  c 480 ÷ (86 − 71) = 32
  d 54 + (12 × 17) = 258
  e 18 × (95 − 56) = 702
  f 208 − (156 ÷ 12) = 195

6 a (45 × 18) − 93 = 717
  b (72 ÷ 18) × 93 = 372
  c 93 − (18 + 45) = 30
  d 67 + (72 − 18) = 121

Extension problem

7 a
NO	74
NO	74
TOO	944
LATE	1092

	b	EAT	819
		THAT	9219
		APPLE	10038
	c	UN	81
		UN	81
		NEUF	1987
		ONZE	2149

How well are you doing?

1 2, 4, 6, 8

2 a $120 \times 16 = 1920$
   b $1200 \times 16 = 19\,200$
   c $120 \times 160 = 19\,200$
   d $12 \times 1.6 = 19.2$
   e $1.2 \times 1.6 = 1.92$
   f $12 \times 17 = 204$

3 6

4 a $1161 = \mathbf{543} + \mathbf{621}$
      $750 = \mathbf{536} + \mathbf{214}$
   b $115 = \mathbf{356} - \mathbf{241}$

5 203

6 a 28×9
      $= (20 \times 9) + (8 \times 9)$
      $= 180 + 72 = 252$
   b $27 \times 28 = 3 \times (9 \times 28)$
      $= 3 \times 252 = 756$

7 $54 \times 3 = 162$

Home book

TASK 1

There are lots of ways to make 100 using the digits 1 to 9, e.g.
$123 - 45 - 67 + 89 = 100$
$123 + 45 - 67 + 8 - 9 = 100$
$12 + 3 - 4 + 5 + 67 + 8 + 9 = 100$

The digits don't necessarily have to be in order, e.g.
$159 + 62 - 34 - 87 = 100$
$257 - 136 - 9 - 8 - 4 = 100$

TASK 2

1 a XXVII
   b CLVI
   c LXXXIX
   d MMIX

2 a 48
   b 217
   c 420
   d 3010

3 a XXIII
   b XI
   c CCXXXIII
   d CCXXIV

TASK 3

1 a $3\mathbf{7} \times \mathbf{4}9 = 1813$
   b $323 \times \mathbf{47} = 15\,18\mathbf{1}$

2 a $(2184 \div 91) - 20 = 4$
   b $(148 + 197) \div 15 = 23$

3 a $96 - (36 + 54) = 6$
   b $(96 \div 12) \times 54 = 432$
   c $(75 \times 12) - 96 = 804$
   d $54 + (75 - 36) = 93$

CD-ROM

Check up
WRITTEN QUESTIONS (NO CALCULATOR)

1 c $80 \times 60 = 4800$

2 1960

3 $30 \times 38 = 1140$

4 a My number must be even.
      A multiple of 4 is divisible by 4, so must also be divisible by 2. It is therefore even.
   b My number could be odd or even.
      20 has both odd and even factors, e.g. the odd number 5 is a factor of 20; the even number 4 is a factor of 20.

5 94, 95, 96

WRITTEN QUESTIONS (CALCULATOR ALLOWED)

6 a 813.75
   b 58.17

7 a 246, 264, 248, 284, 268, 286
      426, 462, 428, 482, 468, 486
   b $82 \times 64 = 5248$

Revision unit 1

Pupils should already be able to apply and use many of the skills shown on the right. This unit offers is an opportunity to consolidate and refine these skills.

Objectives based on NC levels 5 and 6 (mainly level 5)

In this unit, pupils consolidate their ability to:
- identify the mathematical features of a context or problem
- relate the current problem or structure to previous situations
- select appropriate procedures and tools
- calculate accurately, using mental methods or a calculator as appropriate
- manipulate numbers, algebraic expressions and equations, and apply routine algorithms
- make accurate mathematical diagrams and graphs
- estimate, approximate and check working, giving accurate solutions appropriate to the context or problem
- evaluate the efficiency of alternative strategies and approaches
- record methods, solutions and conclusions

and to:

Number
- multiply and divide integers and decimals by 0.1 or 0.01, and derive products such as 6×0.7, 8×0.03

Algebra
- generate terms of a linear sequence using term-to-term and position-to-term rules
- simplify or transform linear expressions by collecting like terms
- derive and substitute integer values into simple formulae and expressions

Geometry
- choose and use units of measurement to measure, continue, calculate and solve problems in a range of contexts
- calculate areas of compound shapes and volumes and surface areas of cuboids and shapes made from cuboids

Statistics
- know that if the probability of an event occurring is p, then the probability of it not occurring is $1 - p$
- use diagrams and tables to record all possible mutually exclusive outcomes for single events and for two successive events
- compare estimated experimental probabilities with theoretical probabilities.

Lessons
1 **Place value**
2 **Solving calculation problems**
3 **Expressions and sequences**
4 **Perimeter, area and volume**
5 **Probability**

About this unit

This unit consists of five revision or support lessons for Tier 4. The lessons are not part of a sequence and have no particular order. They could be taught to the whole class, or to part of the class as extra support, at any point that is appropriate.

The lessons, class book and home book contain National Curriculum test questions at levels 4, 5 and 6 to help pupils to prepare for tests.

The number lessons are adapted from Secondary Strategy materials: *Year 8 and Year 9 Intervention lessons and resources* (see useful websites).

Common errors and misconceptions

Look out for pupils who:

- apply rules of 'to multiply by 10, add a zero' and 'to divide by 10, remove a zero', which don't work with decimals;
- confuse n^2 and $2n$;
- confuse term-to-term rules and position-to-term rules;
- forget to change measurements to the same units when calculating with them;
- confuse surface area and volume, or use cubic units for surface area;
- believe that if an experiment is repeated then the outcomes will be the same;
- fail to appreciate that experimental probability is an estimate of probability that increases in reliability as the number of trials on which it is based increases.

Key terms and notation

problem, solution, method, pattern, relationship, represent, solve, explain, justify

decimal, whole number, multiple, digit, place value, decimal place, units, partition

sequence, difference, ascending, descending, increase, decrease, consecutive, term, term-to-term, position-to-term, rule, nth term, expression, simplify, substitute

length, distance, perimeter, area, surface area, volume, compound shape

likelihood, probability, fair, unfair, biased, unbiased, random, trial, outcome, event

Practical resources

scientific calculators for pupils
a cuboid

individual whiteboards

Exploring maths

Tier 4 teacher's book
R4.1 Mental test, p. 350
Answers for Unit R4.1, pp. 353–355

Tier 4 CD-ROM
PowerPoint files
    R4.1 Slides for lessons 1 to 5
Tools and prepared toolsheets
    R4.1 Toolsheet for lesson 5
    Calculator tool
Tier 4 programs
    Decimal place value
    Simplifying expressions quiz 1
    Area and perimeter

Tier 4 class book
R4.1, pp. 295–313
Tier 4 home book
R4.1, pp. 117–127

Useful websites

Multiplying by 10, 100, …
lgfl.skoool.co.uk/keystage3.aspx?id=65#21_23

Divide and multiply by 10, 100 and 1000, Using decimals
www.bbc.co.uk/skillswise/numbers/

Number patterns 1, Number patterns 2
www.bbc.co.uk/schools/ks3bitesize/maths/algebra/

Expressions
lgfl.skoool.co.uk/keystage3.aspx?id=65#24_30

Animal weigh in
www.bbc.co.uk/education/mathsfile/gameswheel.html

1 Place value

Learning points

- To multiply/divide a number by 10, 100 or 1000, move the digits one, two or three places to the left/right.
- Multiplying by 0.1 is equivalent to multiplying by $\frac{1}{10}$ or dividing by 10.
- Multiplying by 0.01 is equivalent to multiplying by $\frac{1}{100}$ or dividing by 100.
- Dividing by 0.1 is equivalent to dividing by $\frac{1}{10}$ or multiplying by 10.
- Dividing by 0.01 is equivalent to dividing by $\frac{1}{100}$ or multiplying by 100.

Starter

Say that this unit revises previous topics and is an opportunity to practise test questions. This first lesson is about place value.

Remind pupils that when they take mental tests they should:

- listen carefully to the questions — each question will be read twice;
- use jottings if it would be helpful;
- if there is an answer sheet, use the correct box to record each answer.

Give the **R4.1 Mental test** (p. 350). Ask pupils to write answers in their exercise books. Read out the answers (below the questions) for pupils to mark the test. Get pupils to compare methods and say which is most efficient. Point out two-step questions and encourage pupils to jot down the intermediate answer.

Main activity

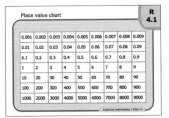

SIM

Show the place value chart on **slide 1.1**. Choose a number such as 7 and discuss what happens when it is multiplied or divided by 10, 100 or 1000. Repeat with other numbers such as 0.3 or 0.06.

Launch **Decimal place value**. Press 'Play' to start the animation, pausing when appropriate, and using it to remind the class of decimal place value.

Ask pupils to write the number 5.7, multiply it by 100 and record the answer. Now ask them to divide 5.7 by 100 and to record the answer. Choose pupils to explain how they arrived at their answers.

What has happened to the digits?

Stress that the decimal point has not moved; the digits have shifted two places to the left for multiplication and to the right for division.

Repeat with other numbers, including decimals, asking pupils to multiply or divide them by 10, 100 or 1000.

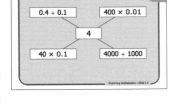

Show **slide 1.2**. Ask pupils to explain the results and, using only the digits 4, 0 and 1, to consider other solutions. Take feedback, asking pupils to talk through their reasoning. Make sure that $4 = 0.04 \div 0.01$ is considered.

Discuss what happens when a number is multiplied/divided by a number less than 1.

Does division always make a number smaller?
Does multiplication always make a number larger?

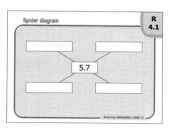

Repeat with **slide 1.3**, which shows 5.7 in the centre of the diagram. Record pupils' responses. Establish that there are several different ways to record the answers, e.g.

0.057×100	$= 5.7$		$0.057 \div 0.01$	$= 5.7$
$0.057 \times 10 \times 10$	$= 5.7$		$0.057 \div 0.1 \div 0.1$	$= 5.7$
0.057×10^2	$= 5.7$		$0.057 \div \frac{1}{100}$	$= 5.7$

Ask pupils to work in groups to develop their own spider diagram showing equivalent calculations for other numbers (e.g. 3.2, 67.3, 0.43). Differentiate by using different starting numbers for different ability groups.

Move pupils on through these stages:

- multiplication/division by 10, 100 and 1000;
- multiplication/division by larger positive integer powers of 10;
- multiplication/division by 0.1 and 0.01.

Ask pupils to do **R4.1 Exercise 1** in the class book (p. 296).

Review   Use the place value target board on **slide 1.4**.

If I divide a number by 0.1 and then again by 0.1 the answer is 0.03. What number did I start with? How do you know?

Why do $3.3 \times 10 \times 10$ and $3.3 \div 0.01$ give the same answer?

Ask similar questions to check pupils' understanding.

What do 10^2 and 10^3 mean?

How do you write 10 000 as a power of 10?
How do you write 10 as a power of 10?

Make sure that pupils recognise that increasing powers of 10 underpin the place value system. Remind them of the meaning of 10^0 and 10^1.

Ask pupils to remember the points on **slides 1.5** and **1.6**.

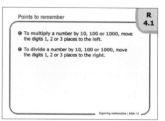

Homework   Ask pupils to do **R4.1 Task 1** in the home book (p. 117).

2 Solving calculation problems

Learning points

When you solve problems:

- ◙ read the question carefully;
- ◙ write down the calculation that you need to do and show your working;
- ◙ check that the answer is reasonable by fitting it to the question.

Starter

Tell pupils that this lesson is about using a calculator to solve number problems.

Write on the board: $950.4 \div \square = 49.5$.

Give pairs 30 seconds then establish a sensible estimate.

Tell the pairs that they can now use a calculator to find the missing number, then invite someone to use the **Calculator tool** to demonstrate how they calculated the answer.

Ask if anyone tackled it in a different way. If so, ask them to demonstrate their method.

Ask pupils how they would check the answer. Establish how this can be done first by checking against the estimate and second by using inverse operation.

Repeat with $\square \times 36.4 = 866.32$.

Main activity

Ask pupils to calculate $136 \div 32$ on their calculators. Ask them to write the answer on whiteboards and hold it up.

Show **slide 2.1**.

> Jim took part in a charity cycle ride.
> He cycled 136 kilometres at 32 kilometres per hour.
> How long did he take to complete the ride?

Confirm that the calculation required is $136 \div 32$. Ask pairs to decide how to interpret the answer in the display. Take feedback.

Set some other questions, involving money and measures, that require interpretation of calculator answers.

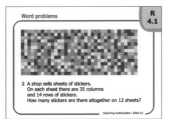

Show **slide 2.2**. Ask pupils how they would tackle it:

> A shop sells sheets of stickers.
> On each sheet there are 35 columns and 14 rows of labels.
> How many stickers are there altogether on 12 sheets?

Model how to approach the problem, e.g.

- ◙ decide what operations are needed;
- ◙ break the problem into parts;
- ◙ estimate the answer, then do and check the calculation;
- ◙ write the answer as a sentence, checking that it makes sense.

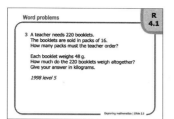

Solve the problem with the class. Ask pupils to try to use a similar approach for a third problem. Show **slide 2.3**.

> A teacher needs 220 booklets.
> The booklets are sold in packs of 16.
> How many packs must the teacher order?

Ask:

> How did you tackle this problem?
> How did you decide what calculation to do?
>
> What calculation did you do?
>
> How did you do the calculation – mentally, using a written method or using a calculator? Why did you decide to do the calculation that way?
>
> How did you interpret the answer in your calculator display?

Ask pupils to work in pairs on the word problems in **R4.1 Exercise 2** in the class book (p. 297). Ask them to read through each problem, estimate the answer and think about how they might solve it, without doing the actual calculation. After a few minutes, check progress and highlight the most effective methods. Now ask pupils to complete the exercise, this time doing the calculations.

Review
Take feedback on the paired work. Discuss answers, using the **Calculator tool** to illustrate methods where appropriate.

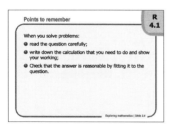

Round off by setting two number puzzles for pupils to solve with their calculators. Ask them first to estimate each missing number, then to use a calculator to work it out.

$$\square \times 24.3 = 400.95 \qquad \text{[Answer: 16.5]}$$
$$24 \times 16.5 \div \square = 79.2 \qquad \text{[Answer: 5]}$$

Summarise the lesson by stressing the points on **slide 2.4**.

Homework
Ask pupils to do **R4.1 Task 2** in the home book (p. 119).

3 Expressions and sequences

Learning points

- A term is one or more numbers or letters combined by multiplication or division.

- Like terms have the same combination of letters. For example, $2a$ and $5a$ and a are all like terms.

- An expression is one or more terms combined by addition or subtraction.

- You can simplify an expression by collecting like terms.

- A sequence is a set of numbers that obey a rule.

Starter

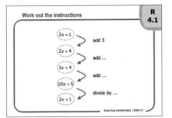

Say that this lesson is about expressions and sequences.

Show **slide 3.1** (Year 8 Optional Test level 5). Say that this is a number chain and that there are instructions that tell you how to move down the chain. Ask pupils to show what to do to move along each step of the chain.

Main activity

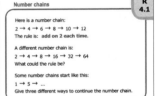

Show **slide 3.2** (1997 level 5). Explain that these are number chains or sequences. Each chain follows a pattern. The first chain goes up in twos.

> **Describe the first chain in a different way.** [e.g. even numbers]

> **Can you find a rule for the second chain?** ['multiply by 2' or 'double']

Look at the beginning of the third chain. Ask pupils to think of ways of continuing the pattern and get them to tell you the rule.

Show **slide 3.3** (1998 level 5). Explain to pupils that they need to read questions very carefully. Tell them this story as they look at the pictures on the slide and respond on their whiteboards.

> Elin has a bag of marbles.
> You cannot see how many marbles are inside the bag.
> Call the number of marbles which Elin starts with in her bag n.
> Elin puts 5 more marbles into her bag.
> Write an expression to show the total number of marbles in Elin's bag now.

> Ravi has another bag of marbles.
> Call the number of marbles which Ravi starts with in his bag t.
> Ravi takes 2 marbles out of his bag.
> Write an expression to show the total number of marbles in Ravi's bag now.

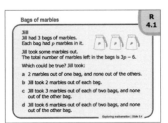

Move on to **slide 3.4**.

> Jill has 3 bags of marbles. Each bag has p marbles inside.
> Jill takes some marbles out.
> Now the total number of marbles in Jill's 3 bags is $3p - 6$.

Ask pupils to imagine what Jill is doing. Reveal the statements on slide 3.4, asking pupils to discuss in pairs which of the statements is true.

Write on the board the expression $7a + 2b + 3a + 5b$. Explain to the class that this is an example of the type of expression that they may be asked to simplify in a mental test. (This example is a level 5 question from 2002.)

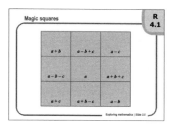

Show **slide 3.5** (2004 level 5). Ask pupils to work in pairs. Ask them to find and simplify the sum of each column, then the sum of each row, and then the sum of each of the two main diagonals, to verify that this is a magic square.

They should then choose and substitute their own values for a, b and c and create their own magic squares, checking that the sum of each row, column and diagonal is the same.

Select individual work from **R4.1 Exercise 3** in the class book (p. 300).

Review

Go through some of the questions from the individual work. Compare methods and discuss how solutions should be set out.

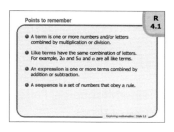

Launch **Simplifying expressions quiz 1**. Use the 'Next' and 'Back' buttons to move through the questions at a pace appropriate for the class. Ask pupils to answer on their whiteboards. For each answer, ask an individual pupil to explain how they worked it out.

Sum up by stressing the points on **slide 3.6**.

Homework

Ask pupils to do **R4.1 Task 3** in the home book (p. 120).

4 Perimeter, area and volume

Learning points

- Learn the formulae for the area of a rectangle, the area of a triangle, the area of a parallelogram and the volume of a cuboid.

- To find the area of a compound shape, divide it up with straight lines into rectangles and triangles.

- Triangles on the same base and with the same perpendicular height are equal in area.

- Parallelograms on the same base and with the same perpendicular height are equal in area.

Starter

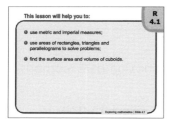

Discuss the objectives for this lesson using **slide 4.1**.

Show **slide 4.2** to remind the class how to convert one measure to a related measure.

Ask pupils to answer questions on their whiteboards.

> What is 390 mm in centimetres? What is 5000 m in centimetres? What is 5000 m in kilometres?
>
> What is 5.6 kg in grams?
>
> What is 6700 ml in litres?

Ask pupils to work in pairs to write a similar question on their whiteboards. Pairs then swap whiteboards and write the answer. Repeat a couple of times.

Main activity

SIM

Remind the class that area and surface area use squared units, e.g. cm², mm².

Launch **Area and perimeter**.

With the grid on, hide the perimeter and area, and select and resize a rectangle, e.g. 10 cm by 7 cm. Ask pupils for the area and perimeter.

Stress that area of a rectangle is:

> length × width or base × height

Now select a triangle. Ask:

> What is the perimeter of this triangle?
>
> What is the area of this triangle?

Ask a pupil to explain how they found the answers. Reveal these on the screen.

With the area result still showing, move vertex B along a horizontal line so that the height remains the same. Ask the class to observe what happens to the area.

Discuss this before reminding them that the area of a triangle is:

$\frac{1}{2} \times$ base $\times$ perpendicular height

Now select a parallelogram. Ask the class to calculate the area. Reveal the answer and discuss methods.

By moving A and B to maintain a parallelogram of the same height, show that the area is constant with the same perpendicular height.

Remind pupils that the area of a parallelogram is:

base $\times$ perpendicular height

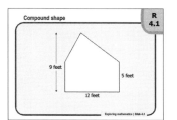

Show **slide 4.3**. Ask pupils to work out the area of the compound shape. Discuss the ways in which the shape could be divided up with straight lines.

Now hold up a cuboid.

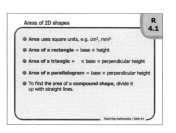

What is meant by the surface area of this cuboid?
How do you calculate it?
What units are used for surface area?

What is meant by the volume of this cuboid? How do you calculate it?
What units are used for volume?

Establish that the volume of a cuboid can be calculated as length $\times$ width $\times$ height, or as area of base $\times$ height. Show that either way the result will be the same.

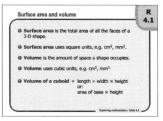

Summarise with the reminders on **slides 4.4** and **4.5**.

> Select individual work from **R4.1 Exercises 4A** (on perimeter and area) and **R4.1 Exercise 4B** (on surface area and volume) in the class book (pp. 304–308).

Review

Go through some of the questions from the exercises on the board, stressing how answers should be set out.

Remind pupils to include the units when using measures. In Key Stage 3 tests there is normally a question on each paper where a mark will be given just for the units.

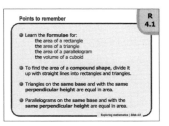

Sum up with the points on **slide 4.6**.

Homework

Ask pupils to do **R4.1 Task 4** in the home book (p. 122).

5 Probability

Learning points

- The theoretical probability of an event is:

$$\frac{\text{number of favourable outcomes}}{\text{total number of possible outcomes}}$$

- The experimental probability of an event is:

$$\frac{\text{number of favourable outcomes}}{\text{total number of possible outcomes}}$$

- Probabilities are written as a fraction, decimal or percentage.

- If p is the probability of an event happening, then the probability of the event **not** happening is $1 - p$.

- Use a two-way table to show all the possible outcomes when two events occur at the same time or one after the other.

Starter

Use **slide 5.1** to discuss the objectives for this lesson.

Use **Toolsheet 5.1** which shows two spinners:

> Spinner 1: 10 sectors, 4 red, 6 blue
> Spinner 2: 8 sectors, 3 red, 5 blue

> On which of the two spinners is the arrow most likely to land on red?

Ask pupils to answer on their whiteboards. Ask pupils with the answer 'Spinner 1' to give a reason for their choice. Then ask pupils with the answer 'Spinner 2' to give a reason.

> How can you work out the probability of the arrow landing on red?

Discuss both theoretical and experimental probability and how they can be worked out.

Work out the theoretical probability of red for the first spinner. Spin the arrow of the first spinner 20 times, recording the number of times it lands on red. Work out the experimental probability.

> Is the experimental probability close to the theoretical probability?

Repeat for the second spinner, then return to the original question:

> On which of the two spinners is the arrow most likely to land on red?

Main activity

Complete the problem on **slide 5.2** with the class.

Show **slide 5.3**. Ask pupils to discuss the four questions in pairs. Check and discuss answers. Repeat with the three questions on **slide 5.4**.

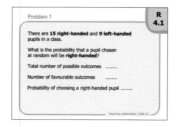

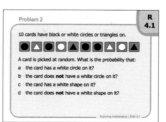

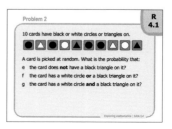

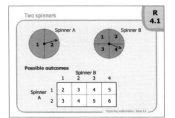

Display **slide 5.5** showing two fair spinners.

> Spinner A has two equal sectors numbered 1 and 2.
> Spinner B has four equal sectors numbered 1, 2, 3 and 4.

Explain that the arrows on the two spinners are to be spun at the same time and the numbers that the arrows land on are added.

Ask pupils to write a list of all the equally likely outcomes on their whiteboards. Encourage them to do this systematically.

Now reveal the two-way table on **slide 5.5**. Ask pupils for the values in various cells. Finally, display the completed two-way table on the slide.

> **How many equally likely outcomes are there?** [8]
>
> **What is the probability of a total of 2?** $[\frac{1}{8}]$
> **Of 3?** $[\frac{1}{4}]$ **Of 4?** $[\frac{1}{4}]$ **Of 5?** $[\frac{1}{4}]$ **Of 6?** $[\frac{1}{8}]$

> Select individual work from **R4.1 Exercise 5A** (calculating theoretical and experimental probabilities) and **R4.1 Exercise 5B** (two successive events) in the class book (pp. 309–313).

Review Go through some of the questions from the individual work.

Compare methods and discuss how solutions should be set out.

Sum up by stressing the points on **slides 5.6 and 5.7**.

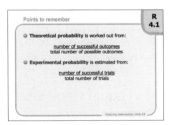
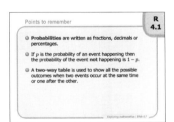

Homework Ask pupils to do **R4.1 Task 5** in the home book (p. 125).

Read each question aloud twice.

Allow from 5 to 15 seconds for pupils to write answers.

1 The population of the United Kingdom is about fifty-nine million.
Write this number in figures.   *2003 KS3*

2 What is six point two multiplied by one thousand?   *2005 KS3*

3 What is twenty per cent of sixty pounds?   *2005 KS3*

4 There are seven red and three blue balls in a bag.
I am going to take a ball out of the bag at random.
What is the probability that the ball will be blue?   *2004 KS3*

5 Multiply eight point seven by two.   *2004 KS3*

6 What is half of two thirds?   *2004 KS3*

7 What is the remainder when you divide three hundred by twenty-nine? *2004 KS3*

8 I am thinking of a two-digit number that is a multiple of eight.
The digits add up to six. What number am I thinking of?   *2003 KS3*

9 Two of the angles in a triangle are sixty degrees and seventy degrees.
What is the size of the third angle?   *2005 KS3*

10 I am thinking of a number. I call it n. I add five to my number.
Write an expression to show the result.   *2003 KS3*

11 I start at seven and count down in equal steps; seven, four, one.
Write down the next two numbers.   *2005 KS3*

12 There are fourteen girls and thirteen boys in a class.
What is the probability that a pupil chosen at random will be a girl? *2004 KS3*

Key:
KS3 Key Stage 3 test

All questions are at level 5.

Answers

1	59 000 000	2	6200
3	£12	4	0.3 or $\frac{3}{10}$
5	17.4	6	$\frac{1}{3}$
7	10	8	24
9	50°	10	$n + 5$
11	$-2, -5$	12	$\frac{14}{27}$

R4.1 Answers

Class book

Exercise 1

1 a 90.7   b 1000
   c 10   d 8.006
   e 30   f 4 600 000
   g 62.03   h 100
   i 1000   j 0.058

2 2.64, 2.75, 2.79, 2.81

3 a 7.5, 7.53, 7.56, 7.6, 7.65
   b 8.02, 8.09, 8.2, 8.29, 8.9, 8.92
   c 0.241, 0.412, 0.421, 1.124, 1.214
   d 6.006, 6.067, 6.07, 6.076, 6.077

4 100×10000 and $10 \times 100\,000$

5 99 990

Exercise 2

1 75p

2 a £288   b 500 people

3 a £33.25   b 14 trees

4 Adult needs $10 \times 4 \times 5 = 200$ ml
   Child needs $5 \times 4 \times 5 = 100$ ml
   There will not be enough cough mixture

5 a 4 m   b £1.40

6 £432.90

7 8 glasses

8 The 6-pack is better value

Extension problem

9 France paid more money
   (France: £506 493.50; Australia: £370 370.37).

Exercise 3

1 a n plum trees
   b $2n$
   c $n + 7$
   d $n + n + 2n + n + 7 = 5n + 7$

2 a $n + 3$
   b $4n$
   c $7n + 3$

3

x	$x + 1$	$2x$	$2x - 1$	$2(x - 1)$
3	**4**	6	**5**	**4**
8	9	**16**	15	**14**
15	**16**	**30**	29	**28**

4 1st pair: $2c + b$ and $3c - 2b$
   2nd pair: a^2 and $a + c$

5 a 20
   b 60
   c Total number of tiles $= \mathbf{4} \times$ the shape
      number

6 a The number of yellow tiles
   b 1 red tile and 36 yellow tiles
   c Pattern number 20
   d $1 + 6N$

Exercise 4A

1 a 12 cm²   b 3 cm²   c 12 cm²

2 Yes

3 a 4 cm   b 5 cm

4 8 cm

5 $h = 8$ cm

6 a 2.5 cm
   b 10 cm
   c Possible solutions:
      $a = 4, b = 1, h = 4$
      $a = 3, b = 2, h = 4$
      Other solutions must fit $(a + b) \times h = 20$
      and $a > b$.

Exercise 4B

1 4 cm³, 16 cm²

2 54 cm²

3 a 60 cm³   b 6 cm

4 a Cuboid A   b 4

Exercise 5A

1 a $\frac{1}{5}$
   b $\frac{4}{5}$
   c 1

2 a $\frac{1}{4}$
   b $\frac{1}{2}$
   c 0
   d $\frac{2}{3}$

3 a $\frac{1}{4}$
   b 1
   c $\frac{12}{100}$ or 0.12 or 12%
   d e.g. 1, 2, 3, 4, 4, 6
      four even numbers (including two 4s) and
      two odd numbers

4 a $\frac{1}{35}$
   b $\frac{16}{35}$
   c $\frac{19}{35}$

Exercise 5B

1 a $\frac{5}{9}$
   b $\frac{1}{3}$
   c

×	2	3	4
2	4	6	8
3	6	9	12
4	8	12	16

   d 16
      4

2 a $\frac{1}{2}$
   b

First coin	Second coin
heads	heads
heads	tails
tails	heads
tails	tails

   c $\frac{1}{4}$
   d $\frac{1}{2}$

Home book

TASK 1

1 a 42 500   b 4 250 000
   c 425   d 42 500

2 a The last digit must be 0.
   b 7400

3 a D (730)
   b B (73 000)
   c F (0.73)
   d E (7.3)
   e C (7300)

TASK 2

1 a £179.40   b 5 children

2 The pens are cheaper in the village shop.

3 3 cm

4 a £729   b £14

TASK 3

1 a $7 + 5t$ b $3b + 17$
   c $4d + 3$ d $4m$

2 a 4 grey tiles
   b The number of grey tiles
   c 1 black tile and 60 grey tiles
   d Pattern number 10
   e Pattern number 20

TASK 4

1 a 3 kg   b 300 millilitres

2 a 4 by 4 square   b 5 by 5 square

3 1 by 6 or 2 by 3 or 3 by 2 or 6 by 1 rectangle

4 a 12 cubes
   b 10 cubes
   c 16 cubes
   d 30 cubes
   e 24 cubes

5 30 cm²

TASK 5

1 The outcomes of picking a pupil, a teacher or
   a member of the canteen staff are not equally
   likely as there are different numbers of them.

2 a $\frac{3}{5}$
   b $\frac{2}{5}$

   c Arrow pointing to 0.6

   d 1

   e Arrow pointing to 1

   f Paige likes any two of the colours.

3 a Plain; $\frac{1}{10}$

   b $\frac{1}{8}$

   c 3 bags of vinegar flavour crisps

4 a 24

       A1, A2, A3, A4, A5, A6

       B1, B2, B3, B4, B5, B6

       C1, C2, C3, C4, C5, C6

       D1, D2, D3, D4, D5, D6

   b $\frac{1}{6}$

Revision unit 2

Pupils should already be able to apply and use many of the skills shown on the right. This unit offers is an opportunity to consolidate and refine these skills.

Objectives based on NC levels 5 and 6 (mainly level 5)

In this unit, pupils consolidate their ability to:

- identify the mathematical features of a context or problem
- relate the current problem or structure to previous situations
- select appropriate procedures and tools
- calculate accurately, using mental methods or a calculator as appropriate
- manipulate numbers, algebraic expressions and equations, and apply routine algorithms
- make accurate mathematical diagrams and graphs
- estimate, approximate and check working, giving accurate solutions appropriate to the context
- evaluate the efficiency of alternative strategies and approaches
- record methods, solutions and conclusions

and to:

Number

- calculate fractions of quantities
- use the unitary method to solve problems involving ratio and direct proportion

Algebra

- construct and solve linear equations with integer coefficients (unknown on either or both sides, without and with brackets)
- plot graphs of linear functions (y given explicitly in terms of x)

Geometry

- identify alternate angles and corresponding angles
- transform 2D shapes by rotation, reflection and translation
- enlarge 2D shapes, given a centre of enlargement and a positive integer scale factor

Statistics

- plan, construct and use two-way tables for recording discrete data
- construct and interpret:
  - bar charts and frequency diagrams for grouped discrete data
  - pie charts for categorical data
  - simple scatter diagrams.

Lessons

1 **Percentages**
2 **Ratio and proportion**
3 **Equations and graphs**
4 **Angles and transformations**
5 **Representing and interpreting data**

About this unit

This unit consists of five revision or support lessons for Tier 4. The lessons are not part of a sequence and have no particular order. They could be taught to the whole class, or to part of the class as extra support, at any point that is appropriate.

The lessons, class book and home book contain National Curriculum test questions at levels 4, 5 and 6 to help pupils to prepare for tests.

The number lessons are adapted from Secondary Strategy materials: *Year 8 and Year 9 Intervention lessons and resources*.

Common errors and misconceptions

Look out for pupils who:

- have difficulty in using percentages greater than 100%;
- have difficulty in applying the unitary method for direct proportion;
- continue to use informal methods to solve equations;
- confuse alternate and corresponding angles;
- have difficulty in determining the scale for the frequency axis of a graph;
- don't take account of the total numbers represented when comparing pie charts.

Key terms and notation

problem, solution, method, relationship, represent, solve, explain, justify, prove

per cent (%), percentage, rate, discount, increase, decrease, direct proportion, ratio, unitary ratio, scale, scale factor, and the notation $a : b$

linear, equation, expression, variable, coefficient, brackets, coordinates, origin, axes, quadrant, gradient, intersect, intersection, straight-line graph

parallel, transversal, alternate angles, corresponding angles, exterior/interior angle, transform, rotate, reflect, translate, enlarge, object, image, centre of enlargement

graph, bar chart, frequency diagram, pie chart, sector, survey, two-way table

Practical resources

scientific calculators for pupils
individual whiteboards

poster paper
squared paper and triangular dotty paper

Exploring maths

Tier 4 teacher's book
R4.2 Mental test, p. 366
Answers for Unit R4.2, pp. 370–373

Tier 4 CD-ROM
PowerPoint files
   R4.2 Slides for lessons 1 to 5
Tools and prepared toolsheets
   Calculator tool
Tier 4 programs and tools
   FDP equivalents quiz
   Solving equations quiz
   Missing angles quiz

Tier 4 class book
R4.2, pp. 314–336

Tier 4 home book
R4.2, pp. 128–138

Tier 4 CD-ROM
R4.2 Pupil resource sheets
   3.1 One per pupil
   3.2 One per pupil

Useful websites

Percentage increase and decrease, Distances, Understanding averages
www.bbc.co.uk/skillswise/numbers/

Division in a given ratio, Map scales, Equations 1, Transformations 1 and 2, Angles, Parallels and polygons
www.bbc.co.uk/schools/ks3bitesize/maths/

Linear equations
lgfl.skoool.co.uk/keystage3.aspx?id=65#24_30

Calculating the mean
www.bbc.co.uk/schools/gcsebitesize/maths/activities/index.shtml

1 Percentages

Learning points

- Percentages such as 10%, 15%, 75% and so on can be calculated mentally or by using jottings.

- Other percentages can be found by using a written method or a calculator.

Starter

Say that this unit revises previous topics and is an opportunity to practise test questions. This first lesson is about percentages.

Remind pupils again that when they take mental tests they should:

- listen carefully to the questions — each question will be read twice;

- use jottings if it would be helpful;

- if there is an answer sheet, take care to use the correct box to record each answer.

Give the **R4.2 Mental test** (p. 368). Ask pupils to write answers in their exercise books. Read out the answers (below the questions) for pupils to mark the test. Get pupils to explain and compare approaches to each question. Discuss which methods are the most efficient. Draw attention to questions that need two steps and encourage pupils to jot down the intermediate step.

Main activity

Say that this lesson will focus on percentage calculations, including finding percentage increases and decreases.

Demonstrate that an increase of 10% results in a total of 110%. For example, 100% can be represented by 10 pencils, so 1 pencil represents 10% and the new amount, 11 pencils, is 110%.

> **How do you write 110% as a decimal? As a fraction?**

Demonstrate that a decrease of 10% leads to 90%. For example, if 10 pencils represent 100%, then 1 pencil represents 10%; the new amount of 9 pencils represents 90%.

> **How do you write 90% as a decimal? As a fraction?**

Repeat with another example, such as a 20% increase/decrease.

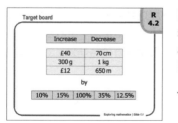

Focus first on calculations that can be done mentally. Use the target board on **slide 1.1** to ask pupils to calculate a percentage increase/decrease of one of the amounts. Encourage them, when appropriate, to jot down steps in their working. Each time, ask one or two pupils to explain how they arrived at their answers.

> **If you increase an amount by 50%, what percentage of the original amount do you then have?**

> **If something increases by 100%, it doubles. What percentage do you then have?**

> **An amount is increased by 500%. How can you describe this?**

Demonstrate that you have the original 100% *plus* the increase of 500%.

An amount increases by 15%. What percentage of the original amount do you then have?

How do you write 115% as a decimal? As a fraction?

Repeat with a decrease of 35%, resulting in a final amount of 65%.

How do you write 65% as a decimal? As a fraction?

Extend to decreasing £450 by 17%. Recap how to work out 83% of £450, reminding pupils of the equivalence of 83%, $\frac{83}{100}$ and 0.83. Use the **Calculator tool** to demonstrate the calculation 0.83 × 450.

How do we interpret the display of 373.5?

How would you increase £450 by 17%?

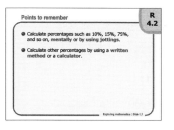

Practise similar calculations using the target board on **slide 1.2**. These examples require the use of calculators.

Select individual work from **R4.2 Exercise 1** in the class book (p. 315).

Review

Discuss these problems:

I start with £250 on January 1st.
This increases by 10% on February 1st. How much do I then have?

By March 1st, my money has increased again by 10%.
How much do I have now?

I start with £250 on January 1st. This increases by 20% on March 1st.
Is this the same result as before?

Discuss how a 10% increase followed by another 10% increase is not the same as a 20% increase. Go on to show how a 20% increase + 20% increase is not the same as a 40% increase.

Finish by launching **FDP equivalents quiz**. Pupils should write the equivalent fraction, decimal or percentage on their whiteboards. 'Next' and 'Back' can be used to move on and back through the questions and answers at a suitable pace. Ask pupils to explain how they arrived at the answer, including 'I just knew!'.

Ask pupils to remember the points on **slide 1.3**.

Homework

Ask pupils to do **R4.2 Task 1** in the home book (p. 128).

2 Ratio and proportion

Learning points

- If you are asked to divide a given quantity into two parts in the ratio 3 : 7, the two parts are $\frac{3}{10}$ and $\frac{7}{10}$ of the quantity.

- If you are given a ratio 2 : 7 and the size of the smaller part, find one share by dividing the smaller part by 2, then multiply by 7 to find the size of the larger part.

Starter

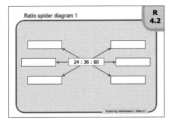

Say that this lesson is revision of calculations involving ratio and proportion.

Show **slide 2.1**. Ask pupils to give ratios equivalent to the one in the centre of the diagram. Annotate the slide with suggestions. Then ask:

> **Which is the simplest form of the ratio? How do you know?**

Discuss simplifying ratios, including those expressed in different units, such as 5p to £1, 400 g to 2 kg, 50 cm to 1.5 m.

Main activity

Remind pupils how to solve a ratio problem where they must divide a quantity into parts in a given ratio.

> **How can we divide £44 into two parts in the ratio 2 : 9?**

Explain that we need 2 + 9 = 11 equal shares. One share is £44 ÷ 11 = £4, two shares are £4 × 2 = £8 and nine shares are £4 × 9 = £36.

This is the same as finding $\frac{2}{11}$ of £44 = £8 and $\frac{9}{11}$ of £44 = £36.

Check that the two parts £8 and £36 sum to £44.

> **How can we divide 84 kg into three parts in the ratio 2 : 3 : 7?**

This time we need 2 + 3 + 7 = 12 equal shares. One share is 84 kg ÷ 12 = 7 kg, so two shares are 14 kg, three shares are 21 kg, and seven shares are 49 kg.

This is the same as finding $\frac{2}{12}$, $\frac{3}{12}$ and $\frac{7}{12}$ of 84 kg.

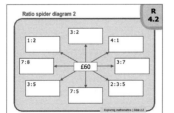

Check that the three parts 14 kg, 21 kg and 49 kg sum to 84 kg.

Show **slide 2.2** and ask pupils to complete the questions mentally. Discuss solutions, annotating the slide with answers. The amount in the centre can be varied to produce questions that require written or calculator methods for solution.

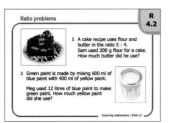

Remind pupils how to solve a problem where we are told a ratio and the size of one part, and must calculate the size of the other part. Show the first problem on **slide 2.3**.

> 1 A cake recipe uses flour and butter in the ratio 5 : 4.
> Sam used 200 g flour to make a cake.
> How much butter did he use?

Explain that the flour is 5 shares, so one share is 200 ÷ 5 = 40 g. The butter is 4 shares, or 40 × 4 = 160 g.

Alternatively, the ratio 5 : 4 must be equivalent to the ratio 200 : ?, where ? is the number of grams of butter. We scale 5 up by multiplying by 40 to get 200, so we do the same to 4 to get $4 \times 40 = 160$ g of butter.

Repeat with the second problem on **slide 2.3**, discussing both approaches.

> 2   Green paint is made by mixing 600 ml of blue paint
>   with 400 ml of yellow paint.
>   Meg used 12 litres of blue paint to make green paint.
>   How much yellow paint did she use?

Explain that the ratio of blue to yellow paint is 600 : 400, or 3 : 2. The blue paint is 3 shares, so 1 share is $12 \div 3 = 4$ litres. The yellow paint is 2 shares, or $4 \times 2 = 8$ litres.

Another way to think about the problem is to say that the ratio 3 : 2 must be equivalent to the ratio 12 : ?, where ? is the number of litres of yellow paint. We scale 3 up by multiplying by 4 to get 12, so we do the same to 2 to get $2 \times 4 = 8$ litres of yellow paint. Remind the class that 4 is the *scale factor*.

> Ask pupils to do **R4.2 Exercise 2** in the class book (p. 318).

Review

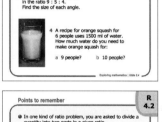

Discuss the first problem on **slide 2.4**.

> 3   The angles in a triangle are in the ratio 9 : 5 : 4.
>   Find the size of each angle.

What fact do you need to know about triangles?

What calculations do you need to do?

How would you set out your working?

Discuss the second problem on **slide 2.4**.

> 4   A recipe for orange squash for 6 people uses 1500 ml of water.
>   How much water do you need to make orange squash for:
>
>   *a* 9 people?   *b* 10 people?

Ask pairs to discuss solutions. Invite a pair to demonstrate how they arrived at their answers.

Sum up using **slides 2.5 and 2.6**. Remind pupils that ratios are simplified similarly to fractions and that there are two types of ratio problems to solve.

Homework

Ask pupils to do **R4.2 Task 2** in the home book (p. 130).

3 Equations and graphs

Learning points

- The linear equation $3x + 7 = 10$ has a unique solution, when $x = 1$.

- The linear equation $3x + 2y = 10$ has an infinite number of solutions. The value of y depends on the value of x.

- When you interpret linear graphs, first work out the scales on the axes.

- When a graph represents a real situation, think what it is about before you answer questions.

Starter

Say that this lesson is about linear equations and graphs.

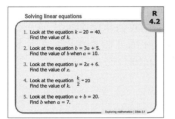

Use the questions on **slide 3.1** to remind pupils how to solve simple linear equations. Ask individual pupils to set out the solutions formally on the board. Discuss how they might solve the equations mentally. Compare different methods.

The questions are taken from these mental tests:

1 2004 Mental test C level 4
2 2004 Mental test C level 5
3 2003 Mental test A level 5
4 2003 Mental test B level 5
5 2003 Mental test C level 4

Main activity

Use the question on **slide 3.2** (level 5). Stress the need to practise reading and comprehending questions. Tell pupils that they can draw pictures or make notes to help them to understand the question.

Read through the introduction to the question. Ask pupils to imagine the three bags of counters. Get them to think about how the bags are filled for each person. Work through each of the questions on the slide.

Go to **slides 3.3 and 3.4**. Ask pupils to write an expression for each person's counters.

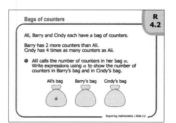  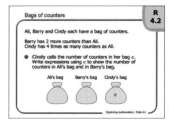

When pupils have completed all three questions, look at the three diagrams and discuss which was the easiest to work out. Explain that when they decide what letters to use to solve a problem they need to think carefully. They can make the problem easier to solve by careful selection.

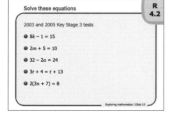

Remind pupils how to solve simple linear equations with the unknown variable on one or both sides. Reveal the equations on **slide 3.5** one by one (they are all taken from the 2003 or 2005 Key Stage 3 tests). Ask pupils to solve the equations on their whiteboards.

Discuss methods, using inverse operations or transforming both sides in the same way.

> Select questions from **R4.2 Exercise 3A** (solving equations) and **R4.2 Exercise 3B** (graphs) in the class book (p. 322–323). They will need some squared paper and a copy of **R4.2 Resource sheet 3.1** for Exercise 3B.

RS

Review Go through some of the questions from the individual work. Compare methods and discuss how solutions should be set out.

Ask pupils some questions from the mental tests.

1 I am thinking of a number. I call it n.
   I double my number then I subtract three.
   Write an expression to show the result.
   [2004 Mental test C level 5]

2 What is the next number in this counting sequence?
   Eight point seven, eight point eight, eight point nine, …
   [2003 Practice test level 3]

3 Look at the equation $k - 20 = 40$. [Write this on the board.]
   Find the value of k.
   [2004 Mental test C level 4]

4 Look at the equation $b = 3a + 5$. [Write this on the board.]
   When $a = 10$, what is the value of b?
   [2004 Mental test C level 5]

5 Look at **slide 3.6**. Which is the graph of $y = x + 1$?

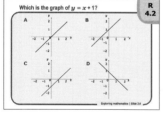

Launch **Solving equations quiz**. Ask pupils to write the solution to the equation on their whiteboards. Click on 'Next' and 'Back' to move on and back through the questions and answers. After each question, ask someone to explain how they worked out the answer. If anyone has done it differently, compare the methods.

QZ

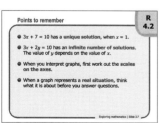

Sum up the key points from the lesson using **slide 3.7**.

Homework Ask pupils to do **R4.2 Task 3** in the home book (p. 132). They will need a copy of **R4.2 Resource sheet 3.2**.

RS

Learning points

- When you identify equal angles in a geometric figure, always give your reasons.
- Look out for vertically opposite angles, corresponding angles and alternate angles.
- Also look out for angles on a straight line, in a triangle or around a point.
- Reflection, rotation and translation leave the size and shape of the object unchanged.
- Enlargement changes the size of the object but not its shape (i.e. angles).

Starter

Say that this lesson is about finding missing angles, transforming shapes and solving problems in geometry.

Launch **Missing angles quiz**. Ask pupils to calculate the missing angle and write the answer on their whiteboards. Click 'Play' to start, and 'Pause' to stop. Use 'Back' and 'Next' to move backwards and forwards through the questions.

Main activity

Write on the board: *vertically opposite angles, corresponding angles, alternate angles*. Remind pupils what these are and that they should always give a reason when they identify equal angles.

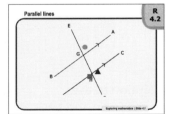

Show **slide 4.1**. Ask pupils to use three letters to identify angles equal to those shown on successive clicks (three in all). They should also give reasons. For example:

- ∠AGE equals:
  ∠BGH (vertically opposite angles);
  ∠CHG (corresponding angles);
  ∠DHF (corresponding and vertically opposite angles).

- ∠DHG equals:
  ∠CHF (vertically opposite angle);
  ∠AGH (alternate angles);
  ∠BGE (corresponding angles).

- ∠CHF equals:
  ∠DHG (vertically opposite angle);
  ∠AGH (corresponding angle);
  ∠BGE (corresponding and vertically opposite angles).

Ask the class:

> **What is the sum of angles in a triangle? On a straight line? At a point?**

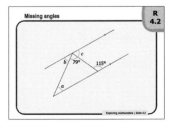

Show **slide 4.2**. Ask pupils in pairs to find the missing angles, giving reasons, writing answers on their whiteboards. [$a = 36°$, $b = 36°$, $c = 65°$. Reasons could include angles in a triangle, alternate or corresponding angles, and angles in a straight line.]

Select individual work from **R4.2 Exercise 4A** in the class book (p. 326). Pupils will need squared paper.

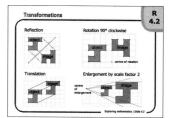

Show **slide 4.3**. Ask pupils to identify each of the transformations. As each diagram appears, ask:

> **What do you need to remember when you answer a question involving reflection (or rotation, translation, enlargement)?**

Stress that with reflection, rotation and translation, the object and image are congruent. Their shape and size are unchanged. With enlargement, the object and image are the same shape (i.e. angles are the same) but the size changes.

> Ask pupils to do **R4.2 Exercise 4B** in the class book (p. 328). They will need squared paper and triangular dotty paper.

Review

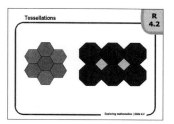

Show **slide 4.4**. Remind pupils how transformations are linked to tessellations. Ask them to spend a short while describing to a partner the different transformations that have been used to create the two tessellations. Choose a couple of pairs to share their descriptions with the whole class.

Summarise with the reminders on **slide 4.5**.

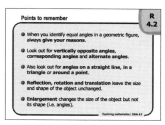

Homework

Ask pupils to do **R4.2 Task 4** in the home book (p. 134). They will need squared paper.

5 Representing and interpreting data

Learning points

- In a pie chart the angle at the centre of the circle is proportional to the frequency for each category.
- A pie chart shows only proportions, not totals.
- A two-way table allows two types of information to be presented and compared.
- A line graph is a useful way of displaying continuous data against time.
- Use the scales to read information from a graph as accurately as you can.

Starter

Say that this lesson is about drawing and interpreting tables, graphs and diagrams.

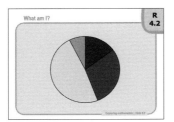

Show pupils the three charts on **slide 5.1**. Establish through questioning that one is a pie chart, one is a scatter graph and one is a bar chart or frequency diagram. Explain that you will show the charts one at a time and will ask the class to discuss in pairs some contexts for each and what the chart or graph might illustrate.

Show **slide 5.2**. Ask questions such as:

> What do you think this pie chart could be about?
>
> What does it show?
>
> Roughly what proportion of the total is each sector?
>
> What are pie charts good for showing? What don't they show?

Repeat with **slide 5.3**, then **slide 5.4**.

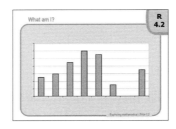
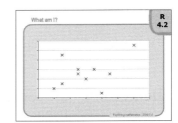

Encourage the class to come up with several suggestions for the context for each graph. For example, the pie chart could show people's eating habits, the way people travel to school, or their favourite sport. The bar chart could show shoe sizes, laps run in a sponsored run, or letters in words in a paragraph of text. The scatter graph could show hand span and foot length, scores in two rounds of the same game or the length of shoe lace and number of eyes in the shoe, and so on.

Main activity

Split the class into groups of three or four. Allocate one of these phrases to each group:

> pie chart
>
> bar chart
>
> scatter graph
>
> mean, median, mode and range

two-way table

survey and questionnaire

line graph

grouped frequency diagram

stem-and-leaf diagram

Give each group a large piece of paper and ask them to make a poster about their topic. They should include all that they can remember about the topic and then produce an example. You could suggest that pupils use their class books and their exercise books to help them to remember some of the details. Refer them to the sections headed 'Points to remember' and the examples.

Select individual work from **R4.2 Exercise 5** in the class book (pp. 332).

Review

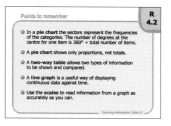

Display all the posters produced earlier. Pick a few posters and ask pupils to explain what they put on them. It would be useful to pick those that contain content not covered in the class book exercises.

Finish with the reminders on **slide 5.5**.

Homework Ask pupils to do **R4.2 Task 5** in the home book (p. 136).

R4.2 Mental test

Read each question aloud twice.

Allow from 5 to 15 seconds for pupils to write answers.

1 Write one and a half million in figures. *2005 KS3*

2 I am thinking of two numbers that add to ten.
The two numbers multiply together to make twenty-one.
What are my two numbers? *2005 KS3*

3 Twenty-five per cent of a number is seven. What is the number? *2003 KS3*

4 I am thinking of a number. I call it *n*.
I double my number then I subtract three.
Write an expression to show the result. *2004 KS3*

5 I face south-west, then I turn through one hundred and eighty degrees.
What direction am I facing now? *2004 KS3*

6 The scale on my map is four centimetres to one kilometre.
On the map the distance to the rail station is twenty centimetres.
How many kilometres is it to the rail station? *2003 KS3*

7 What is three-fifths of forty pounds? *2003 KS3*

8 The perimeter of a rectangle is twenty centimetres.
Its length is seven centimetres. What is the width of the rectangle? *2005 KS3*

9 How many thirds are there in two? *2005 KS3*

10 The probability I will be late for school is one-twentieth.
What is the probability that I will not be late for school? *2005 KS3*

11 A pupil measures his height as six feet.
About how many metres high is that? *2003 KS3*

12 Increase one pound fifty by fifty per cent. *2004 KS3*

Key:

KS3 Key Stage 3 test

All questions are at Level 5.

Answers

1	1 500 000	**2**	3 and 7
3	28	**4**	$2n - 3$
5	North-east	**6**	5 km
7	£24	**8**	3 cm
9	6	**10**	$\frac{19}{20}$
11	2 metres	**12**	£2.25

R4.2 Resource sheets

Draw or write your answers on this sheet.

2004 level 5

A company sells books using the Internet. The graph shows their delivery charges.

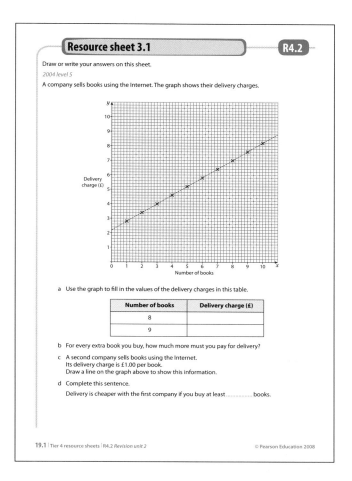

a Use the graph to fill in the values of the delivery charges in this table.

Number of books	Delivery charge (£)
8	
9	

b For every extra book you buy, how much more must you pay for delivery?

c A second company sells books using the Internet.
   Its delivery charge is £1.00 per book.
   Draw a line on the graph above to show this information.

d Complete this sentence.

   Delivery is cheaper with the first company if you buy at least .... books.

Draw or write your answers on this sheet.
You will need this sheet for **Task 3**.

Year 7 Optional Test level 4

The graph shows a straight line through the point (2, 5).

Use a ruler to draw another straight line that is parallel to this line.

The line must go through the point (3, 0).

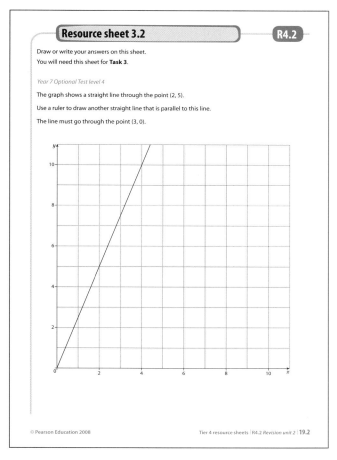

Class book

Exercise 1

1 £63.75

2 a 1 out of 8 squares is shaded.
$\frac{1}{8}$ is equivalent to 25%.
  b Any three squares on this diagram should be shaded, e.g.

3 a **7** out of 10 is the same as 70%.
  b 10 out of 20 is the same as **50**%.
  c **1** out of **20** is the same as 5%.
Any pair of numbers in the ratio 1 : 20 is acceptable.

4 a 75
  b My number is 840.
10% of it is 84.
5% of it is half of 84, or 42.
15% is 10% + 5%, which is 84 + 42 = 126.
  c 105

5 £36

6 60%

7 a Approximately 12.5%
  b 198°

8 48 kg

9 a £556.75   b 7.5% (to 1 d.p.)

10 147.9 million km²

Extension problem

11 19 980 students gained grade A in maths.
13 680 students gained grade A in English.
6300 more students gained grade A in maths.

Exercise 2

1 600 seats downstairs

2 a 1 : 3
  b 2 : 3
  c 1 carton of orange juice

3 a 6 litres of red paint and 14 litres of blue paint
  b 6.5 litres of yellow paint and 3.5 litres of red paint

4 8 oranges

5 £165

6 200 ml

7 If the larger number is 12, the smaller number is 8.
If the smaller number is 12, the larger number is 18.
So the two possibilities are 8 and 18.

Extension problem

8 39 children voted in favour of going to the zoo.

9 75 grams of margarine and 50 grams of lard.

10 a 21 : 15 or 7 : 5
   b 42 : 36 or 7 : 6
   c No. Their ages can never be in the ratio 7 : 7 because this would mean that their ages were the same.

11 160 people were in the survey (100 in favour of milk chocolate, 60 against).

Exercise 3A

1 a $x = 34$ b $y = 8$ c $z = 4$

2 a $s = 12$ b $k = 36$

3 a $k = 4$ b $t = -7$

4 a $x = 14$ b $y = 13$

5 a 91.44 metres
  b 109.36 yards

Extension problem

6 a $k = 2$ b $m = 2.5$ c $t = 4.5$

Exercise 3B

1 a A height in the range 90–92 cm inclusive
  b A height in the range 95–97 cm inclusive
  c 18 months

d

Age (months)	Height at start (cm)	Height at end (cm)	Growth (cm)
12 to 24	74	86	12
24 to 36	86	**about 94**	**8**
36 to 48	**about 94**	**about 102**	**8**

e   198 cm

2 a

Number of books	Delivery charge (£)
8	£7
9	£7.60

b   60p

c   Pupil's graphs

d   Delivery is cheaper with the first company if you buy at least six books

3 a The y-coordinate is 146.

b   The x-coordinate is 18.

c   Yes. The values $x = -10$, $y = -34$ satisfy the equation $y = 3x - 4$.

4 Pupil's graphs of $y = 3$ and $y = x$ on the same grid

5 a The line through B and D

b   The line through A and B

c   The line through C and D

Exercise 4A

1 a D (5, 2)   **b** E (3, 0) or (4, 1) or (6, 3)

2 a Pupil's quadrilateral with exactly 2 right angles

b   Pupil's quadrilateral with exactly 1 right angle

3 a No. The sides are not the same length.

b   Yes. The shape has two pairs of adjacent equal sides and one line of symmetry.

c   No. All sides are not the same length and all angles are not right angles.

4 $a = 50°, b = 130°, c = 20°$

5

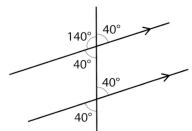

Extension problem

6 $a = 10°$

Exercise 4B

1 a Y

b   90°

2 b, c

3 a (5, 7)

b   (7, 5)

c   (7, 1)

4

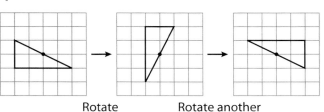

Rotate   Rotate another
90° clockwise   90° clockwise

5 a

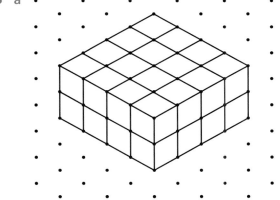

b   24 cubes

Extension problem

6

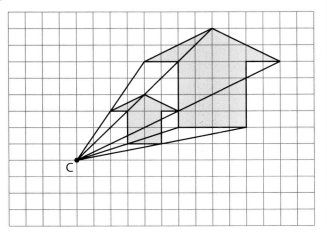

Exercise 5

1 a 54
   b 16
   c

	Yes	No	Don't know
Year 11	10	20	10

   d

	Yes	No
Boys		
Girls		

   (or equivalent)

2 £5.65

3 a Bangor and Hull
   b 289
   c 248
   d 537

4 a About 2 million
   b About 50 million
   c Just over 10 million

5 a Kay was in the lead for **3** minutes.
   b At **1200** metres, Maria and Kay were level again.
   c **Maria** won the race.
      Her total time was **6** minutes.
   d **Kay** finished about **1.5** minutes later.

6 a June
   b Estimates from 18.5 to 19.5 hours are acceptable.
   c December
   d Estimates from 5 to 6 hours are acceptable.

7 a Estimates from 6% to 16% are acceptable.
   b Germany and Norway

8 a £4
   b

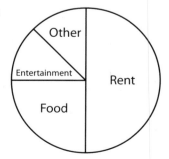

9 a Estimates from 30% to 45% are acceptable, e.g. one third, three eighths

   b Estimates from 15% to 20% are acceptable, e.g. one fifth, one sixth
   c Estimates of 25% to 30% for land are acceptable, e.g.

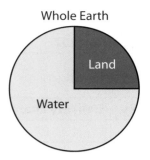

Home book

TASK 1

1 a 20 children are two years old.
   b 30 children are four years old.

2 a Football is sector E.
      Squash is sector D.
   b Approximately 30%
   c Approximately 15%
   d Friday's sports

Sport	Percentage	No of people
Badminton	10%	26
Football	40%	**104**
Squash	5%	**13**

   e 40% of 260 people played football on Friday, i.e. 104 people.
      20% of 700 people played football on Saturday, i.e. 140 people.
      So more people played football on Saturday.

3 a £2.12
   b £12.25
   c 94.5 kg

TASK 2

1 a 18 boys, 9 girls
   b 15 boys, 13 girls
   c 9 boys, 18 girls

2 a 600 ml of water
   b 50 ml of Screenwash
   c No. There are 5 parts altogether. 1 part out of every 5 parts is 20%, not 25%.

3 750 g

Extension problem

4 45 goals at home and 27 goals away is a total of 72 goals.

TASK 3

1 Pupil's graph on Resource sheet 2

2 **a** Any pair of numbers whose sum is 30
   b A different pair of numbers whose sum is 30
   c $b = 10$

3 **a** $x = 3$
   b $2y + 5 = 23 - y, y = 6$
   c $a = 4, b = 7$

TASK 4

1 **a**

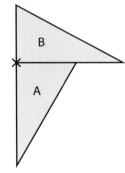

   b 90°

   c

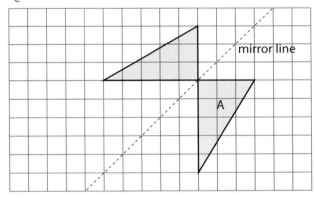

2 B1 Rotate 90° clockwise
   B2 Reflect vertical

TASK 5

1 **a** 80 metres
   b 55 metres
   c 15 mph
   d Mrs Singh must increase her distance from 50 metres to 60 metres.

2 **a** Estimates in the range 20% to 30% are acceptable.
   b Estimates in the range 2 to 3 million are acceptable,
   c The total number of people in each country needs to be taken into account.
   d

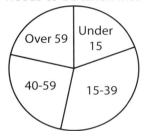

3 **a** 9 hours 15 minutes
   b 15:18

Minimum hardware requirements

For PC

The following hardware is the minimum required for the PC you use to run this CD, whether it is standalone PC or on a network (a client PC):

- IBM compatible PC
- Intel Pentium 4 GHz processor or equivalent
- 1 GB RAM
- 1 GB free space on hard disk
- Sound card and speakers
- CD-ROM drive 16×
- 1024 × 768 screen resolution
- 100Base-T Ethernet NIC for networked installation

For server

The following hardware is the minimum required for the server when installed on the network:

- Pentium 4 2GHz
- 1 GB RAM
- 1000Base-T recommended
- 20% free hard drive space on shared partition

Networks

The following networks are supported:

- Windows 2000 Server
- Windows 2003 Server
- RM Community Connect 3

Grant of Licence:

PEL grants You, provided You only do what is allowed under the 'Yes, You can' table above, and do nothing under the 'No, You cannot' table above, a non-exclusive, non-transferable Licence to use this Exploring Maths: Tier 4 Teacher's Book CD-ROM.

The terms and conditions of this Licence become operative when using this Exploring Maths: Tier 4 Teacher's Book CD-ROM.

Limited Warranty:

PEL warrants that the disk or CD-ROM on which the software is supplied is free from defects in material and workmanship in normal use for ninety (90) days from the date You receive it. This warranty is limited to You and is not transferable.

This limited warranty is void if any damage has resulted from accident, abuse, misapplication, service or modification by someone other than PEL. In no event shall PEL be liable for any damages whatsoever arising out of installation of the software, even if advised of the possibility of such damages. PEL will not be liable for any loss or damage of any nature suffered by any party as a result of reliance upon or reproduction of any errors in the content of the publication.

PEL does not warrant that the functions of the software meet Your requirements or that the media is compatible with any computer system on which it is used or that the operation of the software will be unlimited or error free. You assume responsibility for selecting the software to achieve Your intended results and for the installation of, the use of and the results obtained from the software.

PEL shall not be liable for any loss or damage of any kind (except for personal injury or death) arising from the use of this Exploring Maths: Tier 4 Teacher's Book CD-ROM or from errors, deficiencies or faults therein, whether such loss or damage is caused by negligence or otherwise.

The entire liability of PEL and your only remedy shall be replacement free of charge of the components that do not meet this warranty.

No information or advice (oral, written or otherwise) given by PEL or PEL's agents shall create a warranty or in any way increase the scope of this warranty.

To the extent the law permits, PEL disclaims all other warranties, either express or implied, including by way of example and not limitation, warranties of merchantability and fitness for a particular purpose in respect of this Exploring Maths: Tier 4 Teacher's Book CD-ROM.

Termination:

This Licence shall automatically terminate without notice from PEL if you fail to comply with any of its provisions. PEL may also terminate this Licence by notice in writing. Upon termination for whatever reason You agree to destroy the Exploring Maths: Tier 4 Teacher's Book CD-ROM and any back-up copies and delete any part of the Exploring Maths: Tier 4 Teacher's Book CD-ROM stored on the purchasing institution's servers, secure network or any computer or storage device under the purchasing institution's control.

Governing Law:

This Licence will be governed by and construed in accordance with English law.

This *Exploring maths* teacher's book CD contains printable and editable versions of the lesson notes, resource sheets, check ups, and slide presentations for each unit.

This CD can be installed onto the school network. If you also have *Exploring maths* ActiveTeach installed on your network you will be able to access these resources through the ActiveTeach, via the 'Teacher's book' tab.

Licence Agreement: Exploring Maths: Tier 4 Teacher's Book

Warning:
This is a legally binding agreement between You (the user or purchasing institution) and Pearson Education Limited of Edinburgh Gate, Harlow, Essex, CM20 2JE, United Kingdom ('PEL').

By retaining this Licence, any software media or accompanying written materials or carrying out any of the permitted activities You are agreeing to be bound by the terms and conditions of this Licence. If You do not agree to the terms and conditions of this Licence, do not continue to use the Exploring Maths: Tier 4 Teacher's Book CD-ROM and promptly return the entire publication (this Licence and all software, written materials, packaging and any other component received with it) with Your sales receipt to Your supplier for a full refund.

Intellectual Property Rights:
This Exploring Maths: Tier 4 Teacher's Book CD-ROM consists of copyright software and data. All intellectual property rights, including the copyright is owned by PEL or its licensors and shall remain vested in them at all times. You only own the disk on which the software is supplied. If You do not continue to do only what You are allowed to do as contained in this Licence you will be in breach of the Licence and PEL shall have the right to terminate this Licence by written notice and take action to recover from you any damages suffered by PEL as a result of your breach.

The PEL name, PEL logo, Longman name, Longman logo and all other trademarks appearing on the software and Exploring Maths: Tier 4 Teacher's Book CD-ROM are trademarks of PEL. You shall not utilise any such trademarks for any purpose whatsoever other than as they appear on the software and Exploring Maths: Tier 4 Teacher's Book CD-ROM.

Yes, You can:
1. use this Exploring Maths: Tier 4 Teacher's Book CD-ROM on Your own personal computer as a single individual user:

2. use or install this Exploring Maths: Tier 4 Teacher's Book CD-ROM on a network, server or on more than one personal computer within your school;

No, You cannot:
1. copy this Exploring Maths: Tier 4 Teacher's Book CD-ROM (other than making one copy for back-up purposes);

2. alter, disassemble, or modify this Exploring Maths: Tier 4 Teacher's Book CD-ROM, or in any way reverse engineer, decompile or create a derivative product from the contents of the database or any software included in it:

3. include any materials or software data from the Exploring Maths: Tier 4 Teacher's Book CD-ROM in any other product or software materials;

4. rent, hire, lend, sub-licence or sell the Exploring Maths: Tier 4 Teacher's Book CD-ROM;

5. copy any part of the documentation except where specifically indicated otherwise;

6. use the software in any way not specified above without the prior written consent of PEL;

7. Subject the software, Exploring Maths: Tier 4 Teacher's Book CD-ROM or any PEL content to any derogatory treatment or use them in such a way that would bring PEL into disrepute or cause PEL to incur liability to any third party.